Legal Notice

For information on bulk purchases and licensing agreements, please email

support@SATPrepGet800.com

ISBN-13: 978-0999811757

Acknowledgements

Thanks to Daniel Dimijian, Scott Jeffreys, Dan Seabold, C.R. Sincock, Pete Terlecky, Zoran Sunik, and David Wayne for their helpful input during the creation of this book.

CONNECT WITH DR. STEVE WARNER

www.facebook.com/SATPrepGet800

www.youtube.com/TheSATMathPrep

www.twitter.com/SATPrepGet800

www.linkedin.com/in/DrSteveWarner

www.pinterest.com/SATPrepGet800

plus.google.com/+SteveWarnerPhD

2018

Pure Mathematics
for Beginners

A Rigorous Introduction to Logic, Set Theory, Abstract Algebra, Number Theory, Real Analysis, Topology, Complex Analysis, and Linear Algebra

Dr. Steve Warner

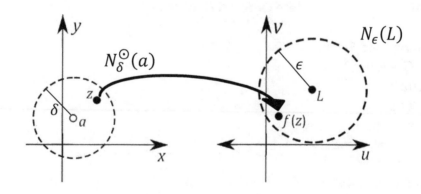

iii

Table of Contents

PURE MATHEMATICS

This book was written to provide a basic but rigorous introduction to pure mathematics, while exposing students to a wide range of mathematical topics in logic, set theory, abstract algebra, number theory, real analysis, topology, complex analysis, and linear algebra.

For students: There are no prerequisites for this book. The content is completely self-contained. Students with a bit of mathematical knowledge may have an easier time getting through some of the material, but no such knowledge is necessary to read this book.

More important than mathematical knowledge is "mathematical maturity." Although there is no single agreed upon definition of mathematical maturity, one reasonable way to define it is as "one's ability to analyze, understand, and communicate mathematics." A student with a higher level of mathematical maturity will be able to move through this book more quickly than a student with a lower level of mathematical maturity.

Whether your level of mathematical maturity is low or high, if you are just starting out in pure mathematics, then you're in the right place. If you read this book the "right way," then your level of mathematical maturity will continually be increasing. This increased level of mathematical maturity will not only help you to succeed in advanced math courses, but it will improve your general problem solving and reasoning skills. This will make it easier to improve your performance in college, in your professional life, and on standardized tests such as the SAT, ACT, GRE, and GMAT.

So, what is the "right way" to read this book? Simply reading each lesson from end to end without any further thought and analysis is not the best way to read the book. You will need to put in some effort to have the best chance of absorbing and retaining the material. When a new theorem is presented, don't just jump right to the proof and read it. Think about what the theorem is saying. Try to describe it in your own words. Do you believe that it is true? If you do believe it, can you give a convincing argument that it is true? If you do not believe that it is true, try to come up with an example that shows it is false, and then figure out why your example does not contradict the theorem. Pick up a pen or pencil. Draw some pictures, come up with your own examples, and try to write your own proof.

You may find that this book goes into more detail than other math books when explaining examples, discussing concepts, and proving theorems. This was done so that any student can read this book, and not just students that are naturally gifted in mathematics. So, it is up to you as the student to try to answer questions before they are answered for you. When a new definition is given, try to think of your own examples before looking at those presented in the book. And when the book provides an example, do not just accept that it satisfies the given definition. Convince yourself. Prove it.

Each lesson is followed by a Problem Set. The problems in each Problem Set have been organized into five levels, Level 1 problems being considered the easiest, and Level 5 problems being considered the most difficult. If you want to get just a small taste of pure mathematics, then you can work on the easier problems. If you want to achieve a deeper understanding of the material, take some time to struggle with the harder problems.

For instructors: This book can be used for a wide range of courses. Although the lessons can be taught in the order presented, they do not need to be. The lessons cycle twice among eight subject areas: logic, set theory, abstract algebra, number theory, real analysis, topology, complex analysis, and linear algebra.

Lessons 1 through 8 give only the most basic material in each of these subjects. Therefore, an instructor that wants to give a brief glimpse into a wide variety of topics might want to cover just the first eight lessons in their course.

Lessons 9 through 16 cover material in each subject area that the author believes is fundamental to a deep understanding of that particular subject.

For a first course in higher mathematics, a high-quality curriculum can be created by choosing among the 16 lessons contained in this book.

As an example, an introductory course focusing on logic, set theory, and real analysis might cover Lessons 1, 2, 5, 9, 10, and 13. Lessons 1 and 9 cover basic sentential logic and proof theory, Lessons 2 and 10 cover basic set theory including relations, functions, and equinumerosity, and Lessons 5 and 13 cover basic real analysis up through a rigorous treatment of limits and continuity. The first three lessons are quite basic, while the latter three lessons are at an intermediate level. Instructors that do not like the idea of leaving a topic and then coming back to it later can cover the lessons in the following order without issue: 1, 9, 2, 10, 5, and 13.

As another example, a course focusing on algebraic structures might cover Lessons 2, 3, 4, 5, 10, and 11. As mentioned in the previous paragraph, Lessons 2 and 10 cover basic set theory. In addition, Lessons 3, 4, 5, and 11 cover semigroups, monoids, groups, rings, and fields. Lesson 4, in addition to a preliminary discussion on rings, also covers divisibility and the principle of mathematical induction. Similarly, Lesson 5, in addition to a preliminary discussion on fields, provides a development of the complete ordered field of real numbers. These topics can be included or omitted, as desired. Instructors that would also like to incorporate vector spaces can include part or all of Lesson 8.

The author strongly recommends covering Lesson 2 in any introductory pure math course. This lesson fixes some basic set theoretical notation that is used throughout the book and includes some important exposition to help students develop strong proof writing skills as quickly as possible.

The author welcomes all feedback from instructors. Any suggestions will be considered for future editions of the book. The author would also love to hear about the various courses that are created using these lessons. Feel free to email Dr. Steve Warner with any feedback at

steve@SATPrepGet800.com

Statements with Words

A **statement** (or **proposition**) is a sentence that can be true or false, but not both simultaneously.

Example 1.1: "Mary is awake" is a statement because at any given time either Mary is awake or Mary is not awake (also known as Mary being asleep), and Mary cannot be both awake and asleep at the same time.

Example 1.2: The sentence "Wake up!" is *not* a statement because it cannot be true or false.

An **atomic statement** expresses a single idea. The statement "Mary is awake" that we discussed above is an example of an atomic statement. Let's look at a few more examples.

Example 1.3: The following sentences are atomic statements:

1. 17 is a prime number.
2. George Washington was the first president of the United States.
3. $5 > 6$.
4. David is left-handed.

Sentences 1 and 2 above are true, and sentence 3 is false. We can't say for certain whether sentence 4 is true or false without knowing who David is. However, it is either true or false. It follows that each of the four sentences above are atomic statements.

We use **logical connectives** to form **compound statements**. The most commonly used logical connectives are "and," "or," "if…then," "if and only if," and "not."

Example 1.4: The following sentences are compound statements:

1. 17 is a prime number and $0 = 1$.
2. Michael is holding a pen or water is a liquid.
3. If Joanna has a cat, then fish have lungs.
4. Albert Einstein is alive today if and only if $5 + 7 = 12$.
5. 16 is not a perfect square.

Sentence 1 above uses the logical connective "and." Since the statement "$0 = 1$" is false, it follows that sentence 1 is false. It does not matter that the statement "17 is a prime number" is true. In fact, "T and F" is always F.

Sentence 2 uses the logical connective "or." Since the statement "water is a liquid" is true, it follows that sentence 2 is true. It does not even matter whether Michael is holding a pen. In fact, "T or T" is always true and "F or T" is always T.

It's worth pausing for a moment to note that in the English language the word "or" has two possible meanings. There is an "inclusive or" and an "exclusive or." The "inclusive or" is true when both statements are true, whereas the "exclusive or" is false when both statements are true. In mathematics, by default, we always use the "inclusive or" unless we are told to do otherwise. To some extent, this is an arbitrary choice that mathematicians have agreed upon. However, it can be argued that it is the better choice since it is used more often and it is easier to work with. Note that we were assuming use of the "inclusive or" in the last paragraph when we said, "In fact, "T or T" is always true." See Problem 4 below for more on the "exclusive or."

Sentence 3 uses the logical connective "if...then." The statement "fish have lungs" is false. We need to know whether Joanna has a cat in order to figure out the truth value of sentence 3. If Joanna does have a cat, then sentence 3 is false ("if T, then F" is always F). If Joanna does not have a cat, then sentence 3 is true ("if F, then F" is always T).

Sentence 4 uses the logical connective "if and only if." Since the two atomic statements have different truth values, it follows that sentence 4 is false. In fact, "F if and only if T" is always F.

Sentence 5 uses the logical connective "not." Since the statement "16 is a perfect square" is true, it follows that sentence 5 is false. In fact, "not T" is always F.

Notes: (1) The logical connectives "and," "or," "if...then," and "if and only if," are called **binary connectives** because they join two statements (the prefix "bi" means "two").

(2) The logical connective "not" is called a **unary connective** because it is applied to just a single statement ("unary" means "acting on a single element").

Example 1.5: The following sentences are **not** statements:

1. Are you happy?
2. Go away!
3. $x - 5 = 7$
4. This sentence is false.
5. This sentence is true.

Sentence 1 above is a question and sentence 2 is a command. Sentence 3 has an unknown variable – it can be turned into a statement by assigning a value to the variable. Sentences 4 and 5 are self-referential (they refer to themselves). They can be neither true nor false. Sentence 4 is called the Liar's paradox and sentence 5 is called a vacuous affirmation.

Statements with Symbols

We will use letters such as $p, q, r,$ and s to denote atomic statements. We sometimes call these letters **propositional variables**, and we will generally assign a truth value of T (for true) or F (for false) to each propositional variable. Formally, we define a **truth assignment** of a list of propositional variables to be a choice of T or F for each propositional variable in the list.

We use the symbols ∧, ∨, →, ↔, and ¬ for the most common logical connectives. The truth value of a compound statement is determined by the truth values of its atomic parts together with applying the following rules for the connectives.

- $p \wedge q$ is called the **conjunction** of p and q. It is pronounced "p and q." $p \wedge q$ is true when both p and q are true, and it is false otherwise.

- $p \vee q$ is called the **disjunction** of p and q. It is pronounced "p or q." $p \vee q$ is true when p or q (or both) are true, and it is false when p and q are both false.

- $p \rightarrow q$ is called a **conditional** or **implication**. It is pronounced "if p, then q" or "p implies q." $p \rightarrow q$ is true when p is false or q is true (or both), and it is false when p is true and q is false.

- $p \leftrightarrow q$ is called a **biconditional**. It is pronounced "p if and only if q." $p \leftrightarrow q$ is true when p and q have the same truth value (both true or both false), and it is false when p and q have opposite truth values (one true and the other false).

- $\neg p$ is called the **negation** of p. It is pronounced "not p." $\neg p$ is true when p is false, and it is false when p is true (p and $\neg p$ have opposite truth values.)

Example 1.6: Let p represent the statement "Fish can swim," and let q represent the statement "$7 < 3$." Note that p is true and q is false.

1. $p \wedge q$ represents "Fish can swim and $7 < 3$." Since q is false, it follows that $p \wedge q$ is false.

2. $p \vee q$ represents "Fish can swim or $7 < 3$." Since p is true, it follows that $p \vee q$ is true.

3. $p \rightarrow q$ represents "If fish can swim, then $7 < 3$." Since p is true and q is false, $p \rightarrow q$ is false.

4. $p \leftrightarrow q$ represents "Fish can swim if and only if $7 < 3$." Since p is true and q is false, $p \leftrightarrow q$ is false.

5. $\neg q$ represents the statement "7 is not less than 3." This is equivalent to "7 is greater than or equal to 3," or equivalently, "$7 \geq 3$." Since q is false, $\neg q$ is true.

6. $\neg p \vee q$ represents the statement "Fish cannot swim or $7 < 3$." Since $\neg p$ and q are both false, $\neg p \vee q$ is false. Note that $\neg p \vee q$ always means $(\neg p) \vee q$. In general, without parentheses present, we always apply negation before any of the other connectives.

7. $\neg (p \vee q)$ represents the statement "It is not the case that either fish can swim or $7 < 3$." This can also be stated as "Neither can fish swim nor is 7 less than 3." Since $p \vee q$ is true (see 2 above), $\neg (p \vee q)$ is false.

8. $\neg p \wedge \neg q$ represents the statement "Fish cannot swim and 7 is not less than 3." This statement can also be stated as "Neither can fish swim nor is 7 less than 3." Since this is the same statement as in 7 above, it should follow that $\neg p \wedge \neg q$ is equivalent to $\neg (p \vee q)$. After completing this lesson, you will be able to verify this. For now, let's observe that since $\neg p$ is false, it follows that $\neg p \wedge \neg q$ is false. This agrees with the truth value we got in 7. (**Note:** The equivalence of $\neg p \wedge \neg q$ with $\neg (p \vee q)$ is one of **De Morgan's laws**. These laws will be explored further in Lesson 9. See also Problem 3 below.)

Truth Tables

A **truth table** can be used to display the possible truth values of a compound statement. We start by labelling the columns of the table with the propositional variables that appear in the statement, followed by the statement itself. We then use the rows to run through every possible combination of truth values for the propositional variables followed by the resulting truth values for the compound statement. Let's look at the truth tables for the five most common logical connectives.

p	q	$p \wedge q$
T	T	T
T	F	F
F	T	F
F	F	F

p	q	$p \vee q$
T	T	T
T	F	T
F	T	T
F	F	F

p	q	$p \rightarrow q$
T	T	T
T	F	F
F	T	T
F	F	T

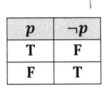

T   F   F

all other comb. T

p	q	$p \leftrightarrow q$
T	T	T
T	F	F
F	T	F
F	F	T

same
dif.
same

T
F
T

p	$\neg p$
T	F
F	T

We can use these five truth tables to compute the truth values of compound statements involving the five basic logical connectives.

Note: For statements involving just 1 propositional variable (such as $\neg p$), the truth table requires 2 rows, 1 for each truth assignment of p (T or F).

For statements involving 2 propositional variables (such as $p \wedge q$), the truth table requires $2 \cdot 2 = 4$ (or $2^2 = 4$) rows, as there are 4 possible combinations for truth assignments of p and q (TT, TF, FT, FF).

In general, for a statement involving n propositional variables, the truth table will require 2^n rows. For example, if we want to build an entire truth table for $\neg p \vee (\neg q \rightarrow r)$, we will need $2^3 = 2 \cdot 2 \cdot 2 = 8$ rows in the truth table. We will create the truth table for this statement in Example 1.8 below (see the third solution).

Example 1.7: If p is true and q is false, then we can compute the truth value of $p \wedge q$ by looking at the second row of the truth table for the conjunction.

p	q	$p \wedge q$
T	T	T
T	F	F
F	T	F
F	F	F

We see from the highlighted row that $p \wedge q \equiv T \wedge F \equiv \textbf{F}$.

Note: Here the symbol $\equiv$ can be read "is logically equivalent to." So, we see that if p is true and q is false, then $p \wedge q$ is logically equivalent to F, or more simply, $p \wedge q$ is false.

Example 1.8: Let p, q, and r be propositional variables with p and q true, and r false. Let's compute the truth value of $\neg p \vee (\neg q \rightarrow r)$.

Solution: We have $\neg p \vee (\neg q \rightarrow r) \equiv \neg T \vee (\neg T \rightarrow F) \equiv F \vee (F \rightarrow F) \equiv F \vee T \equiv \mathbf{T}$.

Notes: (1) For the first equivalence, we simply replaced the propositional variables by their given truth values. We replaced p and q by T, and we replaced r by F.

(2) For the second equivalence, we used the first row of the truth table for the negation (drawn to the right for your convenience).

p	$\neg p$
T	F
F	T

We see from the highlighted row that $\neg T \equiv F$. We applied this result twice.

(3) For the third equivalence, we used the fourth row of the truth table for the conditional.

p	q	$p \rightarrow q$
T	T	T
T	F	F
F	T	T
F	F	T

We see from the highlighted row that $F \rightarrow F \equiv T$.

(4) For the last equivalence, we used the third row of the truth table for the disjunction.

p	q	$p \vee q$
T	T	T
T	F	T
F	T	T
F	F	F

We see from the highlighted row that $F \vee T \equiv T$.

(5) We can save a little time by immediately replacing the negation of a propositional variable by its truth value (which will be the opposite truth value of the propositional variable). For example, since p has truth value T, we can replace $\neg p$ by F. The faster solution would look like this:

$$\neg p \vee (\neg q \rightarrow r) \equiv F \vee (F \rightarrow F) \equiv F \vee T \equiv \mathbf{T}.$$

Quicker solution: Since q has truth value T, it follows that $\neg q$ has truth value F. So, $\neg q \rightarrow r$ has truth value T. Finally, $\neg p \vee (\neg q \rightarrow r)$ must then have truth value T.

Notes: (1) Symbolically, we can write the following:

$$\neg p \vee (\neg q \rightarrow r) \equiv \neg p \vee (\neg T \rightarrow r) \equiv \neg p \vee (F \rightarrow r) \equiv \neg p \vee T \equiv \mathbf{T}$$

(2) We can display this reasoning visually as follows:

$$\neg p \lor (\neg q \to r)$$

```
            | T |
             F
                T
   T
```

The vertical lines have just been included to make sure you see which connective each truth value is written below.

We began by placing a T under the propositional variable q to indicate that q is true. Since $\neg T \equiv F$, we then place an F under the negation symbol. Next, since $F \to r \equiv T$ regardless of the truth value of r, we place a T under the conditional symbol. Finally, since $\neg p \lor T \equiv T$ regardless of the truth value of p, we place a T under the disjunction symbol. We made this last T bold to indicate that we are finished.

(3) Knowing that q has truth value T is enough to determine the truth value of $\neg p \lor (\neg q \to r)$, as we saw in Note 1 above. It's okay if you didn't notice that right away. This kind of reasoning takes a bit of practice and experience.

Truth table solution: An alternative solution is to build the whole truth table of $\neg p \lor (\neg q \to r)$ one column at a time. Since there are 3 propositional variables (p, q, and r), we will need $2^3 = 8$ rows to get all the possible truth values. We then create a column for each compound statement that appears within the given statement starting with the statements of smallest length and working our way up to the given statement. We will need columns for p, q, r (the atomic statements), $\neg p$, $\neg q$, $\neg q \to r$, and finally, the statement itself, $\neg p \lor (\neg q \to r)$. Below is the final truth table with the relevant row highlighted and the final answer circled.

p	q	r	$\neg p$	$\neg q$	$\neg q \to r$	$\neg p \lor (\neg q \to r)$
T	T	T	F	F	T	T
T	T	F	F	F	T	T
T	F	T	F	T	T	T
T	F	F	F	T	F	F
F	T	T	T	F	T	T
F	T	F	T	F	T	T
F	F	T	T	T	T	T
F	F	F	T	T	F	T

Notes: (1) We fill out the first three columns of the truth table by listing all possible combinations of truth assignments for the propositional variables p, q, and r. Notice how down the first column we have 4 T's followed by 4 F's, down the second column we alternate sequences of 2 T's with 2 F's, and down the third column we alternate T's with F's one at a time. This is a nice systematic way to make sure we get all possible combinations of truth assignments.

14

If you're having trouble seeing the pattern of T's and F's, here is another way to think about it: In the first column, the first half of the rows have a T and the remainder have an F. This gives 4 T's followed by 4 F's.

For the second column, we take half the number of consecutive T's in the first column (half of 4 is 2) and then we alternate between 2 T's and 2 F's until we fill out the column.

For the third column, we take half the number of consecutive T's in the second column (half of 2 is 1) and then we alternate between 1 T and 1 F until we fill out the column.

(2) Since the connective $\neg$ has the effect of taking the opposite truth value, we generate the entries in the fourth column by taking the opposite of each truth value in the first column. Similarly, we generate the entries in the fifth column by taking the opposite of each truth value in the second column.

(3) For the sixth column, we apply the connective $\rightarrow$ to the fifth and third columns, respectively, and finally, for the last column, we apply the connective $\vee$ to the fourth and sixth columns, respectively.

(4) The original question is asking us to compute the truth value of $\neg p \vee (\neg q \rightarrow r)$ when p and q are true, and r is false. In terms of the truth table, we are being asked for the entry in the second row and last (seventh) column. Therefore, the answer is **T**.

(5) This is certainly not the most efficient way to answer the given question. However, building truth tables is not too difficult, and it's a foolproof way to determine truth values of compound statements.

Problem Set 1

Full solutions to these problems are available for free download here:

www.SATPrepGet800.com/PMFBXSG

LEVEL 1

1. Determine whether each of the following sentences is an atomic statement, a compound statement, or not a statement at all:

    (i)   I am not going to work today.

    (ii)   What is the meaning of life?

    (iii)   Don't go away mad.

    (iv)   I watched the television show Parks and Recreation.

    (v)   If pigs have wings, then they can fly.

    (vi) $3 < -5$ or $38 > 37$.

    (vii)   This sentence has five words.

    (viii) I cannot swim, but I can run fast.

2. What is the negation of each of the following statements:

    (i)   The banana is my favorite fruit.

    (ii) $7 > -3$.

    (iii)   You are not alone.

    (iv)   The function f is differentiable everywhere.

LEVEL 2

3. Let p represent the statement "9 is a perfect square," let q represent the statement "Orange is a primary color," and let r represent the statement "A frog is a reptile." Rewrite each of the following symbolic statements in words, and state the truth value of each statement:

    (i) $p \land q$

    (ii) $\neg r$

    (iii) $p \rightarrow r$

    (iv) $q \leftrightarrow r$

    (v) $\neg p \land q$

    (vi) $\neg (p \land q)$

    (vii) $\neg p \lor \neg q$

    (viii) $(p \land q) \rightarrow r$

4. Consider the compound sentence "You can have a cookie or ice cream." In English this would most likely mean that you can have one or the other but not both. The word "or" used here is generally called an "exclusive or" because it excludes the possibility of both. The disjunction is an "inclusive or." Using the symbol $\oplus$ for exclusive or, draw the truth table for this connective.

LEVEL 3

5. Let p, q, and r represent true statements. Compute the truth value of each of the following compound statements:

   (i) $(p \vee q) \vee r$

   (ii) $(p \vee q) \wedge \neg r$

   (iii) $\neg p \to (q \vee r)$

   (iv) $\neg(p \leftrightarrow \neg q) \wedge r$

   (v) $\neg[p \wedge (\neg q \to r)]$

   (vi) $\neg[(\neg p \vee \neg q) \leftrightarrow \neg r]$

   (vii) $p \to (q \to \neg r)$

   (viii) $\neg[\neg p \to (q \to \neg r)]$

6. Using only the logical connectives $\neg$, $\wedge$, and $\vee$, produce a statement using the propositional variables p and q that has the same truth values as $p \oplus q$ (this is the "exclusive or" defined in problem 4 above).

LEVEL 4

7. Let p represent a true statement. Decide if this is enough information to determine the truth value of each of the following statements. If so, state that truth value.

   (i) $p \vee q$

   (ii) $p \to q$

   (iii) $\neg p \to \neg(q \vee \neg r)$

   (iv) $\neg(\neg p \wedge q) \leftrightarrow p$

   (v) $(p \leftrightarrow q) \leftrightarrow \neg p$

   (vi) $\neg[(\neg p \wedge \neg q) \leftrightarrow \neg r]$

   (vii) $[(p \wedge \neg p) \to p] \wedge (p \vee \neg p)$

   (viii) $r \to [\neg q \to (\neg p \to \neg r)]$

8. Assume that the given compound statement is true. Determine the truth value of each propositional variable.

  (i) $p \land q$

  (ii) $\neg(p \to q)$

  (iii) $p \leftrightarrow [\neg(p \land q)]$

  (iv) $[p \land (q \lor r)] \land \neg r$

LEVEL 5

9. Show that $[p \land (q \lor r)] \leftrightarrow [(p \land q) \lor (p \land r)]$ is always true.

10. Show that $\big[[(p \land q) \to r] \to s\big] \to [(p \to r) \to s]$ is always true.

LESSON 2 – SET THEORY
SETS AND SUBSETS

Describing Sets

A **set** is simply a collection of "objects." These objects can be numbers, letters, colors, animals, funny quotes, or just about anything else you can imagine. We will usually refer to the objects in a set as the **members** or **elements** of the set.

If a set consists of a small number of elements, we can describe the set simply by listing the elements in the set in curly braces, separating elements by commas.

Example 2.1:

1. {apple, banana} is the set consisting of two elements: *apple* and *banana*.

2. {anteater, elephant, egg, trapezoid} is the set consisting of four elements: *anteater*, *elephant*, *egg*, and *trapezoid*.

3. $\{2, 4, 6, 8, 10\}$ is the set consisting of five elements: 2, 4, 6, 8, and 10. The elements in this set happen to be *numbers*.

A set is determined by its elements, and not the order in which the elements are presented. For example, the set $\{4, 2, 8, 6, 10\}$ is the same as the set $\{2, 4, 6, 8, 10\}$.

Also, the set $\{2, 2, 4, 6, 8, 10, 10, 10\}$ is the same as the set $\{2, 4, 6, 8, 10\}$. If we are describing a set by listing its elements, the most natural way to do this is to list each element just once.

We will usually name sets using capital letters such as A, B, and C. For example, we might write $A = \{1, 2, 3\}$. So, A is the set consisting of the elements 1, 2, and 3.

Example 2.2: Consider the sets $A = \{a, b\}$, $B = \{b, a\}$, $C = \{a, b, a\}$. Then A, B, and C all represent the same set. We can write $A = B = C$.

We use the symbol $\in$ for the membership relation (we will define the term "relation" more carefully in Lesson 10). So, $x \in A$ means "x is an element of A," whereas $x \notin A$ means "x is **not** an element of A."

Example 2.3: Let $A = \{a, k, 3, \boxdot, \oplus\}$. Then $a \in A$, $k \in A$, $3 \in A$, $\boxdot \in A$, and $\oplus \in A$.

If a set consists of many elements, we can use **ellipses** (...) to help describe the set. For example, the set consisting of the natural numbers between 17 and 5326, inclusive, can be written $\{17, 18, 19, \ldots, 5325, 5326\}$ ("inclusive" means that we include 17 and 5326). The ellipses between 19 and 5325 are there to indicate that there are elements in the set that we are not explicitly mentioning.

Ellipses can also be used to help describe **infinite sets**. The set of **natural numbers** can be written $\mathbb{N} = \{0, 1, 2, 3, \ldots\}$, and the set of **integers** can be written $\mathbb{Z} = \{\ldots, -4, -3, -2, -1, 0, 1, 2, 3, 4, \ldots\}$.

Example 2.4: The odd natural numbers can be written $\mathbb{O} = \{1, 3, 5, \dots\}$. The even integers can be written $2\mathbb{Z} = \{\dots, -6, -4, -2, 0, 2, 4, 6, \dots\}$. The primes can be written $\mathbb{P} = \{2, 3, 5, 7, 11, 13, 17, \dots\}$.

A set can also be described by a certain property P that all its elements have in common. In this case, we can use the **set-builder notation** $\{x | P(x)\}$ to describe the set. The expression $\{x | P(x)\}$ can be read "the set of all x such that the property $P(x)$ is true." Note that the symbol "|" is read as "such that."

Example 2.5: Let's look at a few different ways that we can describe the set $\{2, 4, 6, 8, 10\}$. We have already seen that reordering and/or repeating elements does not change the set. For example, $\{2, 2, 6, 4, 10, 8\}$ describes the same set. Here are a few more descriptions using set-builder notation:

- $\{n \mid n$ is an even positive integer less than or equal to $10\}$
- $\{n \in \mathbb{Z} \mid n$ is even, $0 < n \leq 10\}$
- $\{2k \mid k = 1, 2, 3, 4, 5\}$

The first expression in the bulleted list can be read "the set of n such that n is an even positive integer less than or equal to 10." The second expression can be read "the set of integers n such that n is even and n is between 0 and 10, including 10, but excluding 0. Note that the abbreviation "$n \in \mathbb{Z}$" can be read "n is in the set of integers," or more succinctly, "n is an integer." The third expression can be read "the set of $2k$ such that k is $1, 2, 3, 4$, or 5."

If A is a finite set, we define the **cardinality** of A, written $|A|$, to be the number of elements of A. For example, $|\{a, b\}| = 2$. In Lesson 10, we will extend the notion of cardinality to also include infinite sets.

Example 2.6: Let $A = \{\text{anteater}, \text{egg}, \text{trapezoid}\}$, $B = \{2, 3, 3\}$, and $C = \{17, 18, 19, \dots, 5325, 5326\}$. Then $|A| = 3$, $|B| = 2$, and $|C| = 5310$.

Notes: (1) The set A has the three elements "anteater," "egg," and "trapezoid."

(2) The set B has just two elements: 2 and 3. Remember that $\{2, 3, 3\} = \{2, 3\}$.

(3) The number of consecutive integers from m to n, inclusive, is $n - m + 1$. For set C, we have $m = 17$ and $n = 5326$. Therefore, $|C| = 5326 - 17 + 1 = 5310$.

(4) I call the formula "$n - m + 1$" the **fence-post formula**. If you construct a 3-foot fence by placing a fence-post every foot, then the fence will consist of 4 fence-posts ($3 - 0 + 1 = 4$).

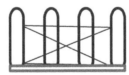

The **empty set** is the unique set with no elements. We use the symbol $\emptyset$ to denote the empty set (some authors use the symbol $\{\ \}$ instead).

Subsets

For two sets A and B, we say that A is a **subset** of B, written $A \subseteq B$, if every element of A is an element of B. That is, $A \subseteq B$ if, for every x, $x \in A$ implies $x \in B$. Symbolically, we can write $\forall x (x \in A \rightarrow x \in B)$.

Notes: (1) The symbol $\forall$ is called a **universal quantifier**, and it is pronounced "For all."

(2) The logical expression $\forall x(x \in A \rightarrow x \in B)$ can be translated into English as "For all x, if x is an element of A, then x is an element of B."

(3) To show that a set A is a subset of a set B, we need to show that the expression $\forall x(x \in A \rightarrow x \in B)$ is true. If the set A is finite and the elements are listed, we can just check that each element of A is also an element of B. However, if the set A is described by a property, say $A = \{x|P(x)\}$, we may need to craft an argument more carefully. We can begin by taking an **arbitrary but specific element** a from A and then arguing that this element a is in B.

What could we possibly mean by an arbitrary but specific element? Aren't the words "arbitrary" and "specific" antonyms? Well, by arbitrary, we mean that we don't know which element we are choosing – it's just some element a that satisfies the property P. So, we are just assuming that $P(a)$ is true. However, once we choose this element a, we use this same a for the rest of the argument, and that is what we mean by it being specific.

(4) To the right we see a physical representation of $A \subseteq B$. This figure is called a **Venn diagram**. These types of diagrams are very useful to help visualize relationships among sets. Notice that set A lies completely inside set B. We assume that all the elements of A and B lie in some **universal set** U.

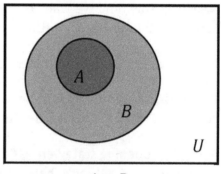

$A \subseteq B$

As an example, let's let U be the set of all species of animals. If we let A be the set of species of cats and we let B be the set of species of mammals, then we have $A \subseteq B \subseteq U$, and we see that the Venn diagram to the right gives a visual representation of this situation. (Note that every cat is a mammal and every mammal is an animal.)

Let's try to prove our first theorem using the definition of a subset together with Note 3 above about arbitrary but specific elements.

Theorem 2.1: Every set A is a subset of itself.

Before writing the proof, let's think about our strategy. We want to prove $A \subseteq A$. In other words, we want to show $\forall x(x \in A \rightarrow x \in A)$. So, we will take an arbitrary but specific $a \in A$ and then argue that $a \in A$. But that's pretty obvious, isn't it? In this case, the property describing the set is precisely the conclusion we are looking for. Here are the details.

Proof of Theorem 2.1: Let A be a set and let $a \in A$. Then $a \in A$. So, $a \in A \rightarrow a \in A$ is true. Since a was arbitrary, $\forall x(x \in A \rightarrow x \in A)$ is true. Therefore, $A \subseteq A$. $\qquad\square$

Notes: (1) The proof begins with the **opening statement** "Let A be a set and let $a \in A$." In general, the opening statement states what is given in the problem and/or fixes any arbitrary but specific objects that we will need.

(2) The proof ends with the **closing statement** "Therefore, $A \subseteq A$." In general, the closing statement states the result.

(3) Everything between the opening statement and the closing statement is known as the **argument**.

(4) We place the symbol □ at the end of the proof to indicate that the proof is complete.

(5) Consider the logical statement $p \rightarrow p$. This statement is always true ($T \rightarrow T \equiv T$ and $F \rightarrow F \equiv T$). $p \rightarrow p$ is an example of a tautology. A **tautology** is a statement that is true for every possible truth assignment of the propositional variables (see Problems 9 and 10 from Lesson 1 for more examples).

(6) If we let p represent the sentence $a \in A$, by Note 5, we see that $a \in A \rightarrow a \in A$ is always true.

Alternate proof of Theorem 2.1: Let A be a set, and let $a \in A$. Since $p \rightarrow p$ is a tautology, we have that $a \in A \rightarrow a \in A$ is true. Since a was arbitrary, $\forall x (x \in A \rightarrow x \in A)$ is true. Therefore, $A \subseteq A$. □

Let's prove another basic but important theorem.

Theorem 2.2: The empty set is a subset of every set.

Analysis: This time we want to prove $\emptyset \subseteq A$. In other words, we want to show $\forall x (x \in \emptyset \rightarrow x \in A)$. Since $x \in \emptyset$ is always false (the empty set has no elements), $x \in \emptyset \rightarrow x \in A$ is always true.

In general, if p is a false statement, then we say that $p \rightarrow q$ is **vacuously true**.

Proof of Theorem 2.2: Let A be a set. The statement $x \in \emptyset \rightarrow x \in A$ is vacuously true for any x, and so, $\forall x (x \in \emptyset \rightarrow x \in A)$ is true. Therefore, $\emptyset \subseteq A$. □

Note: The opening statement is "Let A be a set," the closing statement is "Therefore, $\emptyset \subseteq A$," and the argument is everything in between.

Example 2.7: Let $C = \{a, b, c\}$, $D = \{a, c\}$, $E = \{b, c\}$, $F = \{b, d\}$, and $G = \emptyset$. Then $D \subseteq C$ and $E \subseteq C$. Also, since *the empty set is a subset of every set*, we have $G \subseteq C$, $G \subseteq D$, $G \subseteq E$, $G \subseteq F$, and $G \subseteq G$. *Every set is a subset of itself*, and so, $C \subseteq C$, $D \subseteq D$, $E \subseteq E$, and $F \subseteq F$.

Note: Below are possible Venn diagrams for this problem. The diagram on the left shows the relationship between the sets C, D, E, and F. Notice how D and E are both subsets of C, whereas F is not a subset of C. Also, notice how D and E overlap, E and F overlap, but there is no overlap between D and F (they have no elements in common). The diagram on the right shows the proper placement of the elements. Here, I chose the universal set to be $U = \{a, b, c, d, e, f, g\}$. This choice for the universal set is somewhat arbitrary. Any set containing $\{a, b, c, d\}$ would do.

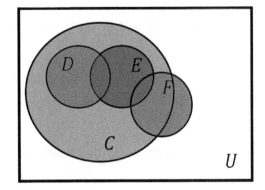
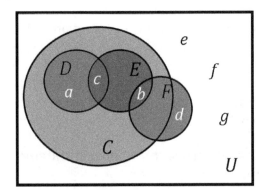

Example 2.8: The set $A = \{a, b\}$ has 2 elements and 4 subsets. The subsets of A are $\emptyset$, $\{a\}$, $\{b\}$, and $\{a, b\}$.

The set $B = \{a, b, c\}$ has 3 elements and 8 subsets. The subsets of B are $\emptyset$, $\{a\}$, $\{b\}$, $\{c\}$, $\{a, b\}$, $\{a, c\}$, $\{b, c\}$, and $\{a, b, c\}$.

Let's draw a **tree diagram** for the subsets of each of the sets A and B.

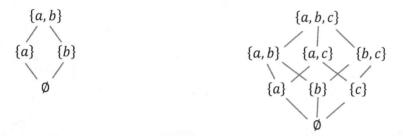

The tree diagram on the left is for the subsets of the set $A = \{a, b\}$. We start by writing the set $A = \{a, b\}$ at the top. On the next line we write the subsets of cardinality 1 ($\{a\}$ and $\{b\}$). On the line below that we write the subsets of cardinality 0 (just $\emptyset$). We draw a line segment between any two sets when the smaller (lower) set is a subset of the larger (higher) set. So, we see that $\emptyset \subseteq \{a\}$, $\emptyset \subseteq \{b\}$, $\{a\} \subseteq \{a, b\}$, and $\{b\} \subseteq \{a, b\}$. There is actually one more subset relationship, namely $\emptyset \subseteq \{a, b\}$ (and of course each set displayed is a subset of itself). We didn't draw a line segment from $\emptyset$ to $\{a, b\}$ to avoid unnecessary clutter. Instead, we can simply trace the path from $\emptyset$ to $\{a\}$ to $\{a, b\}$ (or from $\emptyset$ to $\{b\}$ to $\{a, b\}$). We are using a property called **transitivity** here (see Theorem 2.3 below).

The tree diagram on the right is for the subsets of $B = \{a, b, c\}$. Observe that from top to bottom we write the subsets of B of size 3, then 2, then 1, and then 0. We then draw the appropriate line segments, just as we did for $A = \{a, b\}$.

How many subsets does a set of cardinality n have? Let's start by looking at some examples.

Example 2.9: A set with 0 elements must be $\emptyset$, and this set has exactly 1 subset (the only subset of the empty set is the empty set itself).

A set with 1 element has 2 subsets, namely $\emptyset$ and the set itself.

In the last example, we saw that a set with 2 elements has 4 subsets, and we also saw that a set with 3 elements has 8 subsets.

Do you see the pattern yet? $1 = 2^0, 2 = 2^1, 4 = 2^2, 8 = 2^3$. So, we see that a set with 0 elements has 2^0 subsets, a set with 1 element has 2^1 subsets, a set with 2 elements has 2^2 subsets, and a set with 3 elements has 2^3 subsets. A reasonable guess would be that a set with n elements has 2^n subsets. You will be asked to prove this result later (Problem 12 in Lesson 4). We can also say that if $|A| = n$, then $|\mathcal{P}(A)| = 2^n$, where $\mathcal{P}(A)$ (pronounced the **power set** of A) is the set of all subsets of A. In set-builder notation, we write $\mathcal{P}(A) = \{B \mid B \subseteq A\}$.

Let's get back to the transitivity mentioned above in our discussion of tree diagrams.

Theorem 2.3: Let A, B, and C be sets such that $A \subseteq B$ and $B \subseteq C$. Then $A \subseteq C$.

Proof: Suppose that A, B, and C are sets with $A \subseteq B$ and $B \subseteq C$, and let $a \in A$. Since $A \subseteq B$ and $a \in A$, it follows that $a \in B$. Since $B \subseteq C$ and $a \in B$, it follows that $a \in C$. Since a was an arbitrary element of A, we have shown that every element of A is an element of C. That is, $\forall x(x \in A \rightarrow x \in C)$ is true. Therefore, $A \subseteq C$. $\square$

Note: To the right we have a Venn diagram illustrating Theorem 2.3.

Theorem 2.3 tells us that the relation $\subseteq$ is **transitive**. Since $\subseteq$ is transitive, we can write things like $A \subseteq B \subseteq C \subseteq D$, and without explicitly saying it, we know that $A \subseteq C$, $A \subseteq D$, and $B \subseteq D$.

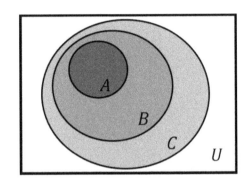

$$A \subseteq B \subseteq C$$

Example 2.10: The membership relation $\in$ is an example of a relation that is **not** transitive. For example, let $A = \{0\}$, $B = \{0, 1, \{0\}\}$, and $C = \{x, y, \{0, 1, \{0\}\}\}$. Observe that $A \in B$ and $B \in C$, but $A \notin C$.

Notes: (1) The set A has just 1 element, namely 0.

(2) The set B has 3 elements, namely 0, 1, and $\{0\}$. But wait! $A = \{0\}$. So, $A \in B$. The set A is circled twice in the above image.

(3) The set C also has 3 elements, namely, x, y, and $\{0, 1, \{0\}\}$. But wait! $B = \{0, 1, \{0\}\}$. So, $B \in C$. The set B has a rectangle around it twice in the above image.

(4) Since $A \neq x$, $A \neq y$, and $A \neq \{0, 1, \{0\}\}$, we see that $A \notin C$.

(5) Is it clear that $\{0\} \notin C$? $\{0\}$ is in a set that's in C (namely, B), but $\{0\}$ is not itself in C.

(6) Here is an even simpler example showing that $\in$ is not transitive: $0 \in \{0\} \in \{\{0\}\}$, but $0 \notin \{\{0\}\}$ The only element of $\{\{0\}\}$ is $\{0\}$.

Unions and Intersections

The **union** of the sets A and B, written $A \cup B$, is the set of elements that are in A or B (or both).

$$A \cup B = \{x \mid x \in A \text{ or } x \in B\}$$

The **intersection** of A and B, written $A \cap B$, is the set of elements that are simultaneously in A and B.

$$A \cap B = \{x \mid x \in A \text{ and } x \in B\}$$

The following Venn diagrams for the union and intersection of two sets can be useful for visualizing these operations.

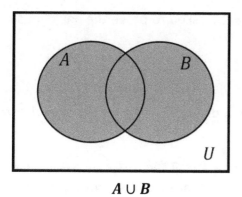

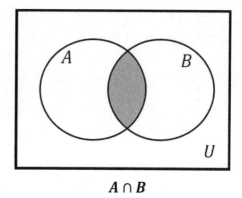

$$A \cup B \qquad\qquad A \cap B$$

Example 2.11:

1. Let $A = \{0, 1, 2, 3, 4\}$ and $B = \{3, 4, 5, 6\}$. Then $A \cup B = \{0, 1, 2, 3, 4, 5, 6\}$ and $A \cap B = \{3, 4\}$. See the figure below for a visual representation of A, B, $A \cup B$ and $A \cap B$.

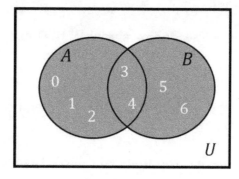

2. Recall that the set of natural numbers is $\mathbb{N} = \{0, 1, 2, 3, \dots\}$ and the set of integers is $\mathbb{Z} = \{\dots, -4, -3, -2, -1, 0, 1, 2, 3, 4, \dots\}$. Observe that in this case, we have $\mathbb{N} \subseteq \mathbb{Z}$. Also, $\mathbb{N} \cup \mathbb{Z} = \mathbb{Z}$ and $\mathbb{N} \cap \mathbb{Z} = \mathbb{N}$.

    In fact, whenever A and B are sets and $B \subseteq A$, then $A \cup B = A$ and $A \cap B = B$. We will prove the first of these two facts in Theorem 2.5. You will be asked to prove the second of these facts in Problem 13 below.

3. Let $\mathbb{E} = \{0, 2, 4, 6, \dots\}$ be the set of even natural numbers and let $\mathbb{O} = \{1, 3, 5, 7, \dots\}$ be the set of odd natural numbers. Then $\mathbb{E} \cup \mathbb{O} = \{0, 1, 2, 3, 4, 5, 6, 7, \dots\} = \mathbb{N}$ and $\mathbb{E} \cap \mathbb{O} = \emptyset$. In general, we say that sets A and B are **disjoint** or **mutually exclusive** if $A \cap B = \emptyset$. Below is a Venn diagram for disjoint sets.

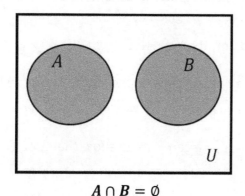

$$A \cap B = \emptyset$$

Let's prove some theorems involving unions of sets. You will be asked to prove the analogous results for intersections of sets in Problems 11 and 13 below.

Theorem 2.4: If A and B are sets, then $A \subseteq A \cup B$.

Before going through the proof, look once more at the Venn diagram above for $A \cup B$ and convince yourself that this theorem should be true.

Proof of Theorem 2.4: Suppose that A and B are sets and let $x \in A$. Then $x \in A$ or $x \in B$. Therefore, $x \in A \cup B$. Since x was an arbitrary element of A, we have shown that every element of A is an element of $A \cup B$. That is, $\forall x(x \in A \rightarrow x \in A \cup B)$ is true. Therefore, $A \subseteq A \cup B$. $\qquad\square$

Note: Recall from Lesson 1 that if p is a true statement, then $p \vee q$ (p or q) is true no matter what the truth value of q is. In the second sentence of the proof above, we are using this fact with p being the statement $x \in A$ and q being the statement $x \in B$.

We will use this same reasoning in the second paragraph of the next proof as well.

Theorem 2.5: $B \subseteq A$ if and only if $A \cup B = A$.

Before going through the proof, it's a good idea to draw a Venn diagram for $B \subseteq A$ and convince yourself that this theorem should be true.

Technical note: Let X and Y be sets. The **Axiom of Extensionality** says that X and Y are the same set if and only if X and Y have precisely the same elements. In symbols, we have

$$X = Y \text{ if and only if } \forall x(x \in X \leftrightarrow x \in Y).$$

It is easy to verify that $p \leftrightarrow q$ is logically equivalent to $(p \rightarrow q) \wedge (q \rightarrow p)$. To see this, we check that all possible truth assignments for p and q lead to the same truth value for the two statements. For example, if p and q are both true, then

$$p \leftrightarrow q \equiv T \leftrightarrow T \equiv T \quad \text{and} \quad (p \rightarrow q) \wedge (q \rightarrow p) \equiv (T \rightarrow T) \wedge (T \rightarrow T) \equiv T \wedge T \equiv T.$$

The reader should check the other three truth assignments for p and q, or draw the entire truth table for both statements.

Letting p be the statement $x \in X$, letting q be the statement $x \in Y$, and replacing $p \leftrightarrow q$ by the logically equivalent statement $(p \rightarrow q) \wedge (q \rightarrow p)$ gives us

$$X = Y \text{ if and only if } \forall x((x \in X \rightarrow x \in Y) \wedge (x \in Y \rightarrow x \in X)).$$

It is also true that $\forall x(p(x) \wedge q(x))$ is logically equivalent to $\forall x(p(x)) \wedge \forall x(q(x))$. And so, we have

$$X = Y \text{ if and only if } \forall x(x \in X \rightarrow x \in Y) \text{ and } \forall x(x \in Y \rightarrow x \in X).$$

In other words, to show that $X = Y$, we can instead show that $X \subseteq Y$ and $Y \subseteq X$.

Proof of Theorem 2.5: Suppose that $B \subseteq A$ and let $x \in A \cup B$. Then $x \in A$ or $x \in B$. If $x \in A$, then $x \in A$ (trivially). If $x \in B$, then since $B \subseteq A$, it follows that $x \in A$. Since x was an arbitrary element of $A \cup B$, we have shown that every element of $A \cup B$ is an element of A. That is, $\forall x (x \in A \cup B \rightarrow x \in A)$ is true. Therefore, $A \cup B \subseteq A$. By Theorem 2.4, $A \subseteq A \cup B$. Since $A \cup B \subseteq A$ and $A \subseteq A \cup B$, it follows that $A \cup B = A$.

Now, suppose that $A \cup B = A$ and let $x \in B$. Since $x \in B$, it follows that $x \in A$ or $x \in B$. Therefore, $x \in A \cup B$. Since $A \cup B = A$, we have $x \in A$. Since x was an arbitrary element of B, we have shown that every element of B is an element of A. That is, $\forall x (x \in B \rightarrow x \in A)$. Therefore, $B \subseteq A$. $\qquad\square$

Problem Set 2

Full solutions to these problems are available for free download here:
www.SATPrepGet800.com/PMFBXSG

LEVEL 1

1. Determine whether each of the following statements is true or false:

   (i) $2 \in \{2\}$

   (ii) $5 \in \emptyset$

   (iii) $\emptyset \in \{1, 2\}$

   (iv) $a \in \{b, \{a\}\}$

   (v) $\emptyset \subseteq \{1, 2\}$

   (vi) $\{\Delta\} \subseteq \{\delta, \Delta\}$

   (vii) $\{a, b, c\} \subseteq \{a, b, c\}$

   (viii) $\{1, a, \{2, b\}\} \subseteq \{1, a, 2, b\}$

2. Determine the cardinality of each of the following sets:

   (i) $\{a, b, c, d, e, f\}$

   (ii) $\{1, 2, 3, 2, 1\}$

   (iii) $\{1, 2, \ldots, 53\}$

   (iv) $\{5, 6, 7, \ldots, 2076, 2077\}$

3. Let $A = \{a, b, \Delta, \delta\}$ and $B = \{b, c, \delta, \gamma\}$. Determine each of the following:

   (i) $A \cup B$

   (ii) $A \cap B$

LEVEL 2

4. Determine whether each of the following statements is true or false:

   (i) $\emptyset \in \emptyset$

   (ii) $\emptyset \in \{\emptyset\}$

   (iii) $\{\emptyset\} \in \emptyset$

   (iv) $\{\emptyset\} \in \{\emptyset\}$

   (v) $\emptyset \subseteq \emptyset$

   (vi) $\emptyset \subseteq \{\emptyset\}$

   (vii) $\{\emptyset\} \subseteq \emptyset$

   (viii) $\{\emptyset\} \subseteq \{\emptyset\}$

5. Determine the cardinality of each of the following sets:

   (i) $\{\emptyset, \{1, 2, 3\}\}$

   (ii) $\{\{\{\emptyset, \{\emptyset\}\}\}\}$

   (iii) $\{\{1,2\}, \emptyset, \{\emptyset\}, \{\emptyset, \{\emptyset, 1, 2\}\}\}$

   (iv) $\{\emptyset, \{\emptyset\}, \{\{\emptyset\}\}, \{\emptyset, \{\emptyset\}, \{\{\emptyset\}\}\}\}$

6. Let $P = \{\emptyset, \{\emptyset\}\}$ and $B = \{\{\emptyset\}, \{\emptyset, \{\emptyset\}\}\}$. Determine each of the following:

   (i) $A \cup B$

   (ii) $A \cap B$

LEVEL 3

7. How many subsets does $\{a, b, c, d\}$ have? Draw a tree diagram for the subsets of $\{a, b, c, d\}$.

8. A set A is transitive if $\forall x (x \in A \rightarrow x \subseteq A)$ (in words, every element of A is also a subset of A). Determine if each of the following sets is transitive:

   (i) $\emptyset$

   (ii) $\{\emptyset\}$

   (iii) $\{\{\emptyset\}\}$

   (iv) $\{\emptyset, \{\emptyset\}, \{\{\emptyset\}\}\}$

LEVEL 4

9. A relation R is **reflexive** if $\forall x(xRx)$ and **symmetric** if $\forall x \forall y (xRy \rightarrow yRx)$. Show that $\subseteq$ is reflexive, but $\in$ is not. Then decide if each of $\subseteq$ and $\in$ is symmetric.

10. Let A, B, C, D, and E be sets such that $A \subseteq B$, $B \subseteq C$, $C \subseteq D$, and $D \subseteq E$. Prove that $A \subseteq E$.

11. Let A and B be sets. Prove that $A \cap B \subseteq A$.

LEVEL 5

12. Let $P(x)$ be the property $x \notin x$. Prove that $\{x | P(x)\}$ cannot be a set.

13. Prove that $B \subseteq A$ if and only if $A \cap B = B$.

14. Let $A = \{a, b, c, d\}$, $B = \{X \mid X \subseteq A \wedge d \notin X\}$, and $C = \{X \mid X \subseteq A \wedge d \in X\}$. Show that there is a natural one-to-one correspondence between the elements of B and the elements of C. Then generalize this result to a set with $n + 1$ elements for $n > 0$.

LESSON 3 – ABSTRACT ALGEBRA
SEMIGROUPS, MONOIDS, AND GROUPS

Binary Operations and Closure

A **binary operation** on a set is a rule that combines two elements of the set to produce another element of the set.

Example 3.1: Let $S = \{0, 1\}$. Multiplication on S is a binary operation, whereas addition on S is **not** a binary operation (here we are thinking of multiplication and addition in the "usual" sense, meaning the way we would think of them in elementary school or middle school).

To see that multiplication is a binary operation on S, observe that $0 \cdot 0 = 0$, $0 \cdot 1 = 0$, $1 \cdot 0 = 0$, and $1 \cdot 1 = 1$. Each of the four computations produces 0 or 1, both of which are in the set S.

To see that addition is not a binary operation on S, just note that $1 + 1 = 2$, and $2 \notin S$.

Let's get a bit more technical and write down the formal definition of a binary operation. The terminology and notation used in this definition will be clarified in the notes below and formalized more rigorously later in Lesson 10.

Formally, a **binary operation** $\star$ on a set S is a **function** $\star : S \times S \to S$. So, if $a, b \in S$, then we have $\star (a, b) \in S$. For easier readability, we will usually write $\star (a, b)$ as $a \star b$.

Notes: (1) If A and B are sets, then $A \times B$ is called the **Cartesian product** of A and B. It consists of the **ordered pairs** (a, b), where $a \in A$ and $b \in B$. A **function** $f : A \times B \to C$ takes each such pair (a, b) to an element $f(a, b) \in C$.

As an example, let $A = \{\text{dog}, \text{fish}\}$, $B = \{\text{cat}, \text{snake}\}$, $C = \{0, 2, 4, 6, 8\}$, and define $f : A \times B \to C$ by $f(a, b) =$ the total number of legs that animals a and b have. Then we have $f(\text{dog}, \text{cat}) = 8$, $f(\text{dog}, \text{snake}) = 4$, $f(\text{fish}, \text{cat}) = 4$, $f(\text{fish}, \text{snake}) = 0$.

We will look at ordered pairs, cartesian products, and functions in more detail in Lesson 10.

(2) For a binary operation, all three sets A, B, and C in the expression $f : A \times B \to C$ are the same.

As we saw in Example 3.1 above, if we let $S = \{0, 1\}$, and we let $\star$ be multiplication, then $\star$ is a binary operation on S. Using function notation, we have $\star (0, 0) = 0$, $\star (0, 1) = 0$, $\star (1, 0) = 0$, and $\star (1, 1) = 1$.

As stated in the formal definition of a binary operation above, we will usually write the computations as $0 \star 0 = 0$, $0 \star 1 = 0$, $1 \star 0 = 0$, and $1 \star 1 = 1$.

We can use symbols other than $\star$ for binary operations. For example, if the operation is multiplication, we would usually use a dot ($\cdot$) for the operation as we did in Example 3.1 above. Similarly, for addition we would usually use $+$, for subtraction we would usually use $-$, and so on.

30

Recall: $\mathbb{N} = \{0, 1, 2, 3, \dots\}$ is the set of natural numbers and $\mathbb{Z} = \{\dots, -4, -3, -2, -1, 0, 1, 2, 3, 4, \dots\}$ is the set of integers.

If A is a set of numbers, we let A^+ be the subset of A consisting of just the positive numbers from A. For example, $\mathbb{Z}^+ = \{1, 2, 3, 4, \dots\}$, and in fact, $\mathbb{N}^+ = \mathbb{Z}^+$.

Example 3.2:

1. The operation of addition on the set of natural numbers is a binary operation because whenever we add two natural numbers we get another natural number. Here, the set S is $\mathbb{N}$ and the operation $\star$ is $+$. Observe that if $a \in \mathbb{N}$ and $b \in \mathbb{N}$, then $a + b \in \mathbb{N}$. For example, if $a = 1$ and $b = 2$ (both elements of $\mathbb{N}$), then $a + b = 1 + 2 = 3$, and $3 \in \mathbb{N}$.

2. The operation of multiplication on the set of positive integers is a binary operation because whenever we multiply two positive integers we get another positive integer. Here, the set S is $\mathbb{Z}^+$ and the operation $\star$ is $\cdot$. Observe that if $a \in \mathbb{Z}^+$ and $b \in \mathbb{Z}^+$, then $a \cdot b \in \mathbb{Z}^+$. For example, if $a = 3$ and $b = 5$ (both elements of $\mathbb{Z}^+$), then $a \cdot b = 3 \cdot 5 = 15$, and $15 \in \mathbb{Z}^+$.

3. Let $S = \mathbb{Z}$ and define $\star$ by $a \star b = \min\{a, b\}$, where $\min\{a, b\}$ is the smallest of a or b. Then $\star$ is a binary operation on $\mathbb{Z}$. For example, if $a = -5$ and $b = 3$ (both elements of $\mathbb{Z}$), then $a \star b = -5$, and $-5 \in \mathbb{Z}$.

4. Subtraction on the set of natural numbers is **not** a binary operation. To see this, we just need to provide a single **counterexample**. (A counterexample is an example that is used to prove that a statement is false.) If we let $a = 1$ and $b = 2$ (both elements of $\mathbb{N}$), then we see that $a - b = 1 - 2$ is not an element of $\mathbb{N}$.

5. Let $S = \{u, v, w\}$ and define $\star$ using the following table:

$\star$	u	v	w
u	v	w	w
v	w	u	u
w	u	v	v

The table given above is called a **multiplication table**. For $a, b \in S$, we evaluate $a \star b$ by taking the entry in the row given by a and the column given by b. For example, $v \star w = u$.

$\star$	u	v	w
u	v	w	w
v	w	u	u
w	u	v	v

$\star$ is a binary operation on S because the only possible "outputs" are u, v, and w.

Some authors refer to a binary operation $\star$ on a set S even when the binary operation is not defined on all pairs of elements $a, b \in S$. We will always refer to these "false operations" as **partial binary operations**.

We say that the set S is **closed** under the partial binary operation $\star$ if whenever $a, b \in S$, we have $a \star b \in S$.

In Example 3.2, part 4 above, we saw that subtraction is a partial binary operation on $\mathbb{N}$ that is not a binary operation. In other words, $\mathbb{N}$ is not **closed** under subtraction.

Semigroups and Associativity

Let $\star$ be a binary operation on a set S. We say that $\star$ is **associative** in S if for all x, y, z in S, we have

$$(x \star y) \star z = x \star (y \star z)$$

A **semigroup** is a pair $(S, \star)$, where S is a set and $\star$ is an associative binary operation on S.

Example 3.3:

1. $(\mathbb{N}, +)$, $(\mathbb{Z}, +)$, $(\mathbb{N}, \cdot)$, and $(\mathbb{Z}, \cdot)$ are all semigroups. In other words, the operations of addition and multiplication are both associative in $\mathbb{N}$ and $\mathbb{Z}$.

2. Let $S = \mathbb{Z}$ and define $\star$ by $a \star b = \min\{a, b\}$, where $\min\{a, b\}$ is the smallest of a or b. Let's check that $\star$ is associative in $\mathbb{Z}$. Let a, b, and c be elements of $\mathbb{Z}$. There are actually 6 cases to consider (see Note 1 below). Let's go through one of these cases in detail. If we assume that $a \le b \le c$, then we have

$$(a \star b) \star c = \min\{a, b\} \star c = a \star c = \min\{a, c\} = a.$$
$$a \star (b \star c) = a \star \min\{b, c\} = a \star b = \min\{a, b\} = a.$$

Since both $(a \star b) \star c = a$ and $a \star (b \star c) = a$, we have $(a \star b) \star c = a \star (b \star c)$. After checking the other 5 cases, we can say the following: Since a, b, and c were arbitrary elements from $\mathbb{Z}$, we have shown that $\star$ is associative in $\mathbb{Z}$. It follows that $(\mathbb{Z}, \star)$ is a semigroup.

3. Subtraction is **not** associative in $\mathbb{Z}$. To see this, we just need to provide a single counterexample. If we let $a = 1$, $b = 2$, and $c = 3$, then $(a - b) - c = (1 - 2) - 3 = -1 - 3 = -4$ and $a - (b - c) = 1 - (2 - 3) = 1 - (-1) = 1 + 1 = 2$. Since $-4 \ne 2$, subtraction is not associative in $\mathbb{Z}$. It follows that $(\mathbb{Z}, -)$ is **not** a semigroup.

   Note that $(\mathbb{N}, -)$ is also not a semigroup, but for a different reason. Subtraction is not even a binary operation on $\mathbb{N}$ (see part 4 in Example 3.2).

4. Let $S = \{u, v, w\}$ and define $\star$ using the following table (this is the same table from part 5 in Example 3.2):

$\star$	u	v	w
u	v	w	w
v	w	u	u
w	u	v	v

Notice that $(u \star v) \star w = w \star w = v$ and $u \star (v \star w) = u \star u = v$.

So, $(u \star v) \star w = u \star (v \star w)$. However, this single computation does **not** show that $\star$ is associative in S. In fact, we have the following counterexample: $(u \star w) \star v = w \star v = v$ and $u \star (w \star v) = u \star v = w$. Thus, $(u \star w) \star v \ne u \star (w \star v)$.

So, $\star$ is **not** associative in S, and therefore, $(S, \star)$ is **not** a semigroup.

5. Let $2\mathbb{Z} = \{\dots, -6, -4, -2, 0, 2, 4, 6, \dots\}$ be the set of even integers. When we multiply two even integers together, we get another even integer (we will prove this in Lesson 4). It follows that multiplication is a binary operation on $2\mathbb{Z}$. Since multiplication is associative in $\mathbb{Z}$ and $2\mathbb{Z} \subseteq \mathbb{Z}$, it follows that multiplication is associative in $2\mathbb{Z}$ (see Note 2 below). So, $(2\mathbb{Z}, \cdot)$ is a semigroup.

Notes: (1) In part 2 above, we must prove the result for each of the following 6 cases:

$$a \leq b \leq c \qquad a \leq c \leq b \qquad b \leq a \leq c \qquad b \leq c \leq a \qquad c \leq a \leq b \qquad c \leq b \leq a$$

The same basic argument can be used for all these cases. For example, we saw in the solution above that for the first case we get

$$(a \star b) \star c = \min\{a, b\} \star c = a \star c = \min\{a, c\} = a.$$
$$a \star (b \star c) = a \star \min\{b, c\} = a \star b = \min\{a, b\} = a.$$

Let's also do the last case $c \leq b \leq a$:

$$(a \star b) \star c = \min\{a, b\} \star c = b \star c = \min\{b, c\} = c.$$
$$a \star (b \star c) = a \star \min\{b, c\} = a \star c = \min\{a, c\} = c.$$

The reader should verify the other 4 cases to complete the proof.

(2) Associativity is **closed downwards**. By this, we mean that if $\star$ is associative in a set A, and $B \subseteq A$, (B is a **subset** of A) then $\star$ is associative in B.

The reason for this is that the definition of associativity involves only a **universal statement**—a statement that describes a property that is true for all elements without mentioning the existence of any new elements. A universal statement begins with the quantifier $\forall$ ("For all" or "Every") and never includes the quantifier $\exists$ ("There exists" or "There is").

As a simple example, if every object in set A is a fruit, and $B \subseteq A$, then every object in B is a fruit. The universal statement we are referring to might be $\forall x(P(x))$, where $P(x)$ is the property "x is a fruit."

In the case of associativity, the universal statement is $\forall x \forall y \forall z((x \star y) \star z = x \star (y \star z))$.

Let $\star$ be a binary operation on a set S. We say that $\star$ is **commutative** (or **Abelian**) in S if for all x, y in S, we have $x \star y = y \star x$.

Example 3.4:

1. $(\mathbb{N}, +)$, $(\mathbb{Z}, +)$, $(\mathbb{N}, \cdot)$, and $(\mathbb{Z}, \cdot)$ are all **commutative semigroups**. In other words, the operations of addition and multiplication are both commutative in $\mathbb{N}$ and $\mathbb{Z}$ (in addition to being associative).

2. The semigroup $(\mathbb{Z}, \star)$, where $\star$ is defined by $a \star b = \min\{a, b\}$ is a commutative semigroup. Let's check that $\star$ is commutative in $\mathbb{Z}$. Let a and b be elements of $\mathbb{Z}$. This time there are just 2 cases to consider ($a \leq b$ and $b \leq a$). Let's do the first case in detail, and assume that $a \leq b$. We then have $a \star b = \min\{a, b\} = a$ and $b \star a = \min\{b, a\} = a$. So, $a \star b = b \star a$. After verifying the other case (which you should do), we can say that $\star$ is commutative in $\mathbb{Z}$.

3. Define the binary operation $\star$ on $\mathbb{N}$ by $a \star b = a$. Then $(\mathbb{N}, \star)$ is a semigroup that is **not** commutative. For associativity, we have $(a \star b) \star c = a \star c = a$ and $a \star (b \star c) = a \star b = a$. Let's use a counterexample to show that $\star$ is not commutative. Well, $2 \star 5 = 2$ and $5 \star 2 = 5$.

Note: In part 3 above, the computation $a \star (b \star c)$ can actually be done in 1 step instead of 2. The way we did it above was to first compute $b \star c = b$, and then to replace $b \star c$ with b to get $a \star (b \star c) = a \star b = a$. However, the definition of $\star$ says that $a \star (\text{anything}) = a$. In this case, the "anything" is $b \star c$. So, we have $a \star (b \star c) = a$ just by appealing to the definition of $\star$.

Monoids and Identity

Let $(S, \star)$ be a semigroup. An element e of S is called an **identity** with respect to the binary operation $\star$ if for all $a \in S$, we have $e \star a = a \star e = a$

A **monoid** is a semigroup with an identity.

Example 3.5:

1. $(\mathbb{N}, +)$ and $(\mathbb{Z}, +)$ are commutative monoids with identity 0 (when we add 0 to any integer a, we get a). $(\mathbb{N}, \cdot)$ and $(\mathbb{Z}, \cdot)$ are commutative monoids with identity 1 (when we multiply any integer a by 1, we get a).

2. The commutative semigroup $(\mathbb{Z}, \star)$, where $\star$ is defined by $a \star b = \min\{a, b\}$ is **not** a monoid. To see this, let $a \in \mathbb{Z}$. Then $a + 1 \in \mathbb{Z}$ and $a \star (a + 1) = a \neq a + 1$. This shows that a is not an identity. Since a was an arbitrary element of $\mathbb{Z}$, we showed that there is no identity. It follows that $(\mathbb{Z}, \star)$ is not a monoid.

3. The noncommutative semigroup $(\mathbb{N}, \star)$, where $a \star b = a$ is also **not** a monoid. Use the same argument given in 2 above with $\mathbb{Z}$ replaced by $\mathbb{N}$.

4. $(2\mathbb{Z}, \cdot)$ is another example of a semigroup that is **not** a monoid. The identity element of $(\mathbb{Z}, \cdot)$ is 1, and this element is missing from $(2\mathbb{Z}, \cdot)$.

Groups and Inverses

Let $(M, \star)$ be a monoid with identity e. An element a of M is called **invertible** if there is an element $b \in M$ such that $a \star b = b \star a = e$.

A **group** is a monoid in which every element is invertible.

Groups appear so often in mathematics that it's worth taking the time to explicitly spell out the full definition of a group.

A **group** is a pair $(G, \star)$ consisting of a set G together with a binary operation $\star$ satisfying:

(1) **(Associativity)** For all $x, y, z \in G$, $(x \star y) \star z = x \star (y \star z)$.

(2) **(Identity)** There exists an element $e \in G$ such that for all $x \in G$, $e \star x = x \star e = x$.

(3) **(Inverse)** For each $x \in G$, there is $y \in G$ such that $x \star y = y \star x = e$.

Notes: (1) If $y \in G$ is an inverse of $x \in G$, we will usually write $y = x^{-1}$.

(2) Recall that the definition of a binary operation already implies closure. However, many books on groups will mention this property explicitly:

> **(Closure)** For all $x, y \in G$, $x \star y \in G$.

(3) A group is **commutative** or **Abelian** if for all $x, y \in G$, $x \star y = y \star x$.

Example 3.6:

1. $(\mathbb{Z}, +)$ is a commutative group with identity 0. The inverse of any integer a is the integer $-a$.

2. $(\mathbb{N}, +)$ is a commutative monoid that is **not** a group. For example, the natural number 1 has no inverse in $\mathbb{N}$. In other words, the equation $x + 1 = 0$ has no solution in $\mathbb{N}$.

3. $(\mathbb{Z}, \cdot)$ is a commutative monoid that is not a group. For example, the integer 2 has no inverse in $\mathbb{Z}$. In other words, the equation $2x = 1$ has no solution in $\mathbb{Z}$.

4. A **rational number** is a number of the form $\frac{a}{b}$, where a and b are integers and $b \neq 0$.

   We identify rational numbers $\frac{a}{b}$ and $\frac{c}{d}$ whenever $ad = bc$. For example, $\frac{1}{2}$ and $\frac{3}{6}$ represent the same rational number because $1 \cdot 6 = 6$ and $2 \cdot 3 = 6$.

   We denote the set of rational numbers by $\mathbb{Q}$. So, we have $\mathbb{Q} = \left\{ \frac{a}{b} \mid a, b \in \mathbb{Z}, b \neq 0 \right\}$. In words, $\mathbb{Q}$ is "the set of quotients a over b such that a and b are integers and b is not zero."

   We identify the rational number $\frac{a}{1}$ with the integer a. In this way, we have $\mathbb{Z} \subseteq \mathbb{Q}$.

   We add two rational numbers using the rule $\frac{a}{b} + \frac{c}{d} = \frac{a \cdot d + b \cdot c}{b \cdot d}$.

   Note that $0 = \frac{0}{1}$ is an identity for $(\mathbb{Q}, +)$ because $\frac{a}{b} + \frac{0}{1} = \frac{a \cdot 1 + b \cdot 0}{b \cdot 1} = \frac{a}{b}$ and $\frac{0}{1} + \frac{a}{b} = \frac{0 \cdot b + 1 \cdot a}{1 \cdot b} = \frac{a}{b}$.

   You will be asked to show in Problem 11 below that $(\mathbb{Q}, +)$ is a commutative group.

5. We multiply two rational numbers using the rule $\frac{a}{b} \cdot \frac{c}{d} = \frac{a \cdot c}{b \cdot d}$.

   Note that $1 = \frac{1}{1}$ is an identity for $(\mathbb{Q}, \cdot)$ because $\frac{a}{b} \cdot \frac{1}{1} = \frac{a \cdot 1}{b \cdot 1} = \frac{a}{b}$ and $\frac{1}{1} \cdot \frac{a}{b} = \frac{1 \cdot a}{1 \cdot b} = \frac{a}{b}$.

   Now, $0 \cdot \frac{a}{b} = \frac{0}{1} \cdot \frac{a}{b} = \frac{0 \cdot a}{1 \cdot b} = \frac{0}{b} = 0$. In particular, when we multiply 0 by any rational number, we can never get 1. So, 0 is a rational number with no multiplicative inverse. It follows that $(\mathbb{Q}, \cdot)$ is **not** a group.

   However, 0 is the **only** rational number without a multiplicative inverse. In fact, you will be asked to show in Problem 9 below that $(\mathbb{Q}^*, \cdot)$ is a commutative group, where $\mathbb{Q}^*$ is the set of rational numbers with 0 removed.

Note: When multiplying two numbers, we sometimes drop the dot ($\cdot$) for easier readability. So, we may write $x \cdot y$ as xy. We may also use parentheses instead of the dot. For example, we might write $\frac{a}{b} \cdot \frac{c}{d}$ as $\left(\frac{a}{b}\right)\left(\frac{c}{d}\right)$, whereas we would probably write $\frac{a \cdot c}{b \cdot d}$ as $\frac{ac}{bd}$. We may even use this simplified notation for arbitrary group operations. So, we could write $a \star b$ as ab. However, we will avoid doing this if it would lead to confusion. For example, we will **not** write $a + b$ as ab.

Problem Set 3

LEVEL 1

1. For each of the following multiplication tables defined on the set $S = \{a, b\}$, determine if each of the following is true or false:

   (i) $\star$ defines a binary operation on S.

   (ii) $\star$ is commutative in S.

   (iii) a is an identity with respect to $\star$.

   (iv) b is an identity with respect to $\star$.

I

$\star$	a	b
a	a	a
b	a	a

II

$\star$	a	b
a	a	b
b	c	a

III

$\star$	a	b
a	a	b
b	b	a

IV

$\star$	a	b
a	a	a
b	b	b

2. Show that there are exactly two monoids on the set $S = \{e, a\}$, where e is the identity. Which of these monoids are groups? Which of these monoids are commutative?

LEVEL 2

3. Let $G = \{e, a, b\}$ and let $(G, \star)$ be a group with identity element e. Draw a multiplication table for $(G, \star)$.

4. Prove that in any monoid $(M, \star)$, the identity element is unique.

LEVEL 3

5. Assume that a group $(G, \star)$ of order 4 exists with $G = \{e, a, b, c\}$, where e is the identity, $a^2 = b$ and $b^2 = e$. Construct the table for the operation of such a group.

6. Prove that in any group $(G, \star)$, each element has a unique inverse.

7. Let $(G, \star)$ be a group with $a, b \in G$, and let a^{-1} and b^{-1} be the inverses of a and b, respectively. Prove

   (i) $(a \star b)^{-1} = b^{-1} \star a^{-1}$.

   (ii)   the inverse of a^{-1} is a.

8. Let $(G, \star)$ be a group such that $a^2 = e$ for all $a \in G$. Prove that $(G, \star)$ is commutative.

9. Prove that $(\mathbb{Q}^*, \cdot)$ is a commutative group.

LEVEL 5

10. Prove that there are exactly two groups of order 4, up to renaming the elements.

11. Show that $(\mathbb{Q}, +)$ is a commutative group.

12. Let $S = \{a, b\}$, where $a \neq b$. How many binary operations are there on S? How many semigroups are there of the form $(S, \star)$, up to renaming the elements?

LESSON 4 – NUMBER THEORY
THE RING OF INTEGERS

Rings and Distributivity

Before giving the general definition of a ring, let's look at an important example.

Example 4.1: Recall that $\mathbb{Z} = \{\ldots, -4, -3, -2, -1, 0, 1, 2, 3, 4, \ldots\}$ is the set of integers. Let's go over some of the properties of addition and multiplication on this set.

1. $\mathbb{Z}$ is **closed** under addition. In other words, whenever we add two integers, we get another integer. For example, 2 and 3 are integers, and we have $2 + 3 = 5$, which is also an integer. As another example, -8 and 6 are integers, and so is $-8 + 6 = -2$.

2. Addition is **commutative** in $\mathbb{Z}$. In other words, when we add two integers, it does not matter which one comes first. For example, $2 + 3 = 5$ and $3 + 2 = 5$. So, we see that $2 + 3 = 3 + 2$. As another example, $-8 + 6 = -2$ and $6 + (-8) = -2$. So, we see that $-8 + 6 = 6 + (-8)$.

3. Addition is **associative** in $\mathbb{Z}$. In other words, when we add three integers, it doesn't matter if we begin by adding the first two or the last two integers. For example, $(2 + 3) + 4 = 5 + 4 = 9$ and $2 + (3 + 4) = 2 + 7 = 9$. So, $(2 + 3) + 4 = 2 + (3 + 4)$. As another example, we have $(-8 + 6) + (-5) = -2 + (-5) = -7$ and $-8 + (6 + (-5)) = -8 + 1 = -7$. So, we see that $(-8 + 6) + (-5) = -8 + (6 + (-5))$.

4. $\mathbb{Z}$ has an **identity** for addition, namely 0. Whenever we add 0 to another integer, the result is that same integer. For example, we have $0 + 3 = 3$ and $3 + 0 = 3$. As another example, $0 + (-5) = -5$ and $(-5) + 0 = -5$.

5. Every integer has an additive **inverse**. This is an integer that we add to the original integer to get 0 (the additive identity). For example, the additive inverse of 5 is -5 because we have $5 + (-5) = 0$ and $-5 + 5 = 0$. Notice that the same two equations also show that the inverse of -5 is 5. We can say that 5 and -5 are additive inverses of each other.

We can summarize the five properties above by saying that $(\mathbb{Z}, +)$ is a **commutative group**.

6. $\mathbb{Z}$ is **closed** under multiplication. In other words, whenever we multiply two integers, we get another integer. For example, 2 and 3 are integers, and we have $2 \cdot 3 = 6$, which is also an integer. As another example, -3 and -4 are integers, and so is $(-3)(-4) = 12$.

7. Multiplication is **commutative** in $\mathbb{Z}$. In other words, when we multiply two integers, it does not matter which one comes first. For example, $2 \cdot 3 = 6$ and $3 \cdot 2 = 6$. So, $2 \cdot 3 = 3 \cdot 2$. As another example, $-8 \cdot 6 = -48$ and $6(-8) = -48$. So, we see that $-8 \cdot 6 = 6(-8)$.

8. Multiplication is **associative** in $\mathbb{Z}$. In other words, when we multiply three integers, it doesn't matter if we begin by multiplying the first two or the last two integers. For example, $(2 \cdot 3) \cdot 4 = 6 \cdot 4 = 24$ and $2 \cdot (3 \cdot 4) = 2 \cdot 12 = 24$. So, $(2 \cdot 3) \cdot 4 = 2 \cdot (3 \cdot 4)$. As another example, $(-5 \cdot 2) \cdot (-6) = -10 \cdot (-6) = 60$ and $-5 \cdot (2 \cdot (-6)) = -5 \cdot (-12) = 60$. So, we see that $(-5 \cdot 2) \cdot (-6) = -5 \cdot (2 \cdot (-6))$.

9. $\mathbb{Z}$ has an **identity** for multiplication, namely 1. Whenever we multiply 1 by another integer, the result is that same integer. For example, we have $1 \cdot 3 = 3$ and $3 \cdot 1 = 3$. As another example $1 \cdot (-5) = -5$ and $(-5) \cdot 1 = -5$.

We can summarize the four properties above by saying that $(\mathbb{Z}, \cdot)$ is a **commutative monoid**.

10. Multiplication is **distributive** over addition in $\mathbb{Z}$. This means that whenever k, m, and n are integers, we have $k \cdot (m + n) = k \cdot m + k \cdot n$. For example, $4 \cdot (2 + 1) = 4 \cdot 3 = 12$ and $4 \cdot 2 + 4 \cdot 1 = 8 + 4 = 12$. So, $4 \cdot (2 + 1) = 4 \cdot 2 + 4 \cdot 1$. As another example, we have $-2 \cdot ((-1) + 3) = -2(2) = -4$ and $-2 \cdot (-1) + (-2) \cdot 3 = 2 - 6 = -4$. Therefore, we see that $-2 \cdot ((-1) + 3) = -2 \cdot (-1) + (-2) \cdot 3$.

Notes: (1) Since the properties listed in 1 through 10 above are satisfied, we say that $(\mathbb{Z}, +, \cdot)$ is a **ring**. We will give the formal definition of a ring below.

(2) Observe that a ring consists of (i) a set (in this case $\mathbb{Z}$), and (ii) **two** binary operations on the set called **addition** and **multiplication**.

(3) $(\mathbb{Z}, +)$ is a commutative group and $(\mathbb{Z}, \cdot)$ is a commutative monoid. The distributive property is the only property mentioned that requires both addition and multiplication.

(4) We see that $\mathbb{Z}$ is missing one nice property—the inverse property for multiplication. For example, 2 has no multiplicative inverse in $\mathbb{Z}$. There is no integer n such that $2 \cdot n = 1$. So, the linear equation $2n - 1 = 0$ has no solution in $\mathbb{Z}$.

(5) If we replace $\mathbb{Z}$ by the set of natural numbers $\mathbb{N} = \{0, 1, 2, \dots\}$, then all the properties mentioned above are satisfied **except** property 5—the inverse property for addition. For example, 1 has no additive inverse in $\mathbb{N}$. There is no natural number n such that $n + 1 = 0$.

(6) $\mathbb{Z}$ actually satisfies two distributive properties. **Left distributivity** says that whenever k, m, and n are integers, we have $k \cdot (m + n) = k \cdot m + k \cdot n$. **Right distributivity** says that whenever k, m, and n are integers, we have $(m + n) \cdot k = m \cdot k + n \cdot k$. Since multiplication is commutative in $\mathbb{Z}$, left distributivity and right distributivity are equivalent.

(7) Let's show that left distributivity together with commutativity of multiplication in $\mathbb{Z}$ implies right distributivity in $\mathbb{Z}$. If we assume that we have left distributivity and commutativity of multiplication, then for integers k, m, and n, we have $(m + n) \cdot k = k(m + n) = k \cdot m + k \cdot n = m \cdot k + n \cdot k$.

We are now ready to give the more general definition of a ring.

A **ring** is a triple $(R, +, \cdot)$, where R is a set and $+$ and $\cdot$ are binary operations on R satisfying

(1) $(R, +)$ is a commutative group.

(2) $(R, \cdot)$ is a monoid.

(3) Multiplication is **distributive** over addition in R. That is, for all $x, y, z \in R$, we have

$$x \cdot (y + z) = x \cdot y + x \cdot z \qquad \text{and} \qquad (y + z) \cdot x = y \cdot x + z \cdot x.$$

Recall: The symbol $\in$ is used for membership in a set. Specifically, the statement $a \in S$ can be read as "a is a member of the set S," or more simply as "a is in S." For example, $2 \in \mathbb{N}$ means "2 is in the set of natural numbers," or more simply, "2 is a natural number."

We will always refer to the operation $+$ as addition and the operation $\cdot$ as multiplication. We will also adjust our notation accordingly. For example, we will refer to the identity for $+$ as 0, and the **additive inverse** of an element $x \in R$ as $-x$. Also, we will refer to the identity for $\cdot$ as 1, and the **multiplicative inverse** of an element $x \in R$ (if it exists) as x^{-1} or $\frac{1}{x}$.

Notes: (1) Recall from Lesson 3 that $(R, +)$ a commutative group means the following:

- **(Closure)** For all $x, y \in R$, $x + y \in R$.
- **(Associativity)** For all $x, y, z \in R$, $(x + y) + z = x + (y + z)$.
- **(Commutativity)** For all $x, y \in R$, $x + y = y + x$.
- **(Identity)** There exists an element $0 \in R$ such that for all $x \in R$, $0 + x = x + 0 = x$.
- **(Inverse)** For each $x \in R$, there is $-x \in R$ such that $x + (-x) = (-x) + x = 0$.

(2) Recall from Lesson 3 that $(R, \cdot)$ a monoid means the following:

- **(Closure)** For all $x, y \in R$, $x \cdot y \in R$.
- **(Associativity)** For all $x, y, z \in R$, $(x \cdot y) \cdot z = x \cdot (y \cdot z)$.
- **(Identity)** There exists an element $1 \in R$ such that for all $x \in R$, $1 \cdot x = x \cdot 1 = x$.

(3) Although commutativity of multiplication is not required for the definition of a ring, our most important example (the ring of integers) satisfies this condition. When multiplication is commutative in R, we call the ring a **commutative ring**. In this case we have the following additional property:

- **(Commutativity)** For all $x, y \in R$, $x \cdot y = y \cdot x$.

(4) Observe that we have two distributive properties in the definition for a ring. The first property is called **left distributivity** and the second is called **right distributivity**.

(5) In a commutative ring, left distributivity implies right distributivity and vice versa. In this case, the distributive property simplifies to

- **(Distributivity)** For all $x, y, z \in R$, $x \cdot (y + z) = x \cdot y + x \cdot z$

(6) Some authors leave out the multiplicative identity property in the definition of a ring and call such a ring a **unital ring** or a **ring with identity**. Since we are mostly concerned with the ring of integers, we will adopt the convention that a ring has a multiplicative identity. If we do not wish to assume that R has a multiplicative identity, then we will call the structure "almost a ring" or rng (note the missing "i").

(7) The properties that define a ring are called the **ring axioms**. In general, an **axiom** is a statement that is assumed to be true. So, the ring axioms are the statements that are **given** to be true in all rings. There are many other statements that are true in rings. However, any additional statements need to be **proved** using the axioms.

Example 4.2:

1. $(\mathbb{Z}, +, \cdot)$ is a commutative ring with additive identity 0 and multiplicative identity 1. The additive inverse of an integer a is the integer $-a$. This is the ring we will be focusing most of our attention on. See Example 4.1 for more details.

2. $(\mathbb{N}, +, \cdot)$ is **not** a ring because $(\mathbb{N}, +)$ is not a group. The only group property that fails is the additive inverse property. For example, the natural number 1 has no additive inverse. That is, $n + 1 = 0$ has no solution in $\mathbb{N}$. Note that $(\mathbb{N}, \cdot)$ is a commutative monoid and the distributive property holds in $\mathbb{N}$. Therefore, $(\mathbb{N}, +, \cdot)$ misses being a commutative ring by just that one property. $(\mathbb{N}, +, \cdot)$ is an example of a structure called a **semiring**.

3. Recall from Example 3.6 (4 and 5) that the set of rational numbers is $\mathbb{Q} = \left\{ \frac{a}{b} \mid a, b \in \mathbb{Z}, b \neq 0 \right\}$ and we define addition and multiplication on $\mathbb{Q}$ by $\frac{a}{b} + \frac{c}{d} = \frac{ad+bc}{bd}$ and $\frac{a}{b} \cdot \frac{c}{d} = \frac{ac}{bd}$.

   $(\mathbb{Q}, +, \cdot)$ is a commutative ring with additive identity $0 = \frac{0}{1}$ and multiplicative identity $1 = \frac{1}{1}$. The additive inverse of a rational number $\frac{a}{b}$ is the rational number $\frac{-a}{b}$.

   $\mathbb{Q}$ has one additional property not required in the definition of a ring. Every nonzero element of $\mathbb{Q}$ has a multiplicative inverse. The inverse of the nonzero rational number $\frac{a}{b}$ is the rational number $\frac{b}{a}$. This is easy to verify: $\frac{a}{b} \cdot \frac{b}{a} = \frac{ab}{ba} = \frac{ab}{ab} = \frac{1}{1} = 1$ and $\frac{b}{a} \cdot \frac{a}{b} = \frac{ba}{ab} = \frac{ab}{ab} = \frac{1}{1} = 1$. So, $(\mathbb{Q}^*, \cdot)$ is a commutative group, where $\mathbb{Q}^*$ is the set of nonzero rational numbers.

   If we replace the condition "$(R, \cdot)$ is a monoid" in the definition of a ring (condition 2) with the condition $(R^*, \cdot)$ is a commutative group, we get a structure called a **field**. By the remarks in the last paragraph, we see that $(\mathbb{Q}, +, \cdot)$ is a field.

Technical note: The definition of semiring has one additional property: $0 \cdot x = x \cdot 0 = 0$. Without the additive inverse property this new property does not follow from the others, and so, it must be listed explicitly.

Divisibility

An integer a is called **even** if there is another integer b such that $a = 2b$.

Example 4.3:

1. 6 is even because $6 = 2 \cdot 3$.

2. -14 is even because $-14 = 2 \cdot (-7)$.

3. We can write $1 = 2 \cdot \frac{1}{2}$, but this does **not** show that 1 is even (and as we all know, it is not). In the definition of even, it is very important that b is an integer. The problem here is that $\frac{1}{2}$ is not an integer, and so, it cannot be used as a value for b in the definition of even.

We define the **sum** of integers a and b to be $a + b$. We define the **product** of a and b to be $a \cdot b$.

Theorem 4.1: The sum of two even integers is even.

Strategy: Before writing the proof, let's think about our strategy. We need to start with two arbitrary but specific even integers. Let's call them m and n. Notice that we need to give them different names because there is no reason that they need to have the same value.

When we try to add m and n, we get $m + n$. Hmmm...I see no reason yet why the expression $m + n$ should represent an even integer.

The problem is that we haven't yet used the definition of even. If we invoke the definition, we get integers j and k such that $m = 2j$ and $n = 2k$.

Now, when we add m and n, we get $m + n = 2j + 2k$.

Is it clear that $2j + 2k$ represents an even integer? Nope...not yet. To be even, our final expression needs to have the form $2b$, where b is an integer.

Here is where we use the fact that $(\mathbb{Z}, +, \cdot)$ is a ring. Specifically, we use the distributive property to rewrite $2j + 2k$ as $2(j + k)$.

It looks like we've done it. We just need to verify one more thing: is $j + k$ an integer? Once again, we can use the fact that $(\mathbb{Z}, +, \cdot)$ is a ring to verify this. Specifically, we use the fact that $+$ is a binary operation on $\mathbb{Z}$.

I think we're now ready to write the proof.

Proof of Theorem 4.1: Let m and n be even integers. Then there are integers j and k such that $m = 2j$ and $n = 2k$. So, $m + n = 2j + 2k = 2(j + k)$ because multiplication is distributive over addition in $\mathbb{Z}$. Since $\mathbb{Z}$ is closed under addition, $j + k \in \mathbb{Z}$. Therefore, $m + n$ is even. $\square$

The property of being even is a special case of the more general notion of divisibility.

An integer a is **divisible** by an integer k, written $k|a$, if there is another integer b such that $a = kb$. We also say that k is a **factor** of a, k is a **divisor** of a, k **divides** a, or a is a **multiple** of k.

Example 4.4:

1. Note that being divisible by 2 is the same as being even.

2. 18 is divisible by 3 because $18 = 3 \cdot 6$.

3. -56 is divisible by 7 because $-56 = 7 \cdot (-8)$.

Theorem 4.2: The product of two integers that are each divisible by k is also divisible by k.

Proof: Let m and n be integers that are divisible by k. Then there are integers b and c such that $m = kb$ and $n = kc$. So, $m \cdot n = (k \cdot b) \cdot (k \cdot c) = k \cdot (b \cdot (k \cdot c))$ because multiplication is associative in $\mathbb{Z}$. Since $\mathbb{Z}$ is closed under multiplication, $b \cdot (k \cdot c) \in \mathbb{Z}$. Thus, $m \cdot n$ is divisible by k. $\square$

Notes: (1) If you're confused about how associativity was used here, it might help to make the substitution $u = (k \cdot c)$. Then we have $(k \cdot b) \cdot (k \cdot c) = (k \cdot b) \cdot u = k \cdot (b \cdot u) = k(b \cdot (k \cdot c))$.

(2) Although it may seem tempting to simplify $k \cdot \left(b \cdot (k \cdot c)\right)$ further, it is unnecessary. The definition of divisibility by k requires us only to generate an expression of the form k times some integer, and that's what we have done.

(3) If the generality of the proof confuses you, try replacing k by a specific integer. For example, if we let $k = 2$, we have $m = 2b$, $n = 2c$, and therefore $m \cdot n = (2b) \cdot (2c) = 2\left(b \cdot (2c)\right)$. Is it clear that this final expression is even (divisible by 2)?

(4) It's worth noting that the product $m \cdot n$ is actually divisible by k^2. Indeed, we have

$$m \cdot n = k \cdot \left(b \cdot (k \cdot c)\right) = k \cdot \left((b \cdot k) \cdot c\right) = k \cdot \left((k \cdot b) \cdot c\right) = k \cdot \left(k \cdot (b \cdot c)\right) = k^2(b \cdot c)$$

Induction

The **Well Ordering Principle** says that every nonempty subset of natural numbers has a least element.

For example, the least element of $\mathbb{N}$ itself is 0.

Theorem 4.3 (The Principle of Mathematical Induction): Let S be a set of natural numbers such that (i) $0 \in S$ and (ii) for all $k \in \mathbb{N}$, $k \in S \rightarrow k + 1 \in S$. Then $S = \mathbb{N}$.

Notes: (1) The Principle of Mathematical Induction works like a chain reaction. We know that $0 \in S$ (this is condition (i)). Substituting 0 in for k in the expression "$k \in S \rightarrow k + 1 \in S$" (condition (ii)) gives us $0 \in S \rightarrow 1 \in S$. So, we have that 0 is in the set S, and "if 0 is in the set S, then 1 is in the set S." So, $1 \in S$ must also be true.

(2) In terms of Lesson 1 on Sentential Logic, if we let p be the statement $0 \in S$ and q the statement $1 \in S$, then we are given that $p \wedge (p \rightarrow q)$ is true. Observe that the only way that this statement can be true is if q is also true. Indeed, we must have both $p \equiv T$ and $p \rightarrow q \equiv T$. If q were false, then we would have $p \rightarrow q \equiv T \rightarrow F \equiv F$. So, we must have $q \equiv T$.

(3) Now that we showed $1 \in S$ is true (from Note 1 above), we can substitute 1 for k in the expression "$k \in S \rightarrow k + 1 \in S$" (condition (ii)) to get $1 \in S \rightarrow 2 \in S$. So, we have $1 \in S \wedge (1 \in S \rightarrow 2 \in S)$ is true. So, $2 \in S$ must also be true.

(4) In general, we get the following chain reaction:

$$0 \in S \rightarrow 1 \in S \rightarrow 2 \in S \rightarrow 3 \in S \rightarrow \cdots$$

I hope that the "argument" presented in Notes 1 through 4 above convinces you that the Principle of Mathematical Induction should be true. Now let's give a proof using the Well Ordering Principle. Proofs involving the Well Ordering Principle are generally done by contradiction.

Proof of Theorem 4.3: Let S be a set of natural numbers such that $0 \in S$ (condition (i)), and such that whenever $k \in S$, $k + 1 \in S$ (condition (ii)). Assume toward contradiction that $S \neq \mathbb{N}$. Let $A = \{k \in \mathbb{N} \mid k \notin S\}$ (so, A is the set of natural numbers **not** in S). Since $S \neq \mathbb{N}$, A is nonempty. So, by the Well Ordering Principle, A has a least element, let's call it a. $a \neq 0$ because $0 \in S$ and $a \notin S$. So, $a - 1 \in \mathbb{N}$. Letting $k = a - 1$, we have $a - 1 \in S \rightarrow k \in S \rightarrow k + 1 \in S \rightarrow (a - 1) + 1 \in S \rightarrow a \in S$. But $a \in A$, which means that $a \notin S$. This is a contradiction, and so, $S = \mathbb{N}$. $\square$

Note: The proof given here is a **proof by contradiction**. A proof by contradiction works as follows:

1. We assume the negation of what we are trying to prove.

2. We use a logically valid argument to derive a statement which is false.

3. Since the argument was logically valid, the only possible error is our original assumption. Therefore, the negation of our original assumption must be true.

In this problem we are trying to prove that $S = \mathbb{N}$. The negation of this statement is that $S \neq \mathbb{N}$, and so that is what we assume.

We then define a set A which contains elements of $\mathbb{N}$ that are not in S. In reality, this set is empty (because the conclusion of the theorem is $S = \mathbb{N}$). However, our (wrong!) assumption that $S \neq \mathbb{N}$ tells us that this set A actually has something in it. Saying that A has something in it is an example of a false statement that was derived from a logically valid argument. This false statement occurred not because of an error in our logic, but because we started with an incorrect assumption ($S \neq \mathbb{N}$).

The Well Ordering Principle then allows us to pick out the least element of this set A. Note that we can do this because A is a subset of $\mathbb{N}$. This wouldn't work if we knew only that A was a subset of $\mathbb{Z}$, as $\mathbb{Z}$ does **not** satisfy the Well Ordering Principle (for example, $\mathbb{Z}$ itself has no least element).

Again, although the argument that A has a least element is logically valid, A does not actually have any elements at all. We are working from the (wrong!) assumption that $S \neq \mathbb{N}$.

Once we have our hands on this least element a, we can get our contradiction. What can this least element a be? Well a was chosen to not be in S, so a cannot be 0 (because 0 **is** in S). Also, we know that $a - 1 \in S$ (because a is the **least** element not in S). But condition (ii) then forces a to be in S (because $a = (a - 1) + 1$).

So, we wind up with $a \in S$, contradicting the fact that a is the least element **not** in S.

The Principle of Mathematical Induction is often written in the following way:

($\star$) Let $P(n)$ be a statement and suppose that (i) $P(0)$ is true and (ii) for all $k \in \mathbb{N}$, $P(k) \to P(k + 1)$. Then $P(n)$ is true for all $n \in \mathbb{N}$.

In Problem 9 below, you will be asked to show that statement ($\star$) is equivalent to Theorem 4.3.

There are essentially two steps involved in a proof by mathematical induction. The first step is to prove that $P(0)$ is true (this is called the **base case**), and the second step is to assume that $P(k)$ is true, and use this to show that $P(k + 1)$ is true (this is called the **inductive step**). While doing the inductive step, the statement "$P(k)$ is true" is often referred to as the **inductive hypothesis**.

Subtraction in $\mathbb{Z}$: For $x, y \in \mathbb{Z}$, we define the **difference** $x - y$ to be equal to the sum $x + (-y)$. For example, $n^2 - n = n^2 + (-n)$ (where n^2 is defined to be the product $n \cdot n$).

Example 4.5: Let's use the Principle of Mathematical Induction to prove that for all natural numbers n, $n^2 - n$ is even.

Base Case ($k = 0$): $0^2 - 0 = 0 = 2 \cdot 0$. So, $0^2 - 0$ is even.

Inductive Step: Let $k \in \mathbb{N}$ and assume that $k^2 - k$ is even. Then $k^2 - k = 2b$ for some integer b. Now,

$$(k+1)^2 - (k+1) = (k+1)[(k+1)-1] = (k+1)[k+(1-1)] = (k+1)(k+0)$$
$$= (k+1) \cdot k = k^2 + k = (k^2 - k) + 2k = 2b + 2k = 2(b+k).$$

Here we used the fact that $(\mathbb{Z}, +, \cdot)$ is a ring. Since $\mathbb{Z}$ is closed under addition, $b + k \in \mathbb{Z}$. Therefore, $(k+1)^2 - (k+1)$ is even.

By the Principle of Mathematical Induction, $n^2 - n$ is even for all $n \in \mathbb{N}$. $\qquad\qquad\square$

Notes: (1) Instead of listing every property that we used at each step, we simply stated that all the computations we made were allowed because $(\mathbb{Z}, +, \cdot)$ is a ring. We will discuss the property we used at each step in the notes below.

(2) We first used left distributivity to rewrite $(k+1)^2 - (k+1)$ as $(k+1)[(k+1)-1]$. If you have trouble seeing this, try working backwards, and making the substitutions $x = (k+1)$, $y = (k+1)$, and $z = -1$. We then have

$$(k+1)[(k+1)-1] = (k+1)[(k+1)+(-1)] = x(y+z) = xy + xz$$
$$= (k+1)(k+1) + (k+1)(-1) = (k+1)^2 + (-1)(k+1) = (k+1)^2 - (k+1).$$

Notice how we also used commutativity of multiplication for the second to last equality.

(3) For the second algebraic step, we used associativity of addition to write

$$(k+1) - 1 = (k+1) + (-1) = k + \big(1 + (-1)\big) = k + (1-1).$$

(4) For the third algebraic step, we used the inverse property for addition to write

$$1 - 1 = 1 + (-1) = 0.$$

(5) For the fourth algebraic step, we used the additive identity property to write $k + 0 = k$.

(6) For the fifth algebraic step, we used right distributivity and the multiplicative identity property to write $(k+1) \cdot k = k \cdot k + 1 \cdot k = k^2 + k$.

(7) For the sixth algebraic step, we used what I call the "**Standard Advanced Calculus Trick**." I sometimes abbreviate this as **SACT**. The trick is simple. If you need something to appear, just put it in. Then correct it by performing the opposite of what you just did.

In this case, in order to use the inductive hypothesis, we need $k^2 - k$ to appear, but unfortunately, we have $k^2 + k$ instead. Using SACT, I do the following:

- I simply put in what I need (and exactly where I need it): $k^2 - \boldsymbol{k} + k$.

- Now, I undo the damage by performing the reverse operation: $k^2 - k + \boldsymbol{k} + k$.

- Finally, I leave the part I need as is, and simplify the rest: $(k^2 - k) + 2k$

(8) For the seventh step, we simply replaced $k^2 - k$ by $2b$. We established that these two quantities were equal in the second sentence of the inductive step.

(9) For the last step, we used left distributivity to write $2b + 2k$ as $2(b + k)$.

Sometimes a statement involving the natural numbers may be false for 0, but true from some natural number on. In this case, we can still use induction. We just need to adjust the base case.

Example 4.6: Let's use the Principle of Mathematical Induction to prove that $n^2 > 2n + 1$ for all natural numbers $n \geq 3$.

Base Case $(k = 3)$: $3^2 = 9$ and $2 \cdot 3 + 1 = 6 + 1 = 7$. So, $3^2 > 2 \cdot 3 + 1$.

Inductive Step: Let $k \in \mathbb{N}$ with $k \geq 3$ and assume that $k^2 > 2k + 1$. Then we have

$$(k + 1)^2 = (k + 1)(k + 1) = (k + 1)k + (k + 1)(1) = k^2 + k + k + 1 > (2k + 1) + k + k + 1$$
$$= 2k + 2 + k + k = 2(k + 1) + k + k \geq 2(k + 1) + 1 \text{ (because } k + k \geq 3 + 3 = 6 \geq 1).$$

By the Principle of Mathematical Induction, $n^2 > 2n + 1$ for all $n \in \mathbb{N}$ with $n \geq 3$. $\qquad\square$

Notes: (1) If we have a sequence of equations and inequalities of the form $=$, $\geq$, and $>$ (with at least one inequality symbol appearing), beginning with a and ending with b, then the final result is $a > b$ if $>$ appears at least once and $a \geq b$ otherwise.

For example, if $a = j = h = m > n = p = q \geq b$, then $a > b$. The sequence that appears in the solution above has this form.

$$(k + 1)^2 = (k + 1)(k + 1) = (k + 1)k + (k + 1)(1) = k^2 + k + k + 1 > (2k + 1) + k + k + 1$$
$$= 2k + 2 + k + k = 2(k + 1) + k + k \geq 2(k + 1) + 1$$

(2) By definition, $x^2 = x \cdot x$. We used this in the first equality in the inductive step to write $(k + 1)^2$ as $(k + 1)(k + 1)$.

(3) For the second equality in the inductive step, we used left distributivity to write $(k + 1)(k + 1)$ as $(k + 1)k + (k + 1)(1)$. If you have trouble seeing this you can make a substitution like we did in Note 2 following Example 4.5.

(4) For the third equality in the inductive step, we used right distributivity to write $(k + 1)k$ as $k \cdot k + 1 \cdot k = k^2 + k$. We also used the multiplicative identity property to write $(k + 1)(1) = k + 1$.

(5) Associativity of addition is being used when we write the expression $k^2 + k + k + 1$. Notice the lack of parentheses. Technically speaking, we should have written $(k^2 + k) + (k + 1)$ and then taken another step to rewrite this as $k^2 + (k + (k + 1))$. However, since we have associativity, we can simply drop all those parentheses.

(6) The inequality "$k^2 + k + k + 1 > (2k + 1) + k + k + 1$" was attained by using the inductive hypothesis "$k^2 > 2k + 1$."

(7) The dedicated reader should verify that the remaining equalities in the proof are valid by determining which ring properties were used at each step.

Example 4.7: Let's use the Principle of Mathematical Induction to prove that for every natural number n, there is a natural number j such that $n = 2j$ or $n = 2j + 1$.

Base Case $(k = 0)$: $0 = 2 \cdot 0$

Inductive Step: Suppose that $k \in \mathbb{N}$ and there is $j \in \mathbb{N}$ such that $k = 2j$ or $k = 2j + 1$. If $k = 2j$, then $k + 1 = 2j + 1$. If $k = 2j + 1$, then $k + 1 = (2j + 1) + 1 = 2j + (1 + 1) = 2j + 2 = 2(j + 1)$. Here we used the fact that $(\mathbb{N}, +, \cdot)$ is a semiring (more specifically, we used associativity of addition in $\mathbb{N}$ and distributivity of multiplication over addition in $\mathbb{N}$). Since $\mathbb{N}$ is closed under addition, $j + 1 \in \mathbb{N}$.

By the Principle of Mathematical Induction, for every natural number n, there is a natural number j such that $n = 2j$ or $n = 2j + 1$. $\qquad\square$

Notes: (1) We can now prove the analogous result for the integers: "For every integer n, there is an integer j such that $n = 2j$ or $n = 2j + 1$."

We already proved the result for $n \geq 0$. If $n < 0$, then $-n > 0$, and so there is a natural number j such that $-n = 2j$ or $-n = 2j + 1$. If $-n = 2j$, then $n = 2(-j)$ (and since $j \in \mathbb{N}$, $-j \in \mathbb{Z}$). If $-n = 2j + 1$, then $n = -(2j + 1) = -2j - 1 = -2j - 1 - 1 + 1$ (SACT) $= -2j - 2 + 1 = 2(-j - 1) + 1$. Here we used the fact that $(\mathbb{Z}, +, \cdot)$ is a ring. Since $\mathbb{Z}$ is closed under addition, $-j - 1 = -j + (-1) \in \mathbb{Z}$.

(2) If there is an integer j such that $n = 2j$, we say that n is **even**. If there is an integer j such that $n = 2j + 1$, we say that n is **odd**.

(3) **An integer n cannot be both even and odd.** Indeed, if $n = 2j$ and $n = 2k + 1$, then $2j = 2k + 1$. So, we have

$$2(j - k) = 2j - 2k = (2k + 1) - 2k = 2k + (1 - 2k) = 2k + (-2k + 1)$$
$$= (2k - 2k) + 1 = 0 + 1 = 1.$$

So, $2(j - k) = 1$. But 2 does not have a multiplicative inverse in $\mathbb{Z}$, and so, this is a contradiction.

Theorem 4.4: The product of two odd integers is odd.

Proof: Let m and n be odd integers. Then there are integers j and k such that $m = 2j + 1$ and $n = 2k + 1$. So,

$$m \cdot n = (2j + 1) \cdot (2k + 1) = (2j + 1)(2k) + (2j + 1)(1) = (2k)(2j + 1) + (2j + 1)$$
$$= \big((2k)(2j) + 2k\big) + (2j + 1) = \big(2(k(2j)) + 2k\big) + (2j + 1) = 2(k(2j) + k) + (2j + 1)$$
$$= (2(k(2j) + k) + 2j) + 1 = 2\big((k(2j) + k) + j\big) + 1.$$

Here we used the fact that $(\mathbb{Z}, +, \cdot)$ is a ring. (Which properties did we use?) Since $\mathbb{Z}$ is closed under addition and multiplication, we have $(k(2j) + k) + j \in \mathbb{Z}$. Therefore, mn is odd. $\qquad\square$

Problem Set 4

Full solutions to these problems are available for free download here:

www.SATPrepGet800.com/PMFBXSG

LEVEL 1

1. The addition and multiplication tables below are defined on the set $S = \{0, 1\}$. Show that $(S, +, \cdot)$ does **not** define a ring.

+	0	1		$\cdot$	0	1
0	0	1		0	1	0
1	1	0		1	0	1

2. Let $S = \{0, 1\}$ and define addition (+) and multiplication ($\cdot$) so that $(S, +, \cdot)$ is a ring. Assume that 0 is the additive identity in S and 1 is the multiplicative identity in S. Draw the tables for addition and multiplication and verify that with these tables, $(S, +, \cdot)$ is a ring.

LEVEL 2

3. Use the Principle of Mathematical Induction to prove the following:

   (i) $2^n > n$ for all natural numbers $n \geq 1$.

   (ii) $0 + 1 + 2 + \cdots + n = \frac{n(n+1)}{2}$ for all natural numbers.

   (iii) $n! > 2^n$ for all natural numbers $n \geq 4$ (where $n! = 1 \cdot 2 \cdots n$ for all natural numbers $n \geq 1$).

   (iv) $2^n \geq n^2$ for all natural numbers $n \geq 4$.

4. Show that the sum of three integers that are divisible by 5 is divisible by 5.

LEVEL 3

5. Prove that if $a, b, c \in \mathbb{Z}$ with $a|b$ and $b|c$, then $a|c$.

6. Prove that $n^3 - n$ is divisible by 3 for all natural numbers n.

LEVEL 4

7. Prove that if $a, b, c, d, e \in \mathbb{Z}$ with $a|b$ and $a|c$, then $a|(db + ec)$.

8. Prove that $3^n - 1$ is even for all natural numbers n.

9. Show that Theorem 4.3 (the Principle of Mathematical Induction) is equivalent to the following statement:

($\star$) Let $P(n)$ be a statement and suppose that (i) $P(0)$ is true and (ii) for all $k \in \mathbb{N}$, $P(k) \rightarrow P(k+1)$. Then $P(n)$ is true for all $n \in \mathbb{N}$.

LEVEL 5

10. The Principle of Strong Induction is the following statement:

($\star\star$) Let $P(n)$ be a statement and suppose that (i) $P(0)$ is true and (ii) for all $k \in \mathbb{N}$, $\forall j \leq k \left(P(j) \right) \rightarrow P(k+1)$. Then $P(n)$ is true for all $n \in \mathbb{N}$.

Use the Principle of Mathematical Induction to prove the Principle of Strong Induction.

11. Show that $(\mathbb{Q}, +, \cdot)$ is a field.

12. Use the Principle of Mathematical Induction to prove that for every $n \in \mathbb{N}$, if S is a set with $|S| = n$, then S has 2^n subsets. (Hint: Use Problem 14 from Lesson 2.)

LESSON 5 – REAL ANALYSIS
THE COMPLETE ORDERED FIELD OF REALS

Fields

Let's review the number systems we have discussed so far.

The set $\mathbb{N} = \{0, 1, 2, 3, \ldots\}$ is the set of **natural numbers** and the structure $(\mathbb{N}, +, \cdot)$ is a **semiring**.

The set $\mathbb{Z} = \{\ldots, -3, -2, -1, 0, 1, 2, 3, \ldots\}$ is the set of **integers** and the structure $(\mathbb{Z}, +, \cdot)$ is a **ring**.

The set $\mathbb{Q} = \{\frac{a}{b} \mid a \in \mathbb{Z}, b \in \mathbb{Z}^*\}$ is the set of **rational numbers** and the structure $(\mathbb{Q}, +, \cdot)$ is a **field**.

And now let's formally introduce the notion of a field (and we will review the definitions of ring and semiring in the notes below).

A **field** is a triple $(F, +, \cdot)$, where F is a set and $+$ and $\cdot$ are binary operations on F satisfying

(1) $(F, +)$ is a commutative group.

(2) $(F^*, \cdot)$ is a commutative group.

(3) $\cdot$ is **distributive** over $+$ in F. That is, for all $x, y, z \in F$, we have

$$x \cdot (y + z) = x \cdot y + x \cdot z \qquad \text{and} \qquad (y + z) \cdot x = y \cdot x + z \cdot x.$$

(4) $0 \neq 1$.

We will refer to the operation $+$ as addition, the operation $\cdot$ as multiplication, the additive identity as 0, the multiplicative identity as 1, the additive inverse of an element $x \in F$ as $-x$, and the multiplicative inverse of an element $x \in F$ as x^{-1}. We will often abbreviate $x \cdot y$ as xy.

Notes: (1) Recall from Lesson 3 that $(F, +)$ a commutative group means the following:

- **(Closure)** For all $x, y \in F$, $x + y \in F$.
- **(Associativity)** For all $x, y, z \in F$, $(x + y) + z = x + (y + z)$.
- **(Commutativity)** For all $x, y \in F$, $x + y = y + x$.
- **(Identity)** There exists an element $0 \in F$ such that for all $x \in F$, $0 + x = x + 0 = x$.
- **(Inverse)** For each $x \in F$, there is $-x \in F$ such that $x + (-x) = (-x) + x = 0$.

(2) Similarly, $(F^*, \cdot)$ a commutative group means the following:

- **(Closure)** For all $x, y \in F^*$, $xy \in F^*$.
- **(Associativity)** For all $x, y, z \in F^*$, $(xy)z = x(yz)$.
- **(Commutativity)** For all $x, y \in F^*$, $xy = yx$.
- **(Identity)** There exists an element $1 \in F^*$ such that for all $x \in F^*$, $1x = x \cdot 1 = x$.
- **(Inverse)** For each $x \in F^*$, there is $x^{-1} \in F^*$ such that $xx^{-1} = x^{-1}x = 1$.

(3) Recall that F^* is the set of nonzero elements of F. We can write $F^* = \{x \in F \mid x \neq 0\}$ (pronounced "the set of x in F such that x is not equal to 0") or $F^* = F \setminus \{0\}$ (pronounced "F with 0 removed").

(4) The properties that define a field are called the **field axioms**. These are the statements that are **given** to be true in all fields. There are many other statements that are true in fields. However, any additional statements need to be **proved** using the axioms.

(5) If we replace the condition that "$(F^*, \cdot)$ is a commutative group" by "$(F, \cdot)$ is a monoid," then the resulting structure is called a **ring**. The most well-known example of a ring is $\mathbb{Z}$, the ring of integers. See Lesson 4 for details about $\mathbb{Z}$ and rings in general.

We also do not require 0 and 1 to be distinct in the definition of a ring. If $0 = 1$, we get the zero ring, which consists of just one element, namely 0 (Why?). The operations of addition and multiplication are defined by $0 + 0 = 0$ and $0 \cdot 0 = 0$. The reader may want to verify that the zero ring is in fact a ring.

The main difference between a ring and a field is that in a ring, there can be nonzero elements that do not have multiplicative inverses. For example, in $\mathbb{Z}$, 2 has no multiplicative inverse. So, the equation $2x = 1$ has no solution.

(6) If we also replace "$(F, +)$ is a commutative group" by "$(F, +)$ is a commutative monoid," then the resulting structure is a **semiring**. The most well-known example of a semiring is $\mathbb{N}$, the semiring of natural numbers.

The main difference between a semiring and a ring is that in a semiring, there can be elements that do not have additive inverses. For example, in $\mathbb{N}$, 1 has no additive inverse. Thus, the equation $x + 1 = 0$ has no solution.

Technical note: For a semiring, we include one additional axiom: For all $x \in F, 0 \cdot x = x \cdot 0 = 0$.

(7) Every field is a commutative ring. Although this is not too hard to show (you will be asked to show this in Problem 6 below), it is worth observing that this is not completely obvious. For example, if $(F, +, \cdot)$ is a ring, then since $(F, \cdot)$ is a monoid with identity 1, it follows that $1 \cdot 0 = 0 \cdot 1 = 0$. However, in the definition of a field given above, this property of 0 is not given as an axiom. We **are** given that $(F^*, \cdot)$ is a commutative group, and so, it follows that 1 is an identity for F^*. But $0 \notin F^*$, and so, $1 \cdot 0 = 0 \cdot 1 = 0$ needs to be proved.

Similarly, in the definition of a field given above, 0 is excluded from associativity and commutativity. These need to be checked.

(8) You were asked to verify that $(\mathbb{Q}, +, \cdot)$ is a field in Problems 9 and 11 from Lesson 3 and Problem 11 from Lesson 4.

Subtraction and Division: If $a, b \in F$, we define $a - b = a + (-b)$ and for $b \neq 0, \frac{a}{b} = ab^{-1}$.

Ordered Rings and Fields

We say that a ring $(R, +, \cdot)$ is ordered if there is a nonempty subset P of R, called the set of **positive elements** of R, satisfying the following three properties:

(1) If $a, b \in P$, then $a + b \in P$.

(2) If $a, b \in P$, then $ab \in P$.

(3) If $a \in R$, then exactly one of the following holds: $a \in P$, $a = 0$, or $-a \in P$.

Note: If $a \in P$, we say that a is **positive** and if $-a \in P$, we say that a is **negative**.

Also, we define $R^+ = P$ and $R^- = \{a \in R \mid -a \in P\}$.

Example 5.1: Let $R = \mathbb{Z}$ and let $P_{\mathbb{Z}} = \{1, 2, 3, \dots\}$. It's easy to see that properties (1), (2), and (3) are satisfied. It follows that $(\mathbb{Z}, +, \cdot)$ is an ordered ring.

Theorem 5.1: $(\mathbb{Q}, +, \cdot)$ is an ordered field.

Note: The proof of this result is a bit technical, but I am including it for completeness. The student just starting out in pure mathematics can feel free to just accept this result and skip the proof.

Recall: (1) Rational numbers have the form $\frac{m}{n}$, where m and n are integers and $n \neq 0$.

(2) Two rational numbers $\frac{m}{n}$ and $\frac{p}{q}$ are equal if and only if $mq = np$.

(3) For rational numbers $\frac{m}{n}$ and $\frac{p}{q}$, we define addition and multiplication by $\frac{m}{n} + \frac{p}{q} = \frac{mq+np}{nq}$ and $\frac{m}{n} \cdot \frac{p}{q} = \frac{mp}{nq}$.

(4) The additive inverse of $\frac{m}{n}$ is $-\frac{m}{n} = \frac{-m}{n}$.

Analysis: Before writing out the proof in detail, let's think about how we would go about it. First of all, we already know from Problem 11 in Lesson 4 that $(\mathbb{Q}, +, \cdot)$ is a field. So, we need only show that it is ordered. To do this, we need to come up with a set P of positive elements from $\mathbb{Q}$. The natural choice would be to take the set of quotients whose numerator (number on the top) and denominator (number on the bottom) are both positive integers. In other words, we will let $P_{\mathbb{Q}}$ be the set of all the rational numbers of the form $\frac{m}{n}$, where m and n are both elements of $P_{\mathbb{Z}}$ (as defined in Example 5.1 above). Since $\frac{-m}{-n} = \frac{m}{n}$ (because $(-m)n = (-n)m$), we must automatically be including all quotients whose numerator and denominator are both negative integers as well.

With this definition of $P_{\mathbb{Q}}$, it is straightforward to verify properties (1) and (2) of an ordered field.

To verify property (3), we need to check three things.

(i) For any rational number a, a is positive, zero, or negative ($a \in P_{\mathbb{Q}}$, $a = 0$, or $-a \in P_{\mathbb{Q}}$). We will show this by assuming $a \notin P_{\mathbb{Q}}$ and $a \neq 0$, and then proving that we must have $-a \in P_{\mathbb{Q}}$.

(ii) For any rational number a, a cannot be both positive and negative. We will show this by assuming $a \in P_{\mathbb{Q}}$ and $-a \in P_{\mathbb{Q}}$, and then deriving a contradiction.

(iii) A positive or negative rational number is not zero, and a rational number that is zero is not positive or negative. This is straightforward to check.

Let's write out the details.

Proof of Theorem 5.1: By Problem 11 from Lesson 4, $(\mathbb{Q}, +, \cdot)$ is a field.

Let $F = \mathbb{Q}$ and let $P_{\mathbb{Q}} = \{x \in \mathbb{Q} \mid x = \frac{m}{n} \text{ with } m, n \in P_{\mathbb{Z}}\}$. Let $a, b \in P_{\mathbb{Q}}$. Then there are $m, n, p, q \in P_{\mathbb{Z}}$ with $a = \frac{m}{n}$ and $b = \frac{p}{q}$. We have $a + b = \frac{m}{n} + \frac{p}{q} = \frac{mq + np}{nq}$. Since $P_{\mathbb{Z}}$ satisfies (2) above, we have $mq, np, nq \in P_{\mathbb{Z}}$. Since $P_{\mathbb{Z}}$ satisfies (1) above, we have $mq + np \in P_{\mathbb{Z}}$. Therefore, $a + b \in P_{\mathbb{Q}}$ and (1) holds. Also, we have $ab = \frac{m}{n} \cdot \frac{p}{q} = \frac{mp}{nq}$. Since $P_{\mathbb{Z}}$ satisfies (2) above, we have $mp, nq \in P_{\mathbb{Z}}$, and therefore, $ab \in P_{\mathbb{Q}}$ and (2) holds.

Now, suppose $a \notin P_{\mathbb{Q}}$ and $a \neq 0$. Since $a \in \mathbb{Q}$, there are $m \in \mathbb{Z}$ and $n \in \mathbb{Z}^*$ such that $a = \frac{m}{n}$. But $a \neq 0$, and so, we must have $m \in \mathbb{Z}^*$. Since $a \notin P_{\mathbb{Q}}$, either $m \notin P_{\mathbb{Z}}$ or $n \notin P_{\mathbb{Z}}$ (or both). If both $m \notin P_{\mathbb{Z}}$ and $n \notin P_{\mathbb{Z}}$, then we have $a = \frac{m}{n} = \frac{-m}{-n}$ (because $m(-n) = n(-m)$). Then $-m, -n \in P_{\mathbb{Z}}$, and so, $a \in P_{\mathbb{Q}}$, contrary to our assumption that $a \notin P_{\mathbb{Q}}$. If $m \notin P_{\mathbb{Z}}$ and $n \in P_{\mathbb{Z}}$, then $-m \in P_{\mathbb{Z}}$, and therefore, $-a = \frac{-m}{n} \in P_{\mathbb{Q}}$. If $m \in P_{\mathbb{Z}}$ and $n \notin P_{\mathbb{Z}}$, then $-n \in P_{\mathbb{Z}}$, and therefore, $-a = \frac{-m}{n} = \frac{m}{-n} \in P_{\mathbb{Q}}$. So, at least one of $a \in P$, $a = 0$, or $-a \in P$ holds.

If $a \in P_{\mathbb{Q}}$ and $-a \in P_{\mathbb{Q}}$, then $a = \frac{m}{n}$ and $-a = \frac{p}{q}$ with $m, n, p, q \in P_{\mathbb{Z}}$. We can also write $-a$ as $-a = \frac{-m}{n}$. So, $\frac{-m}{n} = \frac{p}{q}$, and thus, $(-m)q = np$. Since $n, p \in P_{\mathbb{Z}}$, we have $np \in P_{\mathbb{Z}}$. Since $(-m)q = np$, we must have $(-m)q \in P_{\mathbb{Z}}$. But $-m \notin P_{\mathbb{Z}}$, and so, $-(-m) \in P_{\mathbb{Z}}$. Since we also have $q \in P_{\mathbb{Z}}$, we must have $-(-m)q \in P_{\mathbb{Z}}$. But then by (3) for $P_{\mathbb{Z}}$, $(-m)q \notin P_{\mathbb{Z}}$. This contradiction shows that we cannot have both $a \in P_{\mathbb{Q}}$ and $-a \in P_{\mathbb{Q}}$.

If $a \in P_{\mathbb{Q}}$, then $a = \frac{m}{n}$ with $m, n \in P_{\mathbb{Z}}$. So, $m \neq 0$, and therefore, $a \neq 0$. If $-a \in P_{\mathbb{Q}}$, then $-a = \frac{m}{n}$ with $m, n \in P_{\mathbb{Z}}$. If $a = 0$, then $-a = 0$, and so, $m = 0$. But $m \in P_{\mathbb{Z}}$, and so, $m \neq 0$. Thus, $a \neq 0$.

If $a = 0$, then we have $0 = \frac{0}{1} \notin P_{\mathbb{Q}}$ and $-0 = \frac{-0}{1} = \frac{0}{1} \notin P_{\mathbb{Q}}$.

It follows that $(\mathbb{Q}, +, \cdot)$ is an ordered field. $\square$

If $(R, +, \cdot)$ is an ordered ring and P is the set of positive elements from the ring, we will write $a > 0$ instead of $a \in P$ and $a < 0$ instead of $-a \in P$. If $a - b > 0$, we will write $a > b$ or $b < a$.

We write $a \geq 0$ if $a \in P$ or $a = 0$, we write $a \leq 0$ if $-a \in P$ or $a = 0$, and we write $a \geq b$ or $b \leq a$ if $a - b \geq 0$.

We may use the notation $(R, \leq)$ for an ordered ring, where $\leq$ is the relation defined in the last paragraph. Note that $+$ and $\cdot$ aren't explicitly mentioned, but of course they are still part of the ring.

In the future, we may just use the name of the set for the whole structure when there is no danger of confusion. For example, we may refer to the ring R or the ordered field F instead of the ring $(R, +, \cdot)$ or the ordered field $(F, \leq)$.

Fields are particularly nice to work with because all the arithmetic and algebra we've learned through the years can be used in fields. For example, in the field of rational numbers, we can solve the equation $2x = 1$. The multiplicative inverse property allows us to do this. Indeed, the multiplicative inverse of 2 is $\frac{1}{2}$, and therefore, $x = \frac{1}{2}$ is a solution to the given equation. Compare this to the ring of integers. If we restrict ourselves to the integers, then the equation $2x = 1$ has no solution.

Working with ordered fields is very nice as well. In the problem set below, you will be asked to derive some additional properties of fields and ordered fields that follow from the axioms. We will prove a few of these properties now as examples.

Theorem 5.2: Let $(F, \leq)$ be an ordered field. Then for all $x \in F^*$, $x \cdot x > 0$.

Proof: There are two cases to consider: (i) If $x > 0$, then $x \cdot x > 0$ by property (2) of an ordered field. (ii) If $x < 0$, then $-x > 0$, and so, $(-x)(-x) > 0$, again by property (2) of an ordered field. Now, using Problem 3 (parts (vi) and (vii)) in the problem set below, together with commutativity and associativity of multiplication, and the multiplicative identity property, we have

$$(-x)(-x) = (-1x)(-1x) = (-1)(-1)x \cdot x = 1(x \cdot x) = x \cdot x.$$

So, again we have $x \cdot x > 0$. $\qquad\square$

Theorem 5.3: Every ordered field $(F, \leq)$ contains a copy of the natural numbers. Specifically, F contains a subset $\overline{\mathbb{N}} = \{\overline{n} \mid n \in \mathbb{N}\}$ such that for all $n, m \in \mathbb{N}$, we have $\overline{n + m} = \overline{n} + \overline{m}$, $\overline{n \cdot m} = \overline{n} \cdot \overline{m}$, and $n < m \leftrightarrow \overline{n} < \overline{m}$.

Proof: Let $(F, \leq)$ be an ordered field. By the definition of a field, $0, 1 \in F$ and $0 \neq 1$.

We let $\overline{0} = 0$ and $\overline{n} = 1 + 1 + \cdots + 1$, where 1 appears n times. Let $\overline{\mathbb{N}} = \{\overline{n} \mid n \in \mathbb{N}\}$. Then $\overline{\mathbb{N}} \subseteq F$.

We first prove by induction on m that for all $n, m \in \mathbb{N}$, $\overline{n + m} = \overline{n} + \overline{m}$.

Base case $(k = 0)$: $\overline{n + 0} = \overline{n} = \overline{n} + 0 = \overline{n} + \overline{0}$.

Inductive step: Suppose that $\overline{n + k} = \overline{n} + \overline{k}$. Then we have

$$\overline{n + (k + 1)} = \overline{(n + k) + 1} = \overline{n + k} + 1 = (\overline{n} + \overline{k}) + 1 = \overline{n} + (\overline{k} + 1) = \overline{n} + \overline{k + 1}.$$

By the Principle of Mathematical Induction, for all natural numbers m, $\overline{n + m} = \overline{n} + \overline{m}$.

Similarly, we prove by induction on m that for all $n, m \in \mathbb{N}$, $\overline{n \cdot m} = \overline{n} \cdot \overline{m}$.

Base case $(k = 0)$: $\overline{n \cdot 0} = \overline{0} = \overline{n} \cdot \overline{0}$.

Inductive step: Suppose that $\overline{n \cdot k} = \overline{n} \cdot \overline{k}$. Then we have

$$\overline{n \cdot (k+1)} = \overline{nk + n} = \overline{nk} + \overline{n} = \overline{n} \cdot \overline{k} + \overline{n} = \overline{n}(\overline{k} + 1) = \overline{n}(\overline{k} + \overline{1}) = \overline{n}(\overline{k+1}).$$

By the Principle of Mathematical Induction, for all natural numbers m, $\overline{n \cdot m} = \overline{n} \cdot \overline{m}$.

We now wish to prove that for all $n, m \in \mathbb{N}$, $n < m \leftrightarrow \overline{n} < \overline{m}$.

We first note that for all $n \in \mathbb{N}$, $\overline{n+1} > \overline{n}$ because $\overline{n+1} - \overline{n} = \overline{n} + 1 - \overline{n} = 1 = 1 \cdot 1 > 0$ by Theorem 5.2.

We now prove by induction on n that for all $n \in \mathbb{N}$ with $n > 0$ that $\overline{n} > 0$.

Base case $(k = 1)$: $\overline{1} = 1 = 1 \cdot 1 > 0$ by Theorem 5.2.

Inductive step: Assume that $\overline{k} > 0$. Then $\overline{k+1} = \overline{k} + \overline{1} = \overline{k} + 1 > 0$. Here we have used Order Property 1 together with $\overline{k} > 0$ and $1 > 0$.

By the Principle of Mathematical Induction, for all natural numbers n with $n > 0$, we have $\overline{n} > 0$.

Conversely, if $\overline{n} > 0$, then $n \neq 0$ (because $\overline{0} = 0$). Since $\overline{n}$ is defined only for $n \geq 0$, we have $n > 0$.

So, we have shown that for $n \in \mathbb{N}$, $n > 0$ if and only if $\overline{n} > 0$.

Next, note that if $n < m$, then $\overline{m} = \overline{(m-n) + n} = \overline{m-n} + \overline{n}$. It follows that $\overline{m-n} = \overline{m} - \overline{n}$.

Finally, we have $n < m \leftrightarrow m - n > 0 \leftrightarrow \overline{m-n} > 0 \leftrightarrow \overline{m} - \overline{n} > 0 \leftrightarrow \overline{m} > \overline{n} \leftrightarrow \overline{n} < \overline{m}$. $\qquad \square$

Notes: (1) The function that sends $n \in \mathbb{N}$ to $\overline{n} \in \overline{\mathbb{N}}$ is called an **isomorphism**. It has the following properties: (i) $\overline{n+m} = \overline{n} + \overline{m}$, (ii) $\overline{n \cdot m} = \overline{n} \cdot \overline{m}$, and (iii) $n < m$ if and only if $\overline{n} < \overline{m}$. The function gives a one-to-one correspondence between the elements of $\mathbb{N}$ and the elements of $\overline{\mathbb{N}}$.

So, when we say that every field contains a "copy" of the natural numbers, we mean that there is a subset $\overline{\mathbb{N}}$ of the field so that $(\overline{\mathbb{N}}, \leq)$ is isomorphic to $(\mathbb{N}, \leq)$ (note that addition and multiplication are preserved as well, even though they're not explicitly mentioned in the notation).

(2) We will formally introduce isomorphisms in Lesson 11.

Theorem 5.4: Let $(F, \leq)$ be an ordered field and let $x \in F$ with $x > 0$. Then $\frac{1}{x} > 0$.

Proof: Since $x \neq 0$, $\frac{1}{x} = x^{-1}$ exists and is nonzero.

Assume toward contradiction that $\frac{1}{x} < 0$. Then $-\frac{1}{x} > 0$. Using Problem 3 (part (vi)) from the problem set below, together with commutativity and associativity of multiplication, the multiplicative inverse property, and the multiplicative identity property, $x\left(-\frac{1}{x}\right) = x(-1)x^{-1} = -1xx^{-1} = -1 \cdot 1 = -1$. Since $x > 0$ and $-\frac{1}{x} > 0$, we have $-1 = x\left(-\frac{1}{x}\right) > 0$. So, $1 \not> 0$. But by Theorem 5.2, $1 = 1 \cdot 1 > 0$. This is a contradiction. Therefore, $\frac{1}{x} > 0$. $\qquad\square$

Why Isn't $\mathbb{Q}$ Enough?

At first glance, it would appear that the ordered field of rational numbers would be sufficient to solve all "real world" problems. However, a long time ago, a group of people called the Pythagoreans showed that this was not the case. The problem was first discovered when applying the now well-known Pythagorean Theorem.

Theorem 5.5 (Pythagorean Theorem): In a right triangle with legs of lengths a and b, and a hypotenuse of length c, $c^2 = a^2 + b^2$.

The picture to the right shows a right triangle. The vertical and horizontal segments (labeled a and b, respectively) are called the **legs** of the right triangle, and the side opposite the right angle (labeled c) is called the **hypotenuse** of the right triangle.

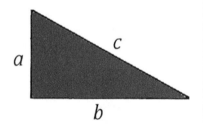

There are many ways to prove the Pythagorean Theorem. Here, we will provide a simple geometric argument. For the proof we will want to recall that the area of a square with side length s is $A = s^2$, and the area of a triangle with base b and height h is $A = \frac{1}{2}bh$. Notice that in our right triangle drawn here, the base is labeled b (how convenient), and the height is labeled a. So, the area of this right triangle is $A = \frac{1}{2}ba = \frac{1}{2}ab$.

Proof of Theorem 5.5: We draw 2 squares, each of side length $a + b$, by rearranging 4 copies of the given triangle in 2 different ways:

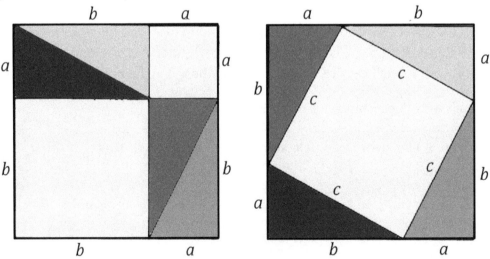

We can get the area of each of these squares by adding the areas of all the figures that comprise each square.

The square on the left consists of 4 copies of the given right triangle, a square of side length a and a square of side length b. It follows that the area of this square is $4 \cdot \frac{1}{2} ab + a^2 + b^2 = 2ab + a^2 + b^2$.

The square on the right consists of 4 copies of the given right triangle, and a square of side length c. It follows that the area of this square is $4 \cdot \frac{1}{2} ab + c^2 = 2ab + c^2$.

Since the areas of both squares of side length $a + b$ are equal (both areas are equal to $(a + b)^2$), $2ab + a^2 + b^2 = 2ab + c^2$. Cancelling $2ab$ from each side of this equation yields $a^2 + b^2 = c^2$. □

Question: In a right triangle where both legs have length 1, what is the length of the hypotenuse?

Let's try to answer this question. If we let c be the length of the hypotenuse of the triangle, then by the Pythagorean Theorem, we have $c^2 = 1^2 + 1^2 = 1 + 1 = 2$. Since $c^2 = c \cdot c$, we need to find a number with the property that when you multiply that number by itself you get 2. The Pythagoreans showed that if we use only numbers in $\mathbb{Q}$, then no such number exists.

Theorem 5.6: There does not exist a rational number a such that $a^2 = 2$.

Analysis: We will prove this Theorem by assuming that there is a rational number a such that $a^2 = 2$, and arguing until we reach a contradiction. A first attempt at a proof would be to let $a = \frac{m}{n} \in \mathbb{Q}$ satisfy $\left(\frac{m}{n}\right)^2 = 2$. It follows that $\boldsymbol{m^2 = 2n^2}$ ($\frac{m^2}{n^2} = \frac{m \cdot m}{n \cdot n} = \frac{m}{n} \cdot \frac{m}{n} = \left(\frac{m}{n}\right)^2$ and $2 = \frac{2}{1} \Rightarrow \frac{m^2}{n^2} = \frac{2}{1} \Rightarrow m^2 = 2n^2$), showing that $\boldsymbol{m^2}$ **is even**. We will then use this information to show that both m and n are even (at this point, you may want to try to use the two statements in bold to prove this yourself).

Now, in our first attempt, the fact that m and n both turned out to be even did not produce a contradiction. However, we can modify the beginning of the argument to make this happen.

Remember that every rational number has infinitely many representations. For example, $\frac{6}{12}$ is the same rational number as $\frac{2}{4}$ (because $6 \cdot 4 = 12 \cdot 2$). Notice that in both representations, the numerator (number on the top) and the denominator (number on the bottom) are even. However, they are both equivalent to $\frac{1}{2}$, which has the property that the numerator is not even.

In Problem 9 below, you will be asked to show that every rational number can be written in the form $\frac{m}{n}$, where at least one of m or n is **not** even. We can now adjust our argument to get the desired contradiction.

Proof of Theorem 5.6: Assume, toward contradiction, that there is a rational number a such that $a^2 = 2$. Since a is a rational number, there are $m \in \mathbb{Z}$ and $n \in \mathbb{Z}^*$, **not both even**, so that $a = \frac{m}{n}$.

So, we have $\frac{m^2}{n^2} = \frac{m \cdot m}{n \cdot n} = \frac{m}{n} \cdot \frac{m}{n} = a \cdot a = a^2 = 2 = \frac{2}{1}$. Thus, $m^2 \cdot 1 = n^2 \cdot 2$. So, $m^2 = 2n^2$. Therefore, m^2 is even. If m were odd, then by Theorem 4.4 (from Lesson 4), $m^2 = m \cdot m$ would be odd. So, **m is even**.

Since m is even, there is $k \in \mathbb{Z}$ such that $m = 2k$. Replacing m by $2k$ in the equation $m^2 = 2n^2$ gives us $2n^2 = m^2 = (2k)^2 = (2k)(2k) = 2\big(k(2k)\big)$. So, $n^2 = k(2k) = (k \cdot 2)k = (2k)k = 2(k \cdot k)$. So, we see that n^2 is even, and again by Theorem 4.4, **n is even**.

So, we have m even and n even, contrary to our original assumption that m and n are not both even. Therefore, there is no rational number a such that $a^2 = 2$. $\qquad\qquad$ □

So, the big question is, "Is there an ordered field F with F containing $\mathbb{Q}$ and $a \in F$ such that $a^2 = 2$?" **Spoiler Alert!** There is! We call it $\mathbb{R}$, the ordered field of real numbers.

Completeness

Let $(F, \leq)$ be an ordered field and let S be a nonempty subset of F. We say that S is **bounded above** if there is $M \in F$ such that for all $s \in S$, $s \leq M$. Each such number M is called an **upper bound** of S.

In words, an upper bound of a set S is simply an element from the field that is at least as big as every element in S.

Similarly, we say that S is **bounded below** if there is $K \in F$ such that for all $s \in S$, $K \leq s$. Each such number K is called a **lower bound** of S.

In words, a lower bound of a set S is simply an element from the field that is no bigger than any element in S.

We will say that S is **bounded** if it is both bounded above and bounded below. Otherwise S is **unbounded**.

A **least upper bound** of a set S is an upper bound that is smaller than any other upper bound of S, and a **greatest lower bound** of S is a lower bound that is larger than any other lower bound of S.

Example 5.2: Let $(F, \leq)$ be an ordered field with $\mathbb{Q} \subseteq F$.

Note: The only two examples of F that we are interested in right now are $\mathbb{Q}$ (the set of rational numbers) and $\mathbb{R}$ (the set of real numbers). Although we haven't finished defining the real numbers, you probably have some intuition as to what they look like—after all, this is the number system you have used throughout high school. As you look at the set in each example below, think about what it looks like as a subset of $\mathbb{Q}$ and as a subset of $\mathbb{R}$.

1. $S = \{1, 2, 3, 4, 5\}$ is bounded.

   5 is an upper bound of S, as is any number larger than 5. The number 5 is special in the sense that there are no upper bounds smaller than it. So, 5 is the **least** upper bound of S.

Similarly, 1 is a lower bound of S, as is any number smaller than 1. The number 1 is the **greatest** lower bound of S because there are no lower bounds larger than it.

Notice that the least upper bound and greatest lower bound of S are inside the set S itself. This will always happen when the set S is finite.

2. $T = \{x \in F \mid -2 < x \le 2\}$ is also bounded. Any number greater than or equal to 2 is an upper bound of T, and any number less than or equal to -2 is a lower bound of T.

   2 is the least upper bound of T and -2 is the greatest lower bound of T.

   Note that the least upper bound of T is in T, whereas the greatest lower bound of T is not in T.

3. $U = \{x \in F \mid x < -3\}$ is bounded above by any number greater than or equal to -3, and -3 is the least upper bound of U. The set U is not bounded below, and therefore, U is unbounded.

4. $V = \{x \in F \mid x^2 < 2\}$ is bounded above by 2. To see this, note that if $x > 2$, then $x^2 > 4 \ge 2$, and therefore, $x \notin V$. Any number greater than 2 is also an upper bound.

   Is 2 the least upper bound of V? It's not! For example, $\frac{3}{2}$ is also an upper bound. Indeed, if $x > \frac{3}{2}$, then $x^2 > \frac{9}{4} \ge 2$ (the reader should verify that for all $a, b \in \mathbb{R}^+, a > b \to a^2 > b^2$).

   Does V have a least upper bound? A moment's thought might lead you to suspect that a least upper bound M would satisfy $M^2 = 2$. And it turns out that you are right! (Proving this, however, is quite difficult). Clearly, this least upper bound M is not in the set V. The big question is "Does M exist at all?"

   Well, if $F = \mathbb{Q}$, then by Theorem 5.6, M **does not** exist in F. In this case, V is an example of a set which is bounded above in $\mathbb{Q}$, but has no least upper bound in $\mathbb{Q}$.

   So, if we want an ordered field F containing $\mathbb{Q}$ where M does exist, we can insist that F has the property that any set which is bounded above in F has a least upper bound in F. It turns out that there is exactly one such ordered field (up to renaming the elements) and we call it the ordered field of real numbers, $\mathbb{R}$.

Many authors use the term **supremum** for "least upper bound" and **infimum** for "greatest lower bound," and they may write sup A and inf A for the supremum and infimum of a set A, respectively (if they exist).

In the examples above, we stated the least upper bound and greatest lower bound of the sets S, T, U, and V without proof. Intuitively, it seems reasonable that those numbers are correct. Let's do one of the examples carefully.

Theorem 5.7: Let $U = \{x \in F \mid x < -3\}$. Then sup $U = -3$.

Analysis: We need to show that -3 is an upper bound of U, and that any number less than -3 is **not** an upper bound of U. That -3 is an upper bound of U follows immediately from the definition of U.

The harder part of the argument is showing that a number less than -3 is not an upper bound of U. However, conceptually it's not hard to see that this is true. If $a < -3$, we simply need to find some number x between a and -3. Here is a picture of the situation.

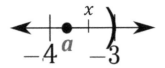

Notice that a can be very close to -3 and we don't know exactly what a is—we know only that it's less than -3. So, we need to be careful how we choose x. The most natural choice for x would be to go midway between a and -3. In other words, we can take the average of a and -3. So, we will let $x = \frac{1}{2}(a + (-3))$. Then we just need to verify that $a < x$ and that $x \in U$ (that is, $x < -3$).

Proof of Theorem 5.7: If $x \in U$, then $x < -3$ by definition, and so, -3 is an upper bound of U.

Suppose that $a < -3$ (or equivalently, $-a - 3 > 0$). We want to show that a is **not** an upper bound of U. To do this, we let $x = \frac{1}{2}(a - 3) = 2^{-1}(a + (-3))$. $x \in F$ because F is closed under addition and multiplication, and the multiplicative inverse property holds in F^*. We will show that $a < x < -3$.

$$x - a = \frac{1}{2}(a - 3) - a = \frac{1}{2}(a - 3) - \frac{1}{2}(2a) = \frac{1}{2}(a - 3 - 2a) = \frac{1}{2}(a - 2a - 3) = \frac{1}{2}(-a - 3).$$

Since $\frac{1}{2} > 0$ (by Theorem 5.4) and $-a - 3 > 0$, it follows that $x - a > 0$, and therefore, $x > a$.

$$-3 - x = -3 - \frac{1}{2}(a - 3) = \frac{1}{2}(-6) - \frac{1}{2}a + \frac{1}{2} \cdot 3 = \frac{1}{2}(-6 - a + 3) = \frac{1}{2}(-a - 3).$$

Again, since $\frac{1}{2} > 0$ and $-a - 3 > 0$, it follows that $-3 - x > 0$, and therefore, $x < -3$. Thus, $x \in U$.

So, we found an element $x \in U$ (because $x < -3$) with $a < x$. This shows that a is **not** an upper bound of U. It follows that $-3 = \sup U$. $\square$

An ordered field $(F, \leq)$ has the **Completeness Property** if every nonempty subset of F that is bounded above in F has a least upper bound in F. In this case, we say that $(F, \leq)$ is a **complete ordered field**.

Theorem 5.8: There is exactly one complete ordered field (up to renaming the elements).

The proof of Theorem 5.8 is quite long and requires some machinery that we haven't yet developed. We will therefore accept it as true for the purpose of this book, and we let $\mathbb{R}$ be the unique complete ordered field guaranteed to exist by the theorem.

We will finish this section by proving two useful theorems about the complete ordered field $\mathbb{R}$.

Theorem 5.9 (The Archimedean Property of $\mathbb{R}$): For every $x \in \mathbb{R}$, there is $n \in \mathbb{N}$ such that $n > x$.

In other words, the Archimedean Property says that the set of natural numbers is unbounded in the reals. In particular, the set of natural numbers is **not** bounded from above in the set of real numbers.

We will prove this theorem by contradiction using the Completeness Property of the reals. If we (wrongly) assume that the set of natural numbers is bounded from above, then the Completeness Property of the reals gives us a least upper bound x. Since x is a **least** upper bound, $x - 1$ is **not** an upper bound. Do you see the problem yet? If $x - 1 < n \in \mathbb{N}$, then $x < n + 1$. But then x is not an upper bound for the set of natural numbers, contrary to our assumption. Let's write out the details.

Proof: Suppose toward contradiction that $\mathbb{N}$ is bounded from above. By the Completeness Property of $\mathbb{R}$, $x = \sup \mathbb{N}$ exists. Since $x - 1$ is **not** an upper bound for $\mathbb{N}$, there is $n \in \mathbb{N}$ such that $x - 1 < n$. Then we have $x = x + (-1 + 1) = (x - 1) + 1 < n + 1$. Since $\mathbb{N}$ is closed under addition, $n + 1 \in \mathbb{N}$. So, x is not an upper bound for $\mathbb{N}$, contradicting the fact that $x = \sup \mathbb{N}$. It follows that $\mathbb{N}$ is not bounded from above. So, for every $x \in \mathbb{R}$, there is $n \in \mathbb{N}$ such that $n > x$. $\qquad \square$

Theorem 5.10 (The Density Theorem): If $x, y \in \mathbb{R}$ with $x < y$, then there is $q \in \mathbb{Q}$ with $x < q < y$.

In other words, the Density Theorem says that between any two real numbers we can always find a rational number. We say that $\mathbb{Q}$ is **dense** in $\mathbb{R}$.

To help understand the proof, let's first run a simple simulation using a specific example. Let's let $x = \frac{16}{3}$ and $y = \frac{17}{3}$. We begin by subtracting to get $y - x = \frac{1}{3}$. This is the distance between x and y. We wish to find a natural number n such that $\frac{1}{n}$ is smaller than this distance. In other words, we want $\frac{1}{n} < \frac{1}{3}$, or equivalently, $n > 3$. So, we can let n be any natural number greater than 3, say $n = 4$. We now want to "shift" $\frac{1}{n} = \frac{1}{4}$ to the right to get a rational number between x and y. We can do this as follows. We multiply n times x to get $nx = 4 \cdot \frac{16}{3} = \frac{64}{3}$. We then let m be the **least** integer greater than nx. So, $m = \frac{66}{3} = 22$. Finally, we let $q = \frac{m}{n} = \frac{22}{4} = \frac{11}{2}$. And we did it! Indeed, we have $\frac{16}{3} < \frac{11}{2} < \frac{17}{3}$. The reader should confirm that these inequalities hold. Let's write out the details of the proof.

Proof: Let's first consider the case where $0 \le x < y$. Let $z = y - x = y + (-x)$. Since $\mathbb{R}$ has the additive inverse property and is closed under addition, $z \in \mathbb{R}$. Also, $z > 0$. By the Archimedean Property, there is $n \in \mathbb{N}$ such that $n > \frac{1}{z}$. Using Problem 5 (part (v)) in the problem set below, we have $\frac{1}{n} < z$. By the Archimedean Property once again, there is $m \in \mathbb{N}$ such that $m > nx$. Therefore, $\frac{m}{n} > x$ (Check this!). So, $\left\{ m \in \mathbb{N} \, \middle| \, \frac{m}{n} > x \right\} \ne \emptyset$. By the Well Ordering Principle, $\left\{ m \in \mathbb{N} \, \middle| \, \frac{m}{n} > x \right\}$ has a least element, let's call it k. Since $k > 0$, (because $x \ge 0$ and $n > 0$) and k is the **least** natural number such that $\frac{k}{n} > x$, it follows that $k - 1 \in \mathbb{N}$ and $\frac{k-1}{n} \le x$, or equivalently, $\frac{k}{n} - \frac{1}{n} \le x$. Therefore, we have $\frac{k}{n} \le x + \frac{1}{n} < x + z = x + (y - x) = y$. Thus, $x < \frac{k}{n} < y$. Since $k, n \in \mathbb{N}$, we have $\frac{k}{n} \in \mathbb{Q}$.

Now, we consider the case where $x < 0$ and $x < y$. By the Archimedean Property, there is $t \in \mathbb{N}$ such that $t > -x$. Then, we have $0 < x + t < y + t$. So, $x + t$ and $y + t$ satisfy the first case above. Thus, there is $q \in \mathbb{Q}$ with $x + t < q < y + t$. It follows that $x < q - t < y$. Since $t \in \mathbb{N}$, $-t \in \mathbb{Z}$. Since $\mathbb{Z} \subseteq \mathbb{Q}$, $-t \in \mathbb{Q}$. So, we have $q, -t \in \mathbb{Q}$. Since $\mathbb{Q}$ is closed under addition, $q - t = q + (-t) \in \mathbb{Q}$. $\qquad \square$

Problem Set 5

Full solutions to these problems are available for free download here:
www.SATPrepGet800.com/PMFBXSG

LEVEL 1

1. The addition and multiplication tables below are defined on the set $S = \{0, 1, 2\}$. Show that $(S, +, \cdot)$ does **not** define a field.

+	0	1	2
0	0	1	2
1	1	2	0
2	2	0	1

$\cdot$	0	1	2
0	0	0	0
1	0	1	2
2	0	2	2

2. Let $F = \{0, 1\}$, where $0 \neq 1$. Show that there is exactly one field $(F, +, \cdot)$, where 0 is the additive identity and $\cdot$ is the multiplicative identity.

LEVEL 2

3. Let $(F, +, \cdot)$ be a field. Prove each of the following:

   (i)   If $a, b \in F$ with $a + b = b$, then $a = 0$.

   (ii)   If $a \in F$, $b \in F^*$, and $ab = b$, then $a = 1$.

   (iii)   If $a \in F$, then $a \cdot 0 = 0$.

   (iv)   If $a \in F^*$, $b \in F$, and $ab = 1$, then $b = \dfrac{1}{a}$.

   (v)   If $a, b \in F$ and $ab = 0$, then $a = 0$ or $b = 0$.

   (vi)   If $a \in F$, then $-a = -1a$

   (vii) $(-1)(-1) = 1$.

4. Let $(F, +, \cdot)$ be a field with $\mathbb{N} \subseteq F$. Prove that $\mathbb{Q} \subseteq F$.

LEVEL 3

5. Let $(F, \leq)$ be an ordered field. Prove each of the following:

   (i)   If $a, b \in F$, exactly one of the following holds: $a < b$, $a = b$, or $a > b$.

   (ii)   If $a, b \in F$, $a \leq b$, and $b \leq a$, then $a = b$.

   (iii)   If $a, b, c \in F$, $a < b$, and $b < c$, then $a < c$.

   (iv)   If $a, b, c \in F$, $a \leq b$, and $b \leq c$, then $a \leq c$.

   (v)   If $a, b \in F^+$ and $a > b$, then $\dfrac{1}{a} < \dfrac{1}{b}$.

   (vi)   If $a, b \in F$, then $a > b$ if and only if $-a < -b$.

   (vii)   If $a, b \in F$, then $a \geq b$ if and only if $-a \leq -b$.

6. Let $(F, +, \cdot)$ be a field. Show that $(F, \cdot)$ is a commutative monoid.

LEVEL 4

7. Prove that there is no smallest positive real number.

8. Let a be a nonnegative real number. Prove that $a = 0$ if and only if a is less than every positive real number. (Note: a nonnegative means that a is positive or zero.)

9. Prove that every rational number can be written in the form $\frac{m}{n}$, where $m \in \mathbb{Z}$, $n \in \mathbb{Z}^*$, and at least one of m or n is **not** even.

LEVEL 5

10. Show that every nonempty set of real numbers that is bounded below has a greatest lower bound in $\mathbb{R}$.

11. Show that between any two real numbers there is a real number that is **not** rational.

12. Let $T = \{x \in F \mid -2 < x \leq 2\}$. Prove $\sup T = 2$ and $\inf T = -2$.

CHALLENGE PROBLEM

13. Let $V = \{x \in F \mid x^2 < 2\}$ and let $a = \sup V$. Prove that $a^2 = 2$.

LESSON 6 – TOPOLOGY
THE TOPOLOGY OF $\mathbb{R}$

Intervals of Real Numbers

A set I of real numbers is called an **interval** if any real number that lies between two numbers in I is also in I. Symbolically, we can write

$$\forall x, y \in I \; \forall z \in \mathbb{R} \; (x < z < y \rightarrow z \in I).$$

The expression above can be read "For all x, y in I and all $z \in \mathbb{R}$, if x is less than z and z is less than y, then z is in I.

Example 6.1:

1. The set $A = \{0, 1\}$ is **not** an interval. A consists of just the two real numbers 0 and 1. There are infinitely many real numbers between 0 and 1. For example, the real number $\frac{1}{2}$ satisfies $0 < \frac{1}{2} < 1$, but $\frac{1}{2} \notin A$.

2. $\mathbb{R}$ is an interval. This follows trivially from the definition. If we replace I by $\mathbb{R}$, we get $\forall x, y \in \mathbb{R} \; \forall z \in \mathbb{R} \; (x < z < y \rightarrow z \in \mathbb{R})$. In other words, if we start with two real numbers, and take a real number between them, then that number is a real number (which we already said).

When we are thinking of $\mathbb{R}$ as an interval, we sometimes use the notation $(-\infty, \infty)$ and refer to this as **the real line**. The following picture gives the standard geometric interpretation of the real line.

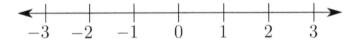

In addition to the real line, there are 8 other types of intervals.

Open Interval: $\qquad\qquad (a, b) = \{x \in \mathbb{R} \mid a < x < b\}$

Closed Interval: $\qquad\qquad [a, b] = \{x \in \mathbb{R} \mid a \leq x \leq b\}$

Half-open Intervals: $\qquad (a, b] = \{x \in \mathbb{R} \mid a < x \leq b\} \qquad [a, b) = \{x \in \mathbb{R} \mid a \leq x < b\}$

Infinite Open Intervals: $\quad (a, \infty) = \{x \in \mathbb{R} \mid x > a\} \qquad (-\infty, b) = \{x \in \mathbb{R} \mid x < b\}$

Infinite Closed Intervals: $[a, \infty) = \{x \in \mathbb{R} \mid x \geq a\} \qquad (-\infty, b] = \{x \in \mathbb{R} \mid x \leq b\}$

It's easy to check that each of these eight types of sets satisfies the definition of being an interval. Conversely, every interval has one of these nine forms. This will follow immediately from Theorem 6.1 and Problem 4 below.

Note that the first four intervals above (the open, closed, and two half-open intervals) are **bounded**. They are each bounded below by a and bounded above by b. In fact, for each of these intervals, a is the **greatest lower bound** and b is the **least upper bound**. Using the notation from Lesson 5, we have for example, $a = \inf(a, b)$ and $b = \sup(a, b)$.

Example 6.2:

1. The half-open interval $(-2, 1] = \{x \in \mathbb{R} \mid -2 < x \leq 1\}$ has the following graph:

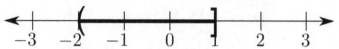

2. The infinite open interval $(0, \infty) = \{x \in \mathbb{R} \mid x > 0\}$ has the following graph:

Theorem 6.1: If an interval I is bounded, then there are $a, b \in \mathbb{R}$ such that one of the following holds: $I = (a, b)$, $I = [a, b]$, $I = (a, b]$, or $I = [a, b)$.

Analysis: We will prove this by letting $a = \inf I$ and $b = \sup I$ (in other words, a is the greatest lower bound of I and b is the least upper bound of I), and then doing each of the following:

(1) We will show $I \subseteq [a, b]$.

(2) We will show $(a, b) \subseteq I$.

(3) We will then look at 4 different cases. As one sample case, if $a, b \in I$, then we will have $I \subseteq [a, b]$ and $[a, b] \subseteq I$. It then follows from the "Axiom of Extensionality" that $I = [a, b]$.

Recall: Given sets X and Y, the **Axiom of Extensionality** says that X and Y are the same set if and only if X and Y have precisely the same elements (See the technical note following Theorem 2.5 in Lesson 2). In symbols,

$$X = Y \text{ if and only if } \forall x(x \in X \leftrightarrow x \in Y).$$

Since $\forall x(x \in X \leftrightarrow x \in Y)$ is logically equivalent to $\forall x(x \in X \to x \in Y) \wedge \forall x(x \in Y \to x \in X)$, we have

$$X = Y \text{ if and only if } \forall x(x \in X \to x \in Y) \text{ and } \forall x(x \in Y \to x \in X).$$

Therefore, to show that $X = Y$, we can instead show that $X \subseteq Y$ and $Y \subseteq X$. This is the approach we will take in the proof below.

Proof of Theorem 6.1: Let I be a bounded interval. Since I is bounded, by the Completeness of $\mathbb{R}$, I has a least upper bound b. By Problem 10 in Lesson 5, I has a greatest lower bound a. If $x \in I$, then by the definitions of upper bound and lower bound, we have $x \in [a, b]$. Since x was an arbitrary element of I, $\forall x(x \in I \to x \in [a, b])$. So, $I \subseteq [a, b]$.

Now, let $z \in (a, b)$. It follows that $a < z < b$. Since b is the **least** upper bound of I, z is **not** an upper bound of I. So, there is $y \in I$ with $z < y$. Since a is the **greatest** lower bound of I, z is **not** a lower bound of I. So, there is $x \in I$ with $x < z$. Since I is an interval, $x, y \in I$, and $x < z < y$, it follows that $z \in I$. Since z was an arbitrary element of (a, b), we have shown $\forall x(x \in (a, b) \to x \in I)$. So, $(a, b) \subseteq I$.

We have shown that $(a, b) \subseteq I$ and $I \subseteq [a, b]$. There are now 4 cases to consider.

Case 1: If both the greatest lower bound of I (namely, a) and the least upper bound of I (namely, b) are elements of I, then we have $[a, b] \subseteq I$ and $I \subseteq [a, b]$. So, $I = [a, b]$.

Case 2: If $a \in I$ and $b \notin I$, then we have $[a, b) \subseteq I$ and $I \subseteq [a, b)$. So, $I = [a, b)$.

Case 3: If $a \notin I$ and $b \in I$, then we have $(a, b] \subseteq I$ and $I \subseteq (a, b]$. So, $I = (a, b]$.

Case 4: If $a \notin I$ and $b \notin I$, then we have $(a, b) \subseteq I$ and $I \subseteq (a, b)$. So, $I = (a, b)$. $\qquad\square$

Note: You will be asked to prove the analogous result for unbounded intervals in Problem 4 below.

Operations on Sets

In Lesson 2 we saw how to take the union and intersection of two sets. We now review the definitions from that lesson and introduce a few more.

The **union** of the sets A and B, written $A \cup B$, is the set of elements that are in A or B (or both).

$$A \cup B = \{x \mid x \in A \text{ or } x \in B\}$$

The **intersection** of A and B, written $A \cap B$, is the set of elements that are simultaneously in A and B.

$$A \cap B = \{x \mid x \in A \text{ and } x \in B\}$$

The following Venn diagrams for the union and intersection of two sets can be useful for visualizing these operations. As usual, U is some "universal" set that contains both A and B.

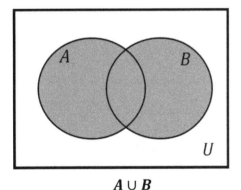

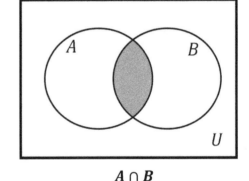

$$A \cup B \qquad\qquad\qquad\qquad A \cap B$$

The **difference** $A \setminus B$ is the set of elements that are in A and not in B.

$$A \setminus B = \{x \mid x \in A \text{ and } x \notin B\}$$

The **symmetric difference** between A and B, written $A \,\Delta\, B$, is the set of elements that are in A or B, but not both.

$$A \,\Delta\, B = (A \setminus B) \cup (B \setminus A)$$

Let's also look at Venn diagrams for the difference and symmetric difference of two sets.

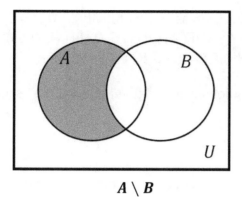

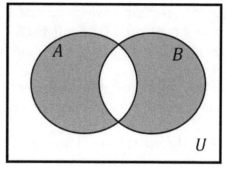

$$A \setminus B \qquad\qquad\qquad A \, \Delta \, B$$

Example 6.3: Let $A = \{0, 1, 2, 3, 4\}$ and $B = \{3, 4, 5, 6\}$. We have

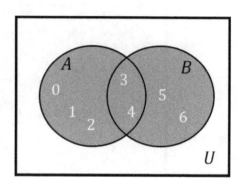

1. $A \cup B = \{0, 1, 2, 3, 4, 5, 6\}$
2. $A \cap B = \{3, 4\}$
3. $A \setminus B = \{0, 1, 2\}$
4. $B \setminus A = \{5, 6\}$
5. $A \, \Delta \, B = \{0, 1, 2\} \cup \{5,6\} = \{0, 1, 2, 5, 6\}$

Example 6.4: Let $A = (-2, 1]$ and $B = (0, \infty)$. We have

1. $A \cup B = (-2, \infty)$
2. $A \cap B = (0, 1]$
3. $A \setminus B = (-2, 0]$
4. $B \setminus A = (1, \infty)$
5. $A \, \Delta \, B = (-2, 0] \cup (1, \infty)$

Note: If you have trouble seeing how to compute these, it may be helpful to draw the graphs of A and B lined up vertically, and then draw vertical lines through the endpoints of each interval.

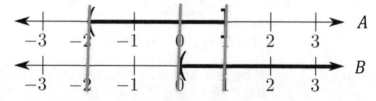

The results follow easily by combining these graphs into a single graph using the vertical lines as guides. For example, let's look at $A \cap B$ in detail. We're looking for all numbers that are in both A and B. The two rightmost vertical lines drawn passing through the two graphs above isolate all those numbers nicely. We see that all numbers between 0 and 1 are in the intersection. We should then think about the two endpoints 0 and 1 separately. $0 \notin B$ and therefore, 0 cannot be in the intersection of A and B. On the other hand, $1 \in A$ and $1 \in B$. Therefore, $1 \in A \cap B$. So, we see that $A \cap B = (0, 1]$.

Unions and intersections have many nice algebraic properties such as commutativity ($A \cup B = B \cup A$ and $A \cap B = B \cap A$), associativity (($A \cup B) \cup C = A \cup (B \cup C)$ and $(A \cap B) \cap C = A \cap (B \cap C)$), and distributivity ($A \cap (B \cup C) = (A \cap B) \cup (A \cap C)$ and $A \cup (B \cap C) = (A \cup B) \cap (A \cup C)$).

As an example, let's prove that the operation of forming unions is associative. You will be asked to prove similar results in the problems below.

Theorem 6.2: The operation of forming unions is associative.

Note: Before beginning the proof, let's draw Venn diagrams of the situation to convince ourselves that the theorem is true.

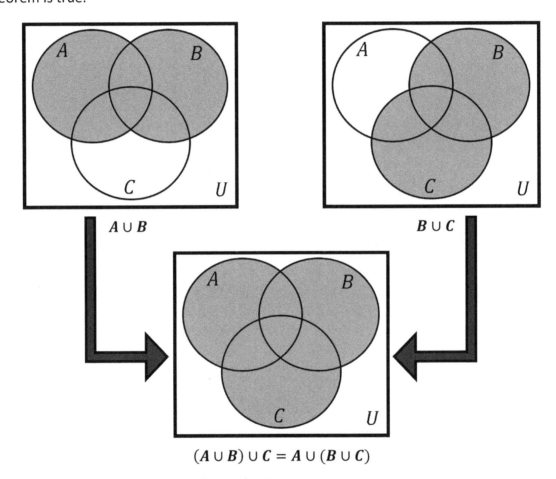

$$(A \cup B) \cup C = A \cup (B \cup C)$$

Proof of Theorem 6.2: Let A, B, and C be sets, and let $x \in (A \cup B) \cup C$. Then $x \in A \cup B$ or $x \in C$. If $x \in C$, then $x \in B$ or $x \in C$. So, $x \in B \cup C$. Then $x \in A$ or $x \in B \cup C$. So, $x \in A \cup (B \cup C)$. If, on the other hand, $x \in A \cup B$, then $x \in A$ or $x \in B$. If $x \in A$, then $x \in A$ or $x \in B \cup C$. So, $x \in A \cup (B \cup C)$. If $x \in B$, then $x \in B$ or $x \in C$. So, $x \in B \cup C$. Then $x \in A$ or $x \in B \cup C$. So, $x \in A \cup (B \cup C)$. Since x was arbitrary, we have shown $\forall x (x \in (A \cup B) \cup C \rightarrow x \in A \cup (B \cup C))$. Therefore, we have shown that $(A \cup B) \cup C \subseteq A \cup (B \cup C)$.

A similar argument can be used to show $A \cup (B \cup C) \subseteq (A \cup B) \cup C$ (the reader should write out the details).

Since $(A \cup B) \cup C \subseteq A \cup (B \cup C)$ and $A \cup (B \cup C) \subseteq (A \cup B) \cup C$, $(A \cup B) \cup C = A \cup (B \cup C)$, and therefore, the operation of forming unions is associative. □

Remember that associativity allows us to drop parentheses. So, we can now simply write $A \cup B \cup C$ when taking the union of the three sets A, B, and C.

Recall from Lesson 2 that sets A and B are called **disjoint** or **mutually exclusive** if $A \cap B = \emptyset$. For example, the sets $(-2, 0]$ and $(1, \infty)$ are disjoint intervals. Here is a typical Venn diagram of disjoint sets A and B.

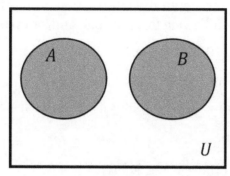

$$A \cap B = \emptyset$$

In topology, we will often want to look at unions and intersections of more than one set. Therefore, we make the following more general definitions.

Let X be a nonempty set of sets.

$$\cup X = \{y \mid \text{there is } Y \in X \text{ with } y \in Y\} \qquad \text{and} \qquad \cap X = \{y \mid \text{for all } Y \in X, y \in Y\}.$$

If you're having trouble understanding what these definitions are saying, you're not alone. The notation probably looks confusing, but the ideas behind these definitions are very simple. You have a whole bunch of sets (possibly infinitely many). To take the union of all these sets, you simply throw all the elements together into one big set. To take the intersection of all these sets, you take only the elements that are in every single one of those sets.

Example 6.5:

1. Let A and B be sets, and let $X = \{A, B\}$. Then

    $$\cup X = \{y \mid \text{there is } Y \in X \text{ with } y \in Y\} = \{y \mid y \in A \text{ or } y \in B\} = A \cup B.$$
    $$\cap X = \{y \mid \text{for all } Y \in X, y \in Y\} = \{y \mid y \in A \text{ and } y \in B\} = A \cap B.$$

2. Let A, B, and C be sets, and let $X = \{A, B, C\}$. Then

    $$\cup X = \{y \mid \text{there is } Y \in X \text{ with } y \in Y\} = \{y \mid y \in A, y \in B, \text{or } y \in C\} = A \cup B \cup C.$$
    $$\cap X = \{y \mid \text{for all } Y \in X, y \in Y\} = \{y \mid y \in A, y \in B, \text{and } y \in C\} = A \cap B \cap C.$$

3. Let $X = \{[0, r) \mid r \in \mathbb{R}^+\}$. Then

    $$\cup X = \{y \mid \text{there is } Y \in X \text{ with } y \in Y\} = \{y \mid \text{there is } r \in \mathbb{R}^+ \text{ with } y \in [0, r)\} = [0, \infty).$$
    $$\cap X = \{y \mid \text{for all } Y \in X, y \in Y\} = \{y \mid \text{for all } r \in \mathbb{R}^+, y \in [0, r)\} = \{0\}.$$

Notes: (1) Examples 1 and 2 give a good idea of what $\cup X$ and $\cap X$ look like when X is finite. More generally, if $X = \{A_1, A_2, \ldots, A_n\}$, then $\cup X = A_1 \cup A_2 \cup \cdots \cup A_n$ and $\cap X = A_1 \cap A_2 \cap \cdots \cap A_n$.

(2) As a specific example of Note 1, let $A_1 = (-\infty, 5]$, $A_2 = (0, 5)$, $A_3 = [2, 6)$, and $A_4 = (4, 99]$. Let $X = \{A_1, A_2, A_3, A_4\}$. Then

$$\cup X = A_1 \cup A_2 \cup A_3 \cup A_4 = (-\infty, 5] \cup (0, 5) \cup [2, 6) \cup (4, 99] = (-\infty, 99].$$

$$\cap X = A_1 \cap A_2 \cap A_3 \cap A_4 = (-\infty, 5] \cap (0, 5) \cap [2, 6) \cap (4, 99] = (4, 5).$$

If you have trouble seeing how to compute the intersection, it may help to line up the graphs of the intervals, as was done in the Note following Example 6.4, and/or take the intersections two at a time:

$(-\infty, 5] \cap (0, 5) = (0, 5)$ because $(0, 5) \subseteq (-\infty, 5]$.

$(0, 5) \cap [2, 6) = [2, 5)$ (draw the line graphs if you don't see this).

$[2, 5) \cap (4, 99] = (4, 5)$ (again, draw the line graphs if you don't see this).

(3) Let's prove carefully that $\{y \mid$ there is $r \in \mathbb{R}^+$ with $y \in [0, r)\} = [0, \infty)$.

For convenience, let's let $A = \{y \mid$ there is $r \in \mathbb{R}^+$ with $y \in [0, r)\}$.

If $y \in A$, then there is $r \in \mathbb{R}^+$ with $y \in [0, r)$. So, $0 \leq y < r$. In particular, $y \geq 0$. So, $y \in [0, \infty)$. Since $y \in A$ was arbitrary, we have shown that $A \subseteq [0, \infty)$.

Let $y \in [0, \infty)$. Since $(y + 1) - y = 1 > 0$, we have $y + 1 > y$. So, $y \in [0, y + 1)$. Since $y + 1 \in \mathbb{R}^+$, $y \in A$. Since $y \in [0, \infty)$ was arbitrary, we have shown that $[0, \infty) \subseteq A$.

Since $A \subseteq [0, \infty)$ and $[0, \infty) \subseteq A$, it follows that $A = [0, \infty)$.

(4) Let's also prove carefully that $\{y \mid$ for all $r \in \mathbb{R}^+, y \in [0, r)\} = \{0\}$.

For convenience, let's let $B = \{y \mid$ for all $r \in \mathbb{R}^+, y \in [0, r)\}$.

If $y \in B$, then for all $r \in \mathbb{R}^+$, $y \in [0, r)$. So, for all $y \in \mathbb{R}^+$, $0 \leq y < r$. So, y is a nonnegative real number that is less than every positive real number. By Problem 8 in Problem Set 5, $y = 0$. Therefore, $y \in \{0\}$. Since $y \in B$ was arbitrary, we have shown that $B \subseteq \{0\}$.

Now, let $y \in \{0\}$. Then $y = 0$. For all $r \in \mathbb{R}^+$, $0 \in [0, r)$. So, $y \in B$. It follows that $\{0\} \subseteq B$.

Since $B \subseteq \{0\}$ and $\{0\} \subseteq B$, it follows that $B = \{0\}$.

(5) Note that the empty union is empty. Indeed, we have $\cup \emptyset = \{y \mid$ there is $Y \in \emptyset$ with $y \in Y\} = \emptyset$.

If X is a nonempty set of sets, we say that X is **disjoint** if $\cap X = \emptyset$. We say that X is **pairwise disjoint** if for all $A, B \in X$ with $A \neq B$, A and B are disjoint. For example, if we let $X = \{(n, n + 1) \mid n \in \mathbb{Z}\}$, then X is both disjoint and pairwise disjoint.

Are the definitions of disjoint and pairwise disjoint equivalent? You will be asked to answer this question in Problem 5 below.

Open and Closed Sets

A subset X of $\mathbb{R}$ is said to be **open** if for every real number $x \in X$, there is an open interval (a, b) with $x \in (a, b)$ and $(a, b) \subseteq X$.

In words, a set is open in $\mathbb{R}$ if every number in the set has "some space" on both sides of that number inside the set. If you think of each point in the set as an animal, then each animal in the set should be able to move a little to the left and a little to the right without ever leaving the set. Another way to think of this is that no number is on "the edge" or "the boundary" of the set, about to fall out of it.

Example 6.6:

1. Every bounded open interval is open. To see this, let $X = (a, b)$ and let $x \in X$. Then $X = (a, b)$ itself is an open interval with $x \in (a, b)$ and $(a, b) \subseteq X$. For example, $(0, 1)$ and $\left(-\sqrt{2}, \frac{3}{5}\right)$ are open sets.

2. We will prove in the theorems below that **all** open intervals are open sets. For example, $(-2, \infty)$, $(-\infty, 5)$, and $(-\infty, \infty)$ are all open sets.

3. $(0, 1]$ is **not** an open set because the "boundary point" 1 is included in the set. If (a, b) is any open interval containing 1, then $(a, b) \nsubseteq (0, 1]$ because there are numbers greater than 1 inside (a, b). For example, let $x = \frac{1}{2}(1 + b)$ (the average of 1 and b). Since $b > 1$, we have that $x > \frac{1}{2}(1 + 1) = \frac{1}{2} \cdot 2 = 1$. So, $x > 1$. Also, since $1 > a$, $x > a$. Now, since $1 < b$, we have that $x < \frac{1}{2}(b + b) = \frac{1}{2}(2b) = \left(\frac{1}{2} \cdot 2\right)b = 1b = b$. So, $x \in (a, b)$.

4. We can use reasoning similar to that used in 3 to see that all half-open intervals and closed intervals are **not** open sets.

Theorem 6.3: Let $a \in \mathbb{R}$. The infinite interval (a, ∞) is an open set.

The idea behind the proof is quite simple. If $x \in (a, \infty)$, then $(a, x + 1)$ is an open interval with x inside of it and with $(a, x + 1) \subseteq (a, \infty)$.

Proof of Theorem 6.3: Let $x \in (a, \infty)$ and let $b = x + 1$.

Since $x \in (a, \infty)$, $x > a$. Since $(x + 1) - x = 1 > 0$, we have $b = x + 1 > x$.

So, we have $a < x < b$. That is, $x \in (a, b)$. Also, $(a, b) \subseteq (a, \infty)$. Since $x \in (a, \infty)$ was arbitrary, (a, ∞) is an open set. $\qquad \square$

In Problem 6 below (part (i)), you will be asked to show that an interval of the form $(-\infty, b)$ is also an open set.

Theorem 6.4: $\emptyset$ and $\mathbb{R}$ are both open sets.

Proof: The statement that $\emptyset$ is open is vacuously true (since $\emptyset$ has no elements, there is nothing to check).

If $x \in \mathbb{R}$, then $x \in (x - 1, x + 1)$ and $(x - 1, x + 1) \subseteq \mathbb{R}$. Since x was an arbitrary element of $\mathbb{R}$, we have shown that for every $x \in \mathbb{R}$, there is an open interval (a, b) with $x \in (a, b)$ and $(a, b) \subseteq \mathbb{R}$. So, $\mathbb{R}$ is open. □

Many authors define "open" in a slightly different way from the definition we've been using. This next Theorem will show that the definition we have been using is equivalent to theirs.

Theorem 6.5: A subset X of $\mathbb{R}$ is open if and only if for every real number $x \in X$, there is a positive real number c such that $(x - c, x + c) \subseteq X$.

Analysis: The harder direction of the proof is showing that if X is open, then for every real number $x \in X$, there is a positive real number c such that $(x - c, x + c) \subseteq X$.

To see this, suppose that X is open and let $x \in X$. Then there is an open interval (a, b) with $x \in (a, b)$ and $(a, b) \subseteq X$. We want to replace the interval (a, b) by an interval that has x right in the center.

The following picture should help us to come up with an argument.

In the picture, we have an open interval (a, b), containing x. In this particular picture, x is a bit closer to a than it is to b. However, we should remember to be careful that our argument doesn't assume this (as we have no control over where x "sits" inside of (a, b)).

In the picture, we see that $x - a$ is the distance from a to x, and $b - x$ is the distance from x to b. Since the distance from a to x is smaller, let's let c be that smaller distance. In other words, we let $c = x - a$. From the picture, it looks like the interval $(x - c, x + c)$ will be inside the interval (a, b).

In general, if x is closer to a, we would let $c = x - a$, and if x is closer to b, we would let $c = b - x$. We can simply define c to be the smaller of $x - a$ and $b - x$. That is, $c = \min\{x - a, b - x\}$. From the picture, it seems like with this choice of c, the interval $(x - c, x + c)$ should give us what we want.

Proof of Theorem 6.5: Let X be an open subset of $\mathbb{R}$ and let $x \in X$. Then there is an open interval (a, b) with $x \in (a, b)$ and $(a, b) \subseteq X$. Let $c = \min\{x - a, b - x\}$. We claim that $(x - c, x + c)$ is an open interval containing x and contained in (a, b). We need to show $a \leq x - c < x < x + c \leq b$.

Since $c = \min\{x - a, b - x\}$, $c \leq x - a$. So, $-c \geq -(x - a)$. It follows that

$$(x - c) - a \geq \big(x - (x - a)\big) - a = (x - x + a) - a = a - a = 0.$$

So, $x - c \geq a$.

Since $c = \min\{x - a, b - x\}$, $c \leq b - x$. So, $-c \geq -(b - x)$. It follows that

$$b - (x + c) = b - x - c \geq b - x - (b - x) = 0.$$

So, $b \geq x + c$, or equivalently, $x + c \leq b$.

Note that $x > a$, so that $x - a > 0$, and $x < b$, so that $b - x > 0$. It follows that $c > 0$.

We have $x - (x - c) = c > 0$, so that $x > x - c$. We also have $(x + c) - x = c > 0$, so that $x + c > x$.

We have shown $a \leq x - c < x < x + c \leq b$, as desired.

Since $(x - c, x + c) \subseteq (a, b)$ and $(a, b) \subseteq X$, by the transitivity of $\subseteq$ (Theorem 2.3 from Lesson 2), we have $(x - c, x + c) \subseteq X$.

The converse is immediate since for $x \in X$, $(x - c, x + c)$ is an open interval containing x. $\square$

The basic definition of a **topological space** involves open sets, unions, and intersections. We're not going to talk about general topological spaces in this lesson (we will look at them in Lesson 14), but in the spirit of the subject, we will prove some results about unions and intersections of open sets in $\mathbb{R}$.

Theorem 6.6: The union of two open sets in $\mathbb{R}$ is an open set in $\mathbb{R}$.

Proof: Let A and B be open sets in $\mathbb{R}$, and let $x \in A \cup B$. Then $x \in A$ or $x \in B$. **Without loss of generality**, we may assume that $x \in A$ (see the Note below). Since A is open in $\mathbb{R}$, there is an interval (a, b) with $x \in (a, b)$ and $(a, b) \subseteq A$. By Theorem 2.4, $A \subseteq A \cup B$. Since $\subseteq$ is transitive (Theorem 2.3), $(a, b) \subseteq A \cup B$. Therefore, $A \cup B$ is open. $\square$

Note: In the proof of Theorem 6.6, we used the expression "Without loss of generality." This expression can be used when an argument can be split up into 2 or more cases, and the proof of each of the cases is nearly identical.

For Theorem 6.6, the two cases are (i) $x \in A$ and (ii) $x \in B$. The argument for case (ii) is the same as the argument for case (i), essentially word for word—only the roles of A and B are interchanged.

Example 6.7: $(-5, 2)$ is open by part 1 of Example 6.6 and $(7, \infty)$ is open by Theorem 6.3. Therefore, by Theorem 6.6, $(-5, 2) \cup (7, \infty)$ is also open.

If you look at the proof of Theorem 6.6 closely, you should notice that the proof would still work if we were taking a union of more than 2 sets. In fact, **any** union of open sets is open, as we now prove.

Theorem 6.7: Let X be a set of open subsets of $\mathbb{R}$. Then $\bigcup X$ is open.

Proof: Let X be a set of open subsets of $\mathbb{R}$ and let $x \in \bigcup X$. Then $x \in A$ for some $A \in X$. Since A is open in $\mathbb{R}$, there is an interval (a, b) with $x \in (a, b)$ and $(a, b) \subseteq A$. By Problem 9 below (part (i)), we have $A \subseteq \bigcup X$. Since $\subseteq$ is transitive (Theorem 2.3), $(a, b) \subseteq \bigcup X$. Therefore, $\bigcup X$ is open. $\square$

Example 6.8:

1. $(1,2) \cup (2,3) \cup (3,4) \cup (4, \infty)$ is open.

2. $\mathbb{R} \setminus \mathbb{Z}$ is open because it is a union of open intervals. It looks like this:

$$\cdots (-2, -1) \cup (-1, 0) \cup (0, 1) \cup (1, 2) \cup \cdots$$

$\mathbb{R} \setminus \mathbb{Z}$ can also be written as

$$\bigcup \{(n, n+1) \mid n \in \mathbb{Z}\} \text{ or } \bigcup_{n \in \mathbb{Z}} (n, n+1)$$

3. If we take the union of all intervals of the form $\left(\frac{1}{n+1}, \frac{1}{n}\right)$ for positive integers n, we get an open set. We can visualize this open set as follows:

$$\bigcup \left\{\left(\frac{1}{n+1}, \frac{1}{n}\right) \mid n \in \mathbb{Z}^+\right\} = \cdots \cup \left(\frac{1}{5}, \frac{1}{4}\right) \cup \left(\frac{1}{4}, \frac{1}{3}\right) \cup \left(\frac{1}{3}, \frac{1}{2}\right) \cup \left(\frac{1}{2}, 1\right)$$

Theorem 6.8: Every open set in $\mathbb{R}$ can be expressed as a union of bounded open intervals.

The main idea of the argument will be the following. Every real number that is in an open set is inside an open interval that is a subset of the set. Just take the union of all these open intervals (one interval for each real number in the set).

Proof of Theorem 6.8: Let X be an open set in $\mathbb{R}$. Since X is open, for each $x \in X$, there is an interval (a_x, b_x) with $x \in (a_x, b_x)$ and $(a_x, b_x) \subseteq X$. We Let $Y = \{(a_x, b_x) \mid x \in X\}$. We will show that $X = \bigcup Y$.

First, let $x \in X$. Then $x \in (a_x, b_x)$. Since $(a_x, b_x) \in Y$, $x \in \bigcup Y$. Since x was arbitrary, $X \subseteq \bigcup Y$.

Now, let $x \in \bigcup Y$. Then there is $z \in X$ with $x \in (a_z, b_z)$. Since $(a_z, b_z) \subseteq X$, $x \in X$. Since $x \in X$ was arbitrary, $\bigcup Y \subseteq X$.

Since $X \subseteq \bigcup Y$ and $\bigcup Y \subseteq X$, it follows that $X = \bigcup Y$. $\quad\square$

Theorem 6.9: The intersection of two open sets in $\mathbb{R}$ is an open set in $\mathbb{R}$.

Proof: Let A and B be open sets in $\mathbb{R}$ and let $x \in A \cap B$. Then $x \in A$ and $x \in B$. Since A is open, there is an open interval (a, b) with $x \in (a, b)$ and $(a, b) \subseteq A$. Since B is open, there is an open interval (c, d) with $x \in (c, d)$ and $(c, d) \subseteq B$. Let $C = (a, b) \cap (c, d)$. Since $x \in (a, b)$ and $x \in (c, d)$, $x \in C$. By Problem 6 below (part (ii)), C is an open interval. By Problem 11 from Lesson 2 and part (ii) of Problem 3 below, $C \subseteq A$ and $C \subseteq B$. It follows that $C \subseteq A \cap B$ (prove this!). Since $x \in A \cap B$ was arbitrary, $A \cap B$ is open. $\quad\square$

In Problem 6 below (part (iii)), you will be asked to show that the intersection of **finitely** many open sets in $\mathbb{R}$ is an open set in $\mathbb{R}$. In problem 8, you will be asked to show that an **arbitrary** intersection of open sets does **not** need to be open.

A subset X of $\mathbb{R}$ is said to be **closed** if $\mathbb{R} \setminus X$ is open.

$\mathbb{R} \setminus X$ is called the **complement** of X in $\mathbb{R}$, or simply the complement of X. It consists of all real numbers **not** in X.

Example 6.9:

1. Every closed interval is a closed set. For example, $[0,1]$ is closed because its complement in $\mathbb{R}$ is $\mathbb{R} \setminus [0,1] = (-\infty, 0) \cup (0, \infty)$. This is a union of open intervals, which is open.

    Similarly, $[3, \infty)$ is a closed set because $\mathbb{R} \setminus [3, \infty) = (-\infty, 3)$, which is open.

2. Half-open intervals are neither open nor closed. For example, we saw in Example 6.6 that $(0,1]$ is **not** an open set. We see that $(0,1]$ is not closed by observing $\mathbb{R} \setminus (0,1] = (-\infty, 0] \cup (1, \infty)$, which is not open.

3. $\emptyset$ is closed because $\mathbb{R} \setminus \emptyset = \mathbb{R}$ is open. $\mathbb{R}$ is closed because $\mathbb{R} \setminus \mathbb{R} = \emptyset$ is open. $\emptyset$ and $\mathbb{R}$ are the only two sets of real numbers that are both open and closed.

Theorem 6.10: The intersection of two closed sets in $\mathbb{R}$ is a closed set in $\mathbb{R}$.

Proof: Let A and B be closed sets in $\mathbb{R}$. Then $\mathbb{R} \setminus A$ and $\mathbb{R} \setminus B$ are open sets in $\mathbb{R}$. By Theorem 6.6 (or 6.7), $(\mathbb{R} \setminus A) \cup (\mathbb{R} \setminus B)$ is open in $\mathbb{R}$. Therefore, $\mathbb{R} \setminus [(\mathbb{R} \setminus A) \cup (\mathbb{R} \setminus B)]$ is closed in $\mathbb{R}$. So, it suffices to show that $A \cap B = \mathbb{R} \setminus [(\mathbb{R} \setminus A) \cup (\mathbb{R} \setminus B)]$. Well, $x \in A \cap B$ if and only if $x \in A$ and $x \in B$ if and only if $x \notin \mathbb{R} \setminus A$ and $x \notin \mathbb{R} \setminus B$ if and only if $x \notin (\mathbb{R} \setminus A) \cup (\mathbb{R} \setminus B)$ if and only if $x \in \mathbb{R} \setminus [(\mathbb{R} \setminus A) \cup (\mathbb{R} \setminus B)]$. So, $A \cap B = \mathbb{R} \setminus [(\mathbb{R} \setminus A) \cup (\mathbb{R} \setminus B)]$, completing the proof. $\square$

A similar argument can be used to show that the union of two closed sets in $\mathbb{R}$ is a closed set in $\mathbb{R}$. This result can be extended to the union of finitely many closed sets in $\mathbb{R}$ with the help of Problem 6 below (part (iii)). The dedicated reader should prove this. In Problem 10 below, you will be asked to show that an arbitrary intersection of closed sets in $\mathbb{R}$ is closed. In problem 8, you will be asked to show that an arbitrary union of closed sets does **not** need to be closed.

Problem Set 6

Full solutions to these problems are available for free download here:
www.SATPrepGet800.com/PMFBXSG

LEVEL 1

1. Draw Venn diagrams for $(A \setminus B) \setminus C$ and $A \setminus (B \setminus C)$. Are these two sets equal for all sets A, B, and C? If so, prove it. If not, provide a counterexample.

2. Let $A = \{\emptyset, \{\emptyset, \{\emptyset\}\}\}$, $B = \{\emptyset, \{\emptyset\}\}$, $C = (-\infty, 2]$, $D = (-1, 3]$. Compute each of the following:

   (i) $A \cup B$

   (ii) $A \cap B$

   (iii) $A \setminus B$

   (iv) $B \setminus A$

   (v) $A \Delta B$

   (vi) $C \cup D$

   (vii) $C \cap D$

   (viii) $C \setminus D$

   (ix) $D \setminus C$

   (x) $C \Delta D$

LEVEL 2

3. Prove the following:

   (i)   The operation of forming unions is commutative.

   (ii)   The operation of forming intersections is commutative.

   (iii)   The operation of forming intersections is associative.

4. Prove that if an interval I is unbounded, then I has one of the following five forms: (a, ∞), $(-\infty, b)$, $[a, \infty)$, $(-\infty, b]$, $(-\infty, \infty)$

LEVEL 3

5. Prove or provide a counterexample:

   (i)   Every pairwise disjoint set of sets is disjoint.

   (ii)   Every disjoint set of sets is pairwise disjoint.

6. Prove the following:

    (i)   For all $b \in \mathbb{R}$, the infinite interval $(-\infty, b)$ is an open set in $\mathbb{R}$.

    (ii)   The intersection of two open intervals in $\mathbb{R}$ is either empty or an open interval in $\mathbb{R}$.

    (iii) The intersection of finitely many open sets in $\mathbb{R}$ is an open set in $\mathbb{R}$.

7. Let A, B, and C be sets. Prove each of the following:

    (i) $A \cap (B \cup C) = (A \cap B) \cup (A \cap C)$.

    (ii) $A \cup (B \cap C) = (A \cup B) \cap (A \cup C)$.

    (iii) $C \setminus (A \cup B) = (C \setminus A) \cap (C \setminus B)$.

    (iv) $C \setminus (A \cap B) = (C \setminus A) \cup (C \setminus B)$.

LEVEL 4

8. Give an example of an infinite collection of open sets whose intersection is not open. Also, give an example of an infinite collection of closed sets whose union is not closed. Provide a proof for each example.

9. Let X be a nonempty set of sets. Prove the following:

    (i)   For all $A \in X$, $A \subseteq \bigcup X$.

    (ii)   For all $A \in X$, $\bigcap X \subseteq A$.

LEVEL 5

10. Prove that if X is a nonempty set of closed subsets of $\mathbb{R}$, then $\bigcap X$ is closed.

11. Let A be a set and let X be a nonempty collection of sets. Prove each of the following:

    (i) $A \cap \bigcup X = \bigcup \{A \cap B \mid B \in X\}$

    (ii) $A \cup \bigcap X = \bigcap \{A \cup B \mid B \in X\}$

    (iii) $A \setminus \bigcup X = \bigcap \{A \setminus B \mid B \in X\}$

    (iv) $A \setminus \bigcap X = \bigcup \{A \setminus B \mid B \in X\}$.

12. Prove that every closed set in $\mathbb{R}$ can be written as an intersection $\bigcap X$, where each element of X is a union of at most 2 closed intervals.

CHALLENGE PROBLEM

13. Prove that every nonempty open set of real numbers can be expressed as a union of pairwise disjoint open intervals.

A Limitation of the Reals

In Lesson 5 we asked (and answered) the question "Why isn't $\mathbb{Q}$ (the field of rational numbers) enough?" We now ask the same question about $\mathbb{R}$, the field of real numbers.

A **linear equation** has the form $ax + b = 0$, where $a \neq 0$. If we are working inside a field, then this equation has the unique solution $x = -ba^{-1} = -\frac{b}{a}$. For example, the equation $2x - 1 = 0$ has the unique solution $x = 2^{-1} = \frac{1}{2}$. Notice how important it is that we are working inside a field here. If we were allowed to use only the properties of a commutative ring, then we might not be able to solve this equation. For example, in $\mathbb{Z}$ (the ring of integers), the equation $2x - 1 = 0$ has no solution.

A **quadratic equation** has the form $ax^2 + bx + c = 0$, where $a \neq 0$. Is working inside a field enough to solve this equation? The answer is no! For example, a solution to the equation $x^2 - 2 = 0$ must satisfy $x^2 = 2$. In Lesson 5, we proved that this equation cannot be solved in $\mathbb{Q}$. This was one of our main motivations for introducing $\mathbb{R}$. And, in fact, the equation $x^2 - 2 = 0$ **can** be solved in $\mathbb{R}$. However, the equation $x^2 + 1 = 0$ **cannot** be solved in $\mathbb{R}$. This follows immediately from Theorem 5.2, which says that if x is an element of an ordered field, then $x^2 = x \cdot x$ can never be negative.

Is there a field containing $\mathbb{R}$, where all quadratic equations can be solved? The answer is **yes**, and in fact, we can do much better than that. In this lesson we will define a field containing the field of real numbers such that every equation of the form $a_n x^n + a_{n-1} x^{n-1} + \cdots + a_1 x + a_0 = 0$ has a solution. Such an equation is called a **polynomial equation**, and a field in which every such polynomial equation has a solution is called an **algebraically closed field**.

The Complex Field

The **standard form of a complex number** is $a + bi$, where a and b are real numbers. So, the set of complex numbers is $\mathbb{C} = \{a + bi \mid a, b \in \mathbb{R}\}$.

If we identify $1 = 1 + 0i$ with the ordered pair $(1, 0)$, and we identify $i = 0 + 1i$ with the ordered pair $(0, 1)$, then it is natural to write the complex number $a + bi$ as the point (a, b). Here is a reasonable justification for this:

$a + bi = a(1,0) + b(0,1) = (a, 0) + (0, b) = (a, b)$

In this way, we can visualize a complex number as a point in **The Complex Plane**. A portion of the Complex Plane is shown to the right with several complex numbers displayed as points of the form (x, y).

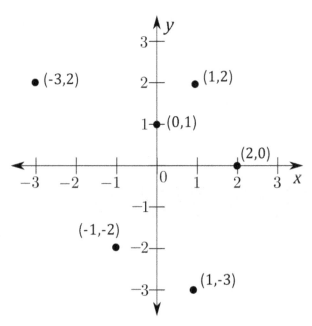

78

The complex plane is formed by taking two copies of the real line and placing one horizontally and the other vertically. The horizontal copy of the real line is called the x-axis or the **real axis** (labeled x in the above figure) and the vertical copy of the real line is called the y-axis or **imaginary axis** (labeled y in the above figure). The two axes intersect at the point $(0, 0)$. This point is called the **origin**.

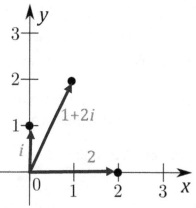

We can also visualize the complex number $a + bi$ as a directed line segment (or **vector**) starting at the origin and ending at the point (a, b). Three examples are shown to the right.

If $z = a + bi$ is a complex number, we call a the **real part** of z and b the **imaginary part** of z, and we write $a = \text{Re } z$ and $b = \text{Im } z$.

Two complex numbers are **equal** if and only if they have the same real part and the same imaginary part. In other words,

$$a + bi = c + di \text{ if and only if } a = c \text{ and } b = d.$$

We add two complex numbers by simply adding their real parts and adding their imaginary parts. So,

$$(a + bi) + (c + di) = (a + c) + (b + d)i.$$

As a point, this sum is $(a + c, b + d)$. We can visualize this sum as the vector starting at the origin that is the diagonal of the parallelogram formed from the vectors $a + bi$ and $c + di$. Here is an example showing that $(1 + 2i) + (-3 + i) = -2 + 3i$.

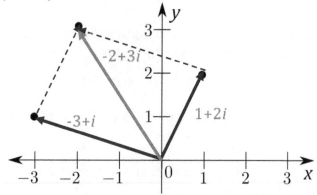

The definition for multiplying two complex numbers is a bit more complicated:

$$(a + bi)(c + di) = (ac - bd) + (ad + bc)i.$$

Notes: (1) If $b = 0$, then we call $a + bi = a + 0i = a$ a **real number**. Note that when we add or multiply two real numbers, we always get another real number.

$$(a + 0i) + (b + 0i) = (a + b) + (0 + 0)i = (a + b) + 0i = a + b.$$
$$(a + 0i)(b + 0i) = (ab - 0 \cdot 0) + (a \cdot 0 + 0b)i = (ab - 0) + (0 + 0)i = ab + 0i = ab.$$

(2) If $a = 0$, then we call $a + bi = 0 + bi = bi$ a **pure imaginary number**.

(3) $i^2 = -1$. To see this, note that $i^2 = i \cdot i = (0 + 1i)(0 + 1i)$, and we have

$$(0 + 1i)(0 + 1i) = (0 \cdot 0 - 1 \cdot 1) + (0 \cdot 1 + 1 \cdot 0)i = (0 - 1) + (0 + 0)i = -1 + 0i = -1.$$

(4) The definition of the product of two complex numbers is motivated by how multiplication should behave in a field, together with replacing i^2 by -1. If we were to naïvely multiply the two complex numbers, we would have

$$(a + bi)(c + di) = (a + bi)c + (a + bi)(di) = ac + bci + adi + bdi^2$$
$$= ac + bci + adi + bd(-1) = ac + (bc + ad)i - bd = (ac - bd) + (ad + bc)i.$$

The dedicated reader should make a note of which field properties were used during this computation.

Those familiar with the mnemonic FOIL may notice that "FOILing" will always work to produce the product of two complex numbers, provided we replace i^2 by -1 and simplify.

Example 7.1: Let $z = 2 - 3i$ and $w = -1 + 5i$. Then

$$z + w = (2 - 3i) + (-1 + 5i) = (2 + (-1)) + (-3 + 5)i = \mathbf{1 + 2i}.$$
$$zw = (2 - 3i)(-1 + 5i) = \big(2(-1) - (-3)(5)\big) + \big(2 \cdot 5 + (-3)(-1)\big)i$$
$$= (-2 + 15) + (10 + 3)i = \mathbf{13 + 13i}.$$

With the definitions we just made for addition and multiplication, we get $(\mathbb{C}, +, \cdot)$, the **field of complex numbers**. See Lesson 5 if you need to review the definition of a field.

Theorem 7.1: $(\mathbb{C}, +, \cdot)$ is field.

The proof that $(\mathbb{C}, +, \cdot)$ is a field is very straightforward and mostly uses the fact that $(\mathbb{R}, +, \cdot)$ is a field. For example, to verify that addition is commutative in $\mathbb{C}$, we have

$$(a + bi) + (c + di) = (a + c) + (b + d)i = (c + a) + (d + b)i = (c + di) + (a + bi).$$

We have $a + c = c + a$ because $a, c \in \mathbb{R}$ and addition is commutative in $\mathbb{R}$. For the same reason, we have $b + d = d + b$.

We leave the full verification that $(\mathbb{C}, +, \cdot)$ is a field as an exercise for the reader (Problem 2 below), and simply note a few things of importance here:

- The identity for addition is $0 = 0 + 0i$.

- The identity for multiplication is $1 = 1 + 0i$

- The additive inverse of $z = a + bi$ is $-z = -(a + bi) = -a - bi$.

- The multiplicative inverse of $z = a + bi$ is $z^{-1} = \dfrac{a}{a^2 + b^2} - \dfrac{b}{a^2 + b^2}i$.

The reader is expected to verify all this in Problem 2.

Remark: By Note 1 above, we see that $(\mathbb{R}, +, \cdot)$ is a **subfield** of $(\mathbb{C}, +, \cdot)$. That is, $\mathbb{R} \subseteq \mathbb{C}$ and $(\mathbb{R}, +, \cdot)$ is a field with respect to the field operations of $(\mathbb{C}, +, \cdot)$ (In other words, we don't need to "change" the definition of addition or multiplication to get the appropriate operations in $\mathbb{R}$—the operations are already behaving correctly). Subfields will be covered in more detail in Lesson 11.

Subtraction: If $z, w \in \mathbb{C}$, with $z = a + bi$ and $w = c + di$, then we define the **difference** $z - w$ by

$$z - w = z + (-w) = (a + bi) + (-c - di) = (a - c) + (b - d)i.$$

As a point, this difference is $(a - c, b - d)$. Here is an example illustrating how subtraction works using the computation $(1 + 2i) - (2 - i) = -1 + 3i$.

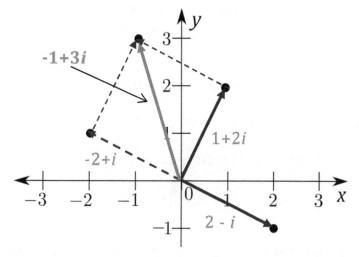

Observe how we first replaced $2 - i$ by $-2 + i$ so that we could change the subtraction problem to the addition problem: $(1 + 2i) + (-2 + i)$. We then formed a parallelogram using $1 + 2i$ and $-2 + i$ as edges, and finally, drew the diagonal of that parallelogram to see the result.

Division: If $z \in \mathbb{C}$ and $w \in \mathbb{C}^*$ with $z = a + bi$ and $w = c + di$, then we define the **quotient** $\frac{z}{w}$ by

$$\frac{z}{w} = zw^{-1} = (a + bi)\left(\frac{c}{c^2 + d^2} - \frac{d}{c^2 + d^2}i\right) = \frac{ac + bd}{c^2 + d^2} + \frac{bc - ad}{c^2 + d^2}i.$$

The definition of division in a field unfortunately led to a messy looking formula. However, when actually performing division, there is an easier way to think about it, as we will see below.

The **conjugate** of the complex number $z = a + bi$ is the complex number $\bar{z} = a - bi$.

Notes: (1) To take the conjugate of a complex number, we simply negate the imaginary part of the number and leave the real part as it is.

(2) If $z = a + bi \neq 0$, then at least one of a or b is not zero. It follows that $\bar{z} = a - bi$ is also not 0.

(3) The product of a complex number with its conjugate is always a nonnegative real number. Specifically, if $z = a + bi$, then $z\bar{z} = (a + bi)(a - bi) = (a^2 + b^2) + (-ab + ab)i = a^2 + b^2$.

(4) We can change the quotient $\frac{z}{w}$ to standard form by multiplying the numerator and denominator by $\bar{w}$. So, if $z = a + bi$ and $w = c + di$, then we have

$$\frac{z}{w} = \frac{z\bar{w}}{w\bar{w}} = \frac{(a + bi)(c - di)}{(c + di)(c - di)} = \frac{(ac + bd) + (bc - ad)i}{c^2 + d^2} = \frac{ac + bd}{c^2 + d^2} + \frac{bc - ad}{c^2 + d^2}i.$$

Example 7.2: Let $z = 2 - 3i$ and $w = -1 + 5i$. Then

$$\overline{z} = 2 + 3i. \qquad\qquad \overline{w} = -1 - 5i.$$

$$\frac{z}{w} = \frac{z\overline{w}}{w\overline{w}} = \frac{(2-3i)(-1-5i)}{(-1+5i)(-1-5i)} = \frac{(-2-15)+(-10+3)i}{(-1)^2+5^2} = \frac{(-17-7i)}{1+25} = -\frac{17}{26} - \frac{7}{26}i.$$

Recall from Lesson 5 that in an ordered field, if $a > 0$ and $b > 0$, then $a + b > 0$ (Order Property 1) and $ab > 0$ (Order Property 2). Also, for every element a, exactly one of the following holds: $a > 0$, $a = 0$, or $a < 0$ (Order Property 3).

Theorem 7.2: The field of complex numbers cannot be ordered.

Proof: Suppose toward contradiction that $<$ is an ordering of $(\mathbb{C}, +, \cdot)$.

If $i > 0$, then $-1 = i^2 = i \cdot i > 0$ by Order Property 2.

If $i < 0$, then $-i > 0$, and therefore, $-1 = i^2 = (-1)(-1)i \cdot i = (-1i)(-1i) = (-i)(-i) > 0$, again by Order Property 2.

So, $-1 > 0$ and it follows that $1 = (-1)(-1) > 0$, again by order property 2. Therefore, we have $-1 > 0$ and $1 > 0$, violating Order Property 3. So, $(\mathbb{C}, +, \cdot)$ cannot be ordered. $\qquad\square$

Absolute Value and Distance

If x and y are real or complex numbers such that $y = x^2$, then we call x a **square root** of y. If x is a positive real number, then we say that x is the **positive square root** of y and we write $x = \sqrt{y}$.

For positive real numbers, we will use the square root symbol only for the positive square root of the number. For complex numbers, we will use the square root symbol for the **principal square root** of the number. The concept of principal square root will be explained in Lesson 15.

Example 7.3:

1. Since $2^2 = 4$, $2 \in \mathbb{R}$, and $2 > 0$, we see that 2 is the positive square root of 4 and we write $2 = \sqrt{4}$.

2. We have $(-2)^2 = 4$, but $-2 < 0$, and so we **do not** write $-2 = \sqrt{4}$. However, -2 is still a square root of 4, and we can write $-2 = -\sqrt{4}$.

3. Since $i^2 = -1$, we see that i is a square root of -1.

4. Since $(-i)^2 = (-i)(-i) = (-1)(-1)i^2 = 1(-1) = -1$, we see that $-i$ is also a square root of -1.

5. $(1+i)^2 = (1+i)(1+i) = (1-1)+(1+1)i = 0 + 2i = 2i$. So, $1 + i$ is a square root of $2i$.

The **absolute value** or **modulus** of the complex number $z = a + bi$ is the nonnegative real number

$$|z| = \sqrt{a^2 + b^2} = \sqrt{(\text{Re } z)^2 + (\text{Im } z)^2}$$

Note: If $z = a + 0i = a$ is a real number, then $|a| = \sqrt{a^2}$. This is equal to a if $a \geq 0$ and $-a$ if $a < 0$.

For example, $|4| = \sqrt{4^2} = \sqrt{16} = 4$ and $|-4| = \sqrt{(-4)^2} = \sqrt{16} = 4 = -(-4)$.

The statement "$|a| = -a$ for $a < 0$" often confuses students. This confusion is understandable, as a minus sign is usually used to indicate that an expression is negative, whereas here we are negating a negative number to make it positive. Unfortunately, this is the simplest way to say, "delete the minus sign in front of the number" using basic notation.

Geometrically, the absolute value of a complex number z is the distance between the point z and the origin.

Example 7.4: Which of the following complex numbers is closest to the origin? $1 + 2i$, $-3 + i$, or $-2 + 3i$?

$$|1 + 2i| = \sqrt{1^2 + 2^2} = \sqrt{1 + 4} = \sqrt{5}$$

$$|-3 + i| = \sqrt{(-3)^2 + 1^2} = \sqrt{9 + 1} = \sqrt{10}$$

$$|-2 + 3i| = \sqrt{(-2)^2 + 3^2} = \sqrt{4 + 9} = \sqrt{13}$$

Since $\sqrt{5} < \sqrt{10} < \sqrt{13}$, we see that $1 + 2i$ is closest to the origin.

Notes: (1) Here we have used the following theorem: If $a, b \in \mathbb{R}^+$, then $a < b$ if and only if $a^2 < b^2$. To see this, observe that $a^2 < b^2$ if and only if $b^2 - a^2 > 0$ if and only if $(b + a)(b - a) > 0$. Since $a > 0$ and $b > 0$, by Order Property 1, $a + b > 0$. It follows that $a^2 < b^2$ if and only if $b - a > 0$ if and only if $b > a$ if and only if $a < b$.

Applying this theorem to $5 < 10 < 13$, we get $\sqrt{5} < \sqrt{10} < \sqrt{13}$.

(2) The definition of the absolute value of a complex number is motivated by the Pythagorean Theorem.

As an example, look at $-3 + i$ in the figure below. Observe that to get from the origin to the point $(-3, 1)$, we move to the left 3 units and then up 1 unit. This gives us a right triangle with legs of lengths 3 and 1. By the Pythagorean Theorem, the hypotenuse has length $\sqrt{3^2 + 1^2} = \sqrt{9 + 1} = \sqrt{10}$.

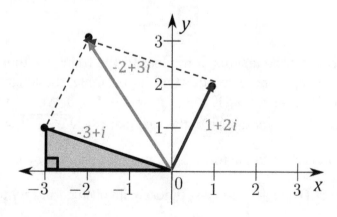

The **distance** between the complex numbers $z = a + bi$ and $w = c + di$ is

$$d(z, w) = |z - w| = \sqrt{(c - a)^2 + (d - b)^2}.$$

Geometrically, we can translate the vector $z - w$ so that the directed line segment begins at the terminal point of w and ends at the terminal point of z. Let's look one more time at the figure we drew for $(1 + 2i) - (2 - i) = -1 + 3i$ and then translate the solution vector as we just suggested.

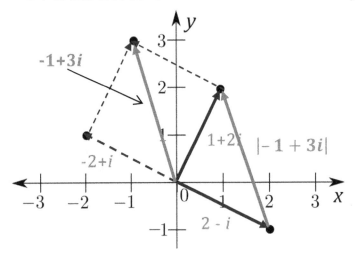

Notice that the expression for the distance between two complex numbers follows from a simple application of the Pythagorean Theorem. Let's continue to use the same example to help us see this.

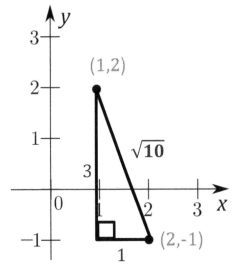

In the figure above, we can get the lengths of the legs of the triangle either by simply counting the units, or by subtracting the appropriate coordinates. For example, the length of the horizontal leg is $2 - 1 = 1$ and the length of the vertical leg is $2 - (-1) = 2 + 1 = 3$. We can then use the Pythagorean Theorem to get the length of the hypotenuse of the triangle: $c = \sqrt{1^2 + 3^2} = \sqrt{1 + 9} = \sqrt{10}$.

Compare this geometric procedure to the formula for distance given above.

While we're on the subject of triangles, the next theorem involving arbitrary triangles is very useful.

Theorem 7.3 (The Triangle Inequality): For all $z, w \in \mathbb{C}$, $|z + w| \leq |z| + |w|$.

Geometrically, the Triangle Inequality says that the length of the third side of a triangle is less than or equal to the sum of the lengths of the other two sides of the triangle. We leave the proof as an exercise (see Problem 4 below).

As an example, let's look at the sum $(1 + 2i) + (-3 + i) = -2 + 3i$. In Example 7.4, we computed

$$|1 + 2i| = \sqrt{5}, |-3 + i| = \sqrt{10}, \text{ and } |-2 + 3i| = \sqrt{13}.$$

Note that $\sqrt{5} + \sqrt{10} > \sqrt{4} + \sqrt{9} = 2 + 3 = 5$, whereas $\sqrt{13} < \sqrt{16} = 4$. So, we see that

$$|(1 + 2i) + (-3 + i)| = |-2 + 3i| = \sqrt{13} < 4 < 5 < \sqrt{5} + \sqrt{10} = |1 + 2i| + |-3 + i|.$$

In the following picture, there are two triangles. We've put dark bold lines around the leftmost triangle and labeled the sides with their lengths.

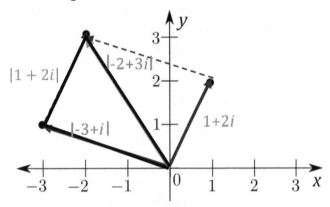

Basic Topology of $\mathbb{C}$

A **circle** in the Complex Plane is the set of all points that are at a fixed distance from a fixed point. The fixed distance is called the **radius** of the circle and the fixed point is called the **center** of the circle.

If a circle has radius $r > 0$ and center $c = a + bi$, then any point $z = x + yi$ on the circle must satisfy $|z - c| = r$, or equivalently, $(x - a)^2 + (y - b)^2 = r^2$.

Note: The equation $|z - c| = r$ says "The distance between z and c is equal to r." In other words, the distance between any point on the circle and the center of the circle is equal to the radius of the circle.

Example 7.5: The circle with equation $|z + 2 - i| = 2$ has center $c = -(2 - i) = -2 + i$ and radius $r = 2$.

Note: $|z + 2 - i| = |z - (-2 + i)|$. So, if we rewrite the equation as $|z - (-2 + i)| = 2$, it is easy to pick out the center and radius of the circle.

A picture of the circle is shown to the right. The center is labeled and a typical radius is drawn.

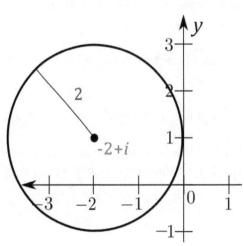

An **open disk** in $\mathbb{C}$ consists of all the points in the interior of a circle. If a is the center of the open disk and r is the radius of the open disk, then any point z inside the disk satisfies $|z - a| < r$.

$N_r(a) = \{z \in \mathbb{C} \mid |z - a| < r\}$ is also called the **r-neighborhood of a**.

Example 7.6: $N_2(-2 + i) = \{z \in \mathbb{C} \mid |z + 2 - i| < 2\}$ is the 2 neighborhood of $-2 + i$. It consists of all points inside the circle $|z + 2 - i| = 2$.

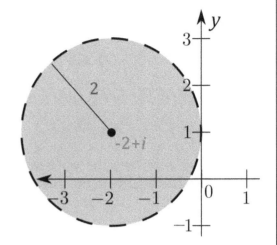

Notes: (1) A picture of the 2-neighborhood of $-2 + i$ is shown to the right. The center is labeled and a typical radius is drawn. We drew the boundary of the disk with dashes to indicate that points on the circle are **not** in the neighborhood and we shaded the interior of the disk to indicate that every point inside the circle is in the neighborhood.

(2) The definitions of open disk and r-neighborhood of a also make sense in $\mathbb{R}$, but the geometry looks a bit different. An open disk in $\mathbb{R}$ is simply an open interval. If x and a are real numbers, then we have

$$x \in N_r(a) \Leftrightarrow |x - a| < r \Leftrightarrow \sqrt{(x - a)^2} < r \Leftrightarrow 0 \le (x - a)^2 < r^2$$
$$\Leftrightarrow -r < x - a < r \Leftrightarrow a - r < x < a + r \Leftrightarrow x \in (a - r, a + r).$$

So, in $\mathbb{R}$, an r-neighborhood of a is the open interval $N_r(a) = (a - r, a + r)$. Notice that the length (or **diameter**) of this interval is $2r$.

As an example, let's draw a picture of $N_2(1) = (1 - 2, 1 + 2) = (-1, 3)$. Observe that the center of this open disk (or open interval or neighborhood) in $\mathbb{R}$ is the real number 1, the radius of the open disk is 2, and the diameter of the open disk (or length of the interval) is 4.

A **closed disk** is the interior of a circle together with the circle itself (the **boundary** is included). If a is the center of the closed disk and r is the radius of the closed disk, then any point z inside the closed disk satisfies $|z - a| \le r$.

Notes: (1) In this case, the circle itself would be drawn solid to indicate that all points on the circle are included.

(2) Just like an open disk in $\mathbb{R}$ is an open interval, a closed disk in $\mathbb{R}$ is a closed interval.

(3) The reader is encouraged to draw a few open and closed disks in both $\mathbb{C}$ and $\mathbb{R}$, and to write down the corresponding sets of points using set builder notation and, in the case of $\mathbb{R}$, interval notation.

A **punctured open disk** consists of all the points in the interior of a circle **except** for the center of the circle. If a is the center of the punctured open disk and r is the radius of the open disk, then any point z inside the punctured disk satisfies $|z - a| < r$ and $z \neq a$.

Note that $z \neq a$ is equivalent to $z - a \neq 0$. In turn, this is equivalent to $|z - a| \neq 0$. Since $|z - a|$ must be nonnegative, $|z - a| \neq 0$ is equivalent to $|z - a| > 0$ or $0 < |z - a|$.

Therefore, a punctured open disk with center a and radius r consists of all points z that satisfy

$$0 < |z - a| < r.$$

$N_r^{\odot}(a) = \{z \mid 0 < |z - a| < r\}$ is also called a **deleted r-neighborhood** of a.

Example 7.7: $N_2^{\odot}(-2 + i) = \{z \in \mathbb{C} \mid 0 < |z + 2 - i| < 2\}$ is the deleted 2 neighborhood of $-2 + i$. It consists of all points inside the circle $|z + 2 - i| = 2$, **except for** $-2 + i$.

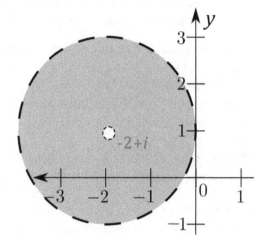

Notes: (1) A picture of the deleted 2-neighborhood of $-2 + i$ is shown to the right. Notice that this time we excluded the center of the disk $-2 + i$, as this point is not included in the set.

(2) In $\mathbb{R}$, we have

$$N_r^{\odot}(a) = (a - r, a + r) \setminus \{a\} = (a - r, a) \cup (a, a + r).$$

This is the open interval centered at a of length (or diameter) $2r$ with a removed.

Let's draw a picture of $N_2^{\odot}(1) = (-1, 3) \setminus \{1\} = (-1, 1) \cup (1, 3)$.

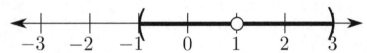

(3) Notice how all the topological definitions we are presenting make sense in both $\mathbb{R}$ and $\mathbb{C}$, but the geometry in each case looks different. You will continue to see this happen. In fact, these definitions make sense for many, many sets and structures, all with their own "look." In general, topology allows us to make definitions and prove theorems that can be applied very broadly and used in many (if not all) branches of mathematics.

A subset X of $\mathbb{C}$ is said to be **open** if for every complex number $z \in X$, there is an open disk D with $z \in D$ and $D \subseteq X$.

In words, a set is open in $\mathbb{C}$ if every point in the set has "space" all around it inside the set. If you think of each point in the set as an animal, then each animal in the set should be able to move a little in any direction it chooses without leaving the set. Another way to think of this is that no number is right on "the edge" or "the boundary" of the set, about to fall out of it.

Example 7.8:

1. Every open disk D is an open set. To see this, simply observe that if $z \in D$, then D itself is an open disk with $z \in D$ and $D \subseteq D$.

2. A closed disk is **not** an open set because it contains its "boundary." As an example, let's look at the closed unit disk $D = \{z \in \mathbb{C} \mid |z| \leq 1\}$. Let's focus on the point i. First note that $i \in D$ because $|i| = \sqrt{0^2 + 1^2} = \sqrt{1} = 1$ and $1 \leq 1$. Now, any open disk N containing i will contain points above i. Let's say $(1 + \epsilon)i \in N$ for some positive real number ϵ. Now, we have $|(1 + \epsilon)i| = \sqrt{0^2 + (1 + \epsilon)^2} = 1 + \epsilon$, which is greater than 1. Therefore, $(1 + \epsilon)i \notin D$. It follows that $N \nsubseteq D$, and so, D is not open.

3. We can use reasoning similar to that used in 2 to see that if we take any subset of a disk that contains any points on the bounding circle, then that set will **not** be open.

4. $\emptyset$ and $\mathbb{C}$ are both open. You will be asked to prove this in Problem 7 below (parts (i) and (ii)).

As we mentioned in Lesson 6 right before Theorem 6.5, many authors define "open" in a slightly different way from the definition we've been using. Once again, let's show that the definition we have been using is equivalent to theirs.

Theorem 7.4: A subset X of $\mathbb{C}$ is open if and only if for every complex number $w \in X$, there is a positive real number d such that $N_d(w) \subseteq X$.

Analysis: The harder direction of the proof is showing that if X is open, then for every complex number $w \in X$, there is a positive real number d such that $N_d(w) \subseteq X$.

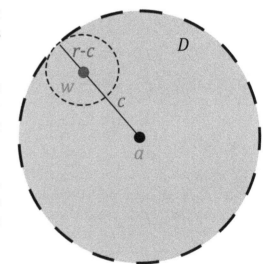

To see this, suppose that X is open and let $w \in X$. Then there is an open disk $D = \{z \in \mathbb{C} \mid |z - a| < r\}$ with $w \in D$ and $D \subseteq X$. We want to replace the disk D with a disk that has w right in the center.

To accomplish this, we let c be the distance from w to a. Then $r - c$ is the distance from w to the boundary of D. We will show that the disk with center w and radius $r - c$ is a subset of D.

The picture to the right illustrates this idea. Notice that $c + (r - c) = r$, the radius of disk D.

Proof of Theorem 7.4: Let X be an open subset of $\mathbb{C}$ and let $w \in X$. Then there is an open disk D with $w \in D$ and $D \subseteq X$.

Suppose that D has center a and radius r. So, $D = \{z \in \mathbb{C} \mid |z - a| < r\}$.

Let $c = |w - a|$ and let $d = r - c$. We will show that $N_d(w) \subseteq D$.

Let $z \in N_d(w)$. Then $|z - w| < d = r - c$.

By the Triangle Inequality (and SACT—see Note 2 below),

$$|z - a| = |(z - w) + (w - a)| \leq |z - w| + |w - a| < (r - c) + c = r.$$

So, $z \in D$. Since z was an arbitrary element of $N_d(w)$, we showed that $N_d(w) \subseteq D$.

So, we have $N_d(w) \subseteq D$ and $D \subseteq X$. By the transitivity of $\subseteq$ (Theorem 2.3 from Lesson 2), we have $N_d(w) \subseteq X$.

The converse is immediate since for $w \in X$, $N_d(w)$ is an open disk containing w. □

Notes: (1) The picture to the right shows how we used the Triangle Inequality. The three sides of the triangle have lengths $|z - w|$, $|w - a|$, and $|z - a|$.

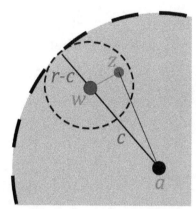

(2) Notice how we used SACT (the Standard Advanced Calculus Trick) here. Starting with $z - a$, we wanted to make $z - w$ and $w - a$ "appear." We were able to do this simply by subtracting and then adding w between z and a. We often use this trick when applying the Triangle Inequality. SACT was introduced in Lesson 4 (Note 7 following Example 4.5).

(3) The same proof used here can be used to prove Theorem 6.5. The geometry looks different (disks and neighborhoods are open intervals instead of the interiors of circles, and points appear on the real line instead of in the complex plane), but the argument is identical. Compare this proof to the proof we used in Theorem 6.5.

A subset X of $\mathbb{C}$ is said to be **closed** if $\mathbb{C} \setminus X$ is open.

$\mathbb{C} \setminus X$ is called the **complement** of X in $\mathbb{C}$, or simply the complement of X. It consists of all complex numbers **not** in X.

Example 7.9:

1. Every closed disk is a closed set. For example, $D = \{z \in \mathbb{C} \mid |z| \leq 1\}$ is closed because its complement in $\mathbb{C}$ is $\mathbb{C} \setminus D = \{z \in \mathbb{C} \mid |z| > 1\}$. You will be asked to prove that this set D is open in Problem 7 below (part (iii)).

2. If we take any subset of a closed disk that includes the interior of the disk, but is missing at least one point on the bounding circle, then that set will **not** be closed. You will be asked to prove this for the closed unit disk $\{z \in \mathbb{C} \mid |z| \leq 1\}$ in Problem 10 below.

3. $\emptyset$ is closed because $\mathbb{C} \setminus \emptyset = \mathbb{C}$ is open. $\mathbb{C}$ is closed because $\mathbb{C} \setminus \mathbb{C} = \emptyset$ is open. $\emptyset$ and $\mathbb{C}$ are the only two sets of complex numbers that are both open and closed.

Full solutions to these problems are available for free download here:
www.SATPrepGet800.com/PMFBXSG

LEVEL 1

1. Let $z = -4 - i$ and $w = 3 - 5i$. Compute each of the following:

    (i) $z + w$

    (ii) zw

    (iii) $\text{Im } w$

    (iv) $2z - w$

    (v) $\overline{w}$

    (vi) $\dfrac{z}{w}$

    (vii) $|z|$

    (viii) the distance between z and w

LEVEL 2

2. Prove that $(\mathbb{C}, +, \cdot)$ is field.

3. Let z and w be complex numbers. Prove the following:

    (i) $\text{Re } z = \dfrac{z + \overline{z}}{2}$

    (ii) $\text{Im } z = \dfrac{z - \overline{z}}{2i}$

    (iii) $\overline{z + w} = \overline{z} + \overline{w}$

    (iv) $\overline{zw} = \overline{z} \cdot \overline{w}$

    (v) $\overline{\left(\dfrac{z}{w}\right)} = \dfrac{\overline{z}}{\overline{w}}$

    (vi) $z\overline{z} = |z|^2$

    (vii) $|zw| = |z||w|$

    (viii) If $w \neq 0$, then $\left|\dfrac{z}{w}\right| = \dfrac{|z|}{|w|}$

    (ix) $\text{Re } z \leq |z|$

    (x) $\text{Im } z \leq |z|$

LEVEL 3

4. Prove the Triangle Inequality (Theorem 7.3).

5. Let z and w be complex numbers. Prove $\big||z| - |w|\big| \le |z \pm w| \le |z| + |w|$.

6. A point w is an **accumulation point** of a set S of complex numbers if each deleted neighborhood of w contains at least one point in S. Determine the accumulation points of each of the following sets:

   (i) $\left\{ \frac{1}{n} \,\middle|\, n \in \mathbb{Z}^+ \right\}$

   (ii) $\left\{ \frac{i}{n} \,\middle|\, n \in \mathbb{Z}^+ \right\}$

   (iii) $\{ i^n \mid n \in \mathbb{Z}^+ \}$

   (iv) $\left\{ \frac{i^n}{n} \,\middle|\, n \in \mathbb{Z}^+ \right\}$

   (v) $\{ z \mid |z| < 1 \}$

   (vi) $\{ z \mid 0 < |z - 2| \le 3 \}$

LEVEL 4

7. Determine if each of the following subsets of $\mathbb{C}$ is open, closed, both, or neither. Give a proof in each case.

   (i) $\emptyset$

   (ii) $\mathbb{C}$

   (iii) $\{ z \in \mathbb{C} \mid |z| > 1 \}$

   (iv) $\{ z \in \mathbb{C} \mid \operatorname{Im} z \le -2 \}$

   (v) $\{ i^n \mid n \in \mathbb{Z}^+ \}$

   (vi) $\{ z \in \mathbb{C} \mid 2 < |z - 2| < 4 \}$

8. Prove the following:

   (i)   An arbitrary union of open sets in $\mathbb{C}$ is an open set in $\mathbb{C}$.

   (ii) A finite intersection of open sets in $\mathbb{C}$ is an open set in $\mathbb{C}$.

   (iii) An arbitrary intersection of closed sets in $\mathbb{C}$ is a closed set in $\mathbb{C}$.

   (iv) A finite union of closed sets in $\mathbb{C}$ is a closed set in $\mathbb{C}$.

   (v)   Every open set in $\mathbb{C}$ can be expressed as a union of open disks.

9. A complex number z is an **interior point** of a set S of complex numbers if there is a neighborhood of z that contains only points in S, whereas w is a **boundary point** of S if each neighborhood of w contains at least one point in S and one point not in S. Prove the following:

    (i) A set of complex numbers is open if and only if each point in S is an interior point of S.

    (ii) A set of complex numbers is open if and only if it contains none of its boundary points.

    (iii) A set of complex numbers is closed if and only if it contains all its boundary points.

10. Let $D = \{z \in \mathbb{C} \mid |z| \leq 1\}$ be the closed unit disk and let S be a subset of D that includes the interior of the disk but is missing at least one point on the bounding circle of the disk. Show that S is not a closed set.

11. Prove that a set of complex numbers is closed if and only if it contains all its accumulation points. (See Problem 6 for the definition of an accumulation point.)

12. Prove that a set consisting of finitely many complex numbers is a closed set in $\mathbb{C}$. (Hint: Show that a finite set has no accumulation points.)

LESSON 8 – LINEAR ALGEBRA
VECTOR SPACES

Vector Spaces Over Fields

Recall the following:

1. In previous lessons, we looked at three structures called fields: $\mathbb{Q}$ (the field of rational numbers), $\mathbb{R}$ (the field of real numbers), and $\mathbb{C}$ (the field of complex numbers). Each of these fields come with two operations called addition and multiplication. Also, $\mathbb{Q}$ is a subfield of $\mathbb{R}$ and $\mathbb{R}$ is a subfield of $\mathbb{C}$. This means that every rational number is a real number, every real number is a complex number, and addition and multiplication in $\mathbb{Q}$, $\mathbb{R}$, and $\mathbb{C}$ all work the same way.

2. Fields have a particularly nice structure. When working in a field, we can perform all the arithmetic and algebra that we remember from elementary and middle school. In particular, we have closure, associativity, commutativity, identity elements, and inverse properties for both addition and multiplication (with the exception that 0 has no multiplicative inverse), and multiplication is distributive over addition.

3. The standard form of a complex number is $a + bi$, where a and b are real numbers. We add two complex numbers using the rule $(a + bi) + (c + di) = (a + c) + (b + d)i$.

To give some motivation for the definition of a vector space, let's begin with an example.

Example 8.1: Consider the set $\mathbb{C}$ of complex numbers together with the usual definition of addition. Let's also consider another operation, which we will call **scalar multiplication**. For each $k \in \mathbb{R}$ and $z = a + bi \in \mathbb{C}$, we define kz to be $ka + kbi$.

The operation of scalar multiplication is a little different from other types of operations we have looked at previously because instead of multiplying two elements from $\mathbb{C}$ together, we are multiplying an element of $\mathbb{R}$ with an element of $\mathbb{C}$. In this case, we will call the elements of $\mathbb{R}$ **scalars**.

Let's observe that we have the following properties:

1. $(\mathbb{C}, +)$ **is a commutative group.** In other words, for addition in $\mathbb{C}$, we have closure, associativity, commutativity, an identity element (called 0), and the inverse property (the inverse of $a + bi$ is $-a - bi$). This follows immediately from the fact that $(\mathbb{C}, +, \cdot)$ is a field. When we choose to think of $\mathbb{C}$ as a vector space, we will "forget about" the multiplication in $\mathbb{C}$, and just consider $\mathbb{C}$ together with addition. In doing so, we lose much of the field structure of the complex numbers, but we retain the group structure of $(\mathbb{C}, +)$.

2. $\mathbb{C}$ **is closed under scalar multiplication.** That is, **for all $k \in \mathbb{R}$ and $z \in \mathbb{C}$, we have $kz \in \mathbb{C}$.** To see this, let $z = a + bi \in \mathbb{C}$ and let $k \in \mathbb{R}$. Then, by definition, $kz = ka + kbi$. Since $a, b \in \mathbb{R}$, and $\mathbb{R}$ is closed under multiplication, $ka \in \mathbb{R}$ and $kb \in \mathbb{R}$. It follows that $ka + kbi \in \mathbb{C}$.

3. $\mathbf{1z = z.}$ To see this, consider $1 \in \mathbb{R}$ and let $z = a + bi \in \mathbb{C}$. Then, since 1 is the multiplicative identity for $\mathbb{R}$, we have $1z = 1a + 1bi = a + bi = z$.

4. **For all $j, k \in \mathbb{R}$ and $z \in \mathbb{C}$, $(jk)z = j(kz)$ (Associativity of scalar multiplication).** To see this, let $j, k \in \mathbb{R}$ and $z = a + bi \in \mathbb{C}$. Then since multiplication is associative in $\mathbb{R}$, we have

$$(jk)z = (jk)(a + bi) = (jk)a + (jk)bi = j(ka) + j(kb)i = j(ka + kbi) = j(kz).$$

5. **For all $k \in \mathbb{R}$ and $z, w \in \mathbb{C}$, $k(z + w) = kz + kw$ (Distributivity of 1 scalar over 2 vectors).** To see this, let $k \in \mathbb{R}$ and $z = a + bi, w = c + di \in \mathbb{C}$. Then since multiplication distributes over addition in $\mathbb{R}$, we have

$$k(z + w) = k\big((a + bi) + (c + di)\big) = k\big((a + c) + (b + d)i\big) = k(a + c) + k(b + d)i$$
$$= (ka + kc) + (kb + kd)i = (ka + kbi) + (kc + kdi) = k(a + bi) + k(c + di) = kz + kw.$$

6. **For all $j, k \in \mathbb{R}$ and $z \in \mathbb{C}$, $(j + k)z = jz + kz$ (Distributivity of 2 scalars over 1 vector).** To see this, let $j, k \in \mathbb{R}$ and $z = a + bi \in \mathbb{C}$. Then since multiplication distributes over addition in $\mathbb{R}$, we have

$$(j + k)z = (j + k)(a + bi) = (j + k)a + (j + k)bi = (ja + ka) + (jb + kb)i$$
$$= (ja + jbi) + (ka + kbi) = j(a + bi) + k(a + bi) = jz + kz.$$

Notes: (1) Since the properties listed in 1 through 6 above are satisfied, we say that $\mathbb{C}$ is a **vector space** over $\mathbb{R}$. We will give the formal definition of a vector space below.

(2) Note that a vector space consists of (i) a set of **vectors** (in this case $\mathbb{C}$), (ii) a field (in this case $\mathbb{R}$), and (iii) two operations called **addition** and **scalar multiplication**.

(3) The operation of addition is a binary operation on the set of vectors, and the set of vectors together with this binary operation forms a commutative group. In the previous example (Example 8.1), we have that $(\mathbb{C}, +)$ is a commutative group.

(4) Scalar multiplication is **not** a binary operation on the set of vectors. It takes pairs of the form (k, v), where k is in the field and v is a vector to a vector kv. Formally speaking, scalar multiplication is a function $f: \mathbb{F} \times V \to V$, where $\mathbb{F}$ is the field of scalars and V is the set of vectors (see the beginning of Lesson 3 for a brief explanation of this notation).

(5) We started with the example of $\mathbb{C}$ as a vector space over $\mathbb{R}$ because it has a geometric interpretation where we can draw simple pictures to visualize what the vector space looks like. Recall from Lesson 7 that we can think of the complex number $a + bi$ as a directed line segment (which from now on we will call a **vector**) in the complex plane that begins at the origin and terminates at the point (a, b).

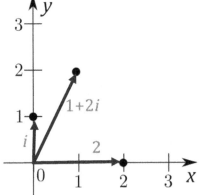

For example, pictured to the right, we can see the vectors $i = 0 + 1i$, $1 + 2i$, and $2 = 2 + 0i$ in the complex plane.

We can visualize the sum of two vectors as the vector starting at the origin that is the diagonal of the parallelogram formed from the original vectors. We see this in the first figure on the left below. In this figure, we have removed the complex plane and focused on the vectors $1 + 2i$ and 2, together with their sum $(1 + 2i) + (2 + 0i) = (1 + 2) + (2 + 0)i = 3 + 2i$.

A second way to visualize the sum of two vectors is to translate one of the vectors so that its initial point coincides with the terminal point of the other vector. The sum of the two vectors is then the vector whose initial point coincides with the initial point of the "unmoved" vector and whose terminal point coincides with the terminal point of the "moved" vector. We see two ways to do this in the center and rightmost figures below.

Technically speaking, the center figure shows the sum $(1 + 2i) + 2$ and the rightmost figure shows the sum $2 + (1 + 2i)$. If we superimpose one figure on top of the other, we can see strong evidence that commutativity holds for addition.

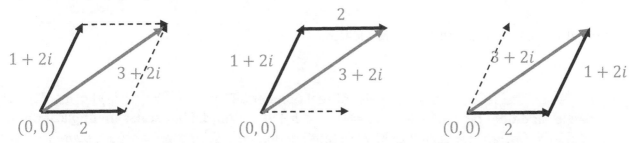

We can visualize a scalar multiple of a vector as follows: (i) if k is a positive real number and $z \in \mathbb{C}$, then the vector kz points in the same direction as z and has a length that is k times the length of z; (ii) if k is a negative real number and $z \in \mathbb{C}$, then the vector kz points in the direction opposite of z and has a length that is $|k|$ times the length of z; (iii) if $k = 0$ and $z \in \mathbb{C}$, then kz is a point.

In the figures below, we have a vector $z \in \mathbb{C}$, together with several scalar multiples of z.

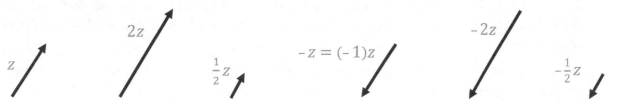

We are now ready for the general definition of a vector space.

A **vector space** over a field $\mathbb{F}$ is a set V together with a binary operation $+$ on V (called **addition**) and an operation called **scalar multiplication** satisfying:

(1) $(V, +)$ is a commutative group.

(2) **(Closure under scalar multiplication)** For all $k \in \mathbb{F}$ and $v \in V$, $kv \in V$.

(3) **(Scalar multiplication identity)** If 1 is the multiplicative identity of $\mathbb{F}$ and $v \in V$, then $1v = v$.

(4) **(Associativity of scalar multiplication)** For all $j, k \in \mathbb{F}$ and $v \in V$, $(jk)v = j(kv)$.

(5) **(Distributivity of 1 scalar over 2 vectors)** For all $k \in \mathbb{F}$ and $v, w \in V$, $k(v + w) = kv + kw$.

(6) **(Distributivity of 2 scalars over 1 vector)** For all $j, k \in \mathbb{F}$ and $v \in V$, $(j + k)v = jv + kv$.

Notes: (1) Recall from Lesson 3 that $(V, +)$ a commutative group means the following:

- **(Closure)** For all $v, w \in V$, $v + w \in V$.

- **(Associativity)** For all $v, w, u \in V$, $(v + w) + u = v + (w + u)$.

- **(Commutativity)** For all $v, w \in V$, $v + w = w + v$.

- **(Identity)** There exists an element $0 \in V$ such that for all $v \in V$, $0 + v = v + 0 = v$.

- **(Inverse)** For each $v \in V$, there is $- v \in V$ such that $v + (-v) = (-v) + v = 0$.

(2) The fields that we are familiar with are $\mathbb{Q}$ (the field of rational numbers), $\mathbb{R}$ (the field of real numbers), and $\mathbb{C}$ (the field of complex numbers). For our purposes here, we can always assume that $\mathbb{F}$ is one of these three fields.

Let's look at some basic examples of vector spaces.

Example 8.2:

1. Let $\mathbb{R}^2$ be the set of all ordered pairs of real numbers. That is, $\mathbb{R}^2 = \{(a, b) \mid a, b \in \mathbb{R}\}$ We define **addition** by $(a, b) + (c, d) = (a + c, b + d)$. We define **scalar multiplication** by $k(a, b) = (ka, kb)$ for each $k \in \mathbb{R}$. With these definitions, $\mathbb{R}^2$ is a vector space over $\mathbb{R}$.

   Notice that $\mathbb{R}^2$ looks just like $\mathbb{C}$. In fact, (a, b) is sometimes used as another notation for $a + bi$. Therefore, the verification that $\mathbb{R}^2$ is a vector space over $\mathbb{R}$ is nearly identical to what we did in Example 8.1 above.

   We can visualize elements of $\mathbb{R}^2$ as points or vectors in a plane in exactly the same way that we visualize complex numbers as points or vectors in the complex plane.

2. $\mathbb{R}^3 = \{(a, b, c) \mid a, b, c \in \mathbb{R}\}$ is a vector space over $\mathbb{R}$, where we define addition and scalar multiplication by $(a, b, c) + (d, e, f) = (a + d, b + e, c + f)$ and $k(a, b, c) = (ka, kb, kc)$, respectively.

   We can visualize elements of $\mathbb{R}^3$ as points in space in a way similar to visualizing elements of $\mathbb{R}^2$ and $\mathbb{C}$ as points in a plane.

3. More generally, we can let $\mathbb{R}^n = \{(a_1, a_2, \ldots, a_n) \mid a_i \in \mathbb{R} \text{ for each } i = 1, 2, \ldots, n\}$. Then $\mathbb{R}^n$ is a vector space over $\mathbb{R}$, where we define addition and scalar multiplication by

$$(a_1, a_2, \ldots, a_n) + (b_1, b_2, \ldots, b_n) = (a_1 + b_1, a_2 + b_2, \ldots, a_n + b_n).$$
$$k(a_1, a_2, \ldots, a_n) = (ka_1, ka_2, \ldots, ka_n).$$

4. More generally still, if $\mathbb{F}$ is any field (for our purposes, we can think of $\mathbb{F}$ as $\mathbb{Q}$, $\mathbb{R}$, or $\mathbb{C}$), we let $\mathbb{F}^n = \{(a_1, a_2, \ldots, a_n) \mid a_i \in \mathbb{F} \text{ for each } i = 1, 2, \ldots, n\}$. Then $\mathbb{F}^n$ is a vector space over $\mathbb{F}$, where we define addition and scalar multiplication by

$$(a_1, a_2, \ldots, a_n) + (b_1, b_2, \ldots, b_n) = (a_1 + b_1, a_2 + b_2, \ldots, a_n + b_n).$$
$$k(a_1, a_2, \ldots, a_n) = (ka_1, ka_2, \ldots, ka_n).$$

Notes: (1) Ordered pairs have the property that $(a, b) = (c, d)$ if and only if $a = c$ and $b = d$. So, for example, $(1,2) \neq (2,1)$. Compare this to the unordered pair (or set) $\{1, 2\}$. Recall that a set is determined by its elements and not the order in which the elements are listed. So, $\{1, 2\} = \{2, 1\}$.

We will learn more about ordered pairs in Lesson 10.

(2) $(a_1, a_2, \ldots, a_n)$ is called an **n-tuple**. So, $\mathbb{R}^n$ consists of all n-tuples of elements from $\mathbb{R}$, and more generally, $\mathbb{F}^n$ consists of all n-tuples of elements from the field $\mathbb{F}$.

For example, $\left(3, 2 - i, \sqrt{2} + \sqrt{3}i, -3i\right) \in \mathbb{C}^4$ and $\left(1, \frac{1}{2}, \frac{1}{3}, \frac{1}{4}, \frac{1}{5}, \frac{1}{6}, \frac{1}{7}, \frac{1}{8}\right) \in \mathbb{Q}^8$ (and since $\mathbb{Q}^8 \subseteq \mathbb{R}^8 \subseteq \mathbb{C}^8$, we can also say that this 8-tuple is in $\mathbb{R}^8$ or $\mathbb{C}^8$).

(3) Similar to what we said in Note 1, we have $(a_1, a_2, \ldots, a_n) = (b_1, b_2, \ldots, b_n)$ if and only if $a_i = b_i$ for all $i = 1, 2, \ldots, n$. So, for example, $\left(2, 5, \sqrt{2}, \sqrt{2}\right)$ and $\left(2, \sqrt{2}, 5, \sqrt{2}\right)$ are distinct elements from $\mathbb{R}^4$.

(4) You will be asked to verify that $\mathbb{F}^n$ is a vector space over the field $\mathbb{F}$ in Problem 3 below. Unless stated otherwise, from now on we will always consider the vector space $\mathbb{F}^n$ to be over the field $\mathbb{F}$.

Let's look at a few other examples of vector spaces.

Example 8.3:

1. Let $M = \left\{\begin{bmatrix} a & b \\ c & d \end{bmatrix} \,\middle|\, a, b, c, d \in \mathbb{R}\right\}$ be the set of all 2×2 matrices of real numbers. We add two matrices using the rule $\begin{bmatrix} a & b \\ c & d \end{bmatrix} + \begin{bmatrix} e & f \\ g & h \end{bmatrix} = \begin{bmatrix} a + e & b + f \\ c + g & d + h \end{bmatrix}$, and we multiply a matrix by a real number using the rule $k\begin{bmatrix} a & b \\ c & d \end{bmatrix} = \begin{bmatrix} ka & kb \\ kc & kd \end{bmatrix}$. It is straightforward to check that M is a vector space over $\mathbb{R}$.

2. For $m, n \in \mathbb{Z}^+$, an $m \times n$ **matrix** over a field $\mathbb{F}$ is a rectangular array with m rows and n columns, and entries in $\mathbb{F}$. For example, the matrix $A = \begin{bmatrix} 5 & 2 & \frac{1}{5} \\ -3 & \sqrt{3} & 7 \end{bmatrix}$ is a 2×3 matrix over $\mathbb{R}$. We will generally use a capital letter to represent a matrix, and the corresponding lowercase letter with double subscripts to represent the entries of the matrix. We use the first subscript for the row and the second subscript for the column. Using the matrix A above as an example, we see that $a_{21} = -3$ because the entry in row 2 and column 1 is -3. Similarly, we have $a_{11} = 5$, $a_{12} = 2$, $a_{13} = \frac{1}{5}$, $a_{22} = \sqrt{3}$, and $a_{23} = 7$.

Let $M_{mn}^{\mathbb{F}}$ be the set of all $m \times n$ matrices over the field $\mathbb{F}$. We add two matrices $A, B \in M_{mn}^{\mathbb{F}}$ to get $A + B \in M_{mn}^{\mathbb{F}}$ using the rule $(a + b)_{ij} = a_{ij} + b_{ij}$. We multiply a matrix $A \in M_{mn}^{\mathbb{F}}$ by a scalar $k \in \mathbb{F}$ using the rule $(ka)_{ij} = ka_{ij}$.

For example, if we let A be the matrix above and $B = \begin{bmatrix} 2 & -5 & \frac{4}{5} \\ -1 & -\sqrt{3} & 1 \end{bmatrix}$, then we have

$$A + B = \begin{bmatrix} 7 & -3 & 1 \\ -4 & 0 & 8 \end{bmatrix} \quad \text{and} \quad 2A = \begin{bmatrix} 10 & 4 & \frac{2}{5} \\ -6 & 2\sqrt{3} & 14 \end{bmatrix}.$$

Notice that we get the entry in the first row and first column of $A + B$ as follows:

$$(a + b)_{11} = a_{11} + b_{11} = 5 + 2 = 7$$

Similarly, we get the other two entries in the first row like this:

$$(a + b)_{12} = a_{12} + b_{12} = 2 + (-5) = -3 \qquad (a + b)_{13} = a_{13} + b_{13} = \frac{1}{5} + \frac{4}{5} = \frac{5}{5} = 1$$

I leave it to the reader to write out the details for computing the entries in the second row of $A + B$.

We get the entries in the first row of $2A$ as follows:

$$(2a)_{11} = 2a_{11} = 2 \cdot 5 = 10 \qquad (2a)_{12} = 2a_{12} = 2 \cdot 2 = 4 \qquad (2a)_{13} = 2a_{13} = 2 \cdot \frac{1}{5} = \frac{2}{5}$$

I leave it to the reader to write out the details for computing the entries in the second row of $2A$.

With the operations of addition and scalar multiplication defined as we have above, it is not too hard to show that $M_{mn}^{\mathbb{F}}$ is a vector space over $\mathbb{F}$.

3. Let $P = \{ax^2 + bx + c \mid a, b, c \in \mathbb{R}\}$ be the set of **polynomials of degree 2 with real coefficients.** We define addition and scalar multiplication (with scalars in $\mathbb{R}$) on this set of polynomials as follows:

$$(ax^2 + bx + c) + (dx^2 + ex + f) = (a + d)x^2 + (b + e)x + (c + f).$$
$$k(ax^2 + bx + c) = (ka)x^2 + (kb)x + (kc).$$

For example, if $p(x) = 2x^2 + 3x - 5$ and $q(x) = -5x + 4$, then $p(x), q(x) \in P$ and we have

$$p(x) + q(x) = (2x^2 + 3x - 5) + (-5x + 4) = 2x^2 - 2x - 1.$$
$$3p(x) = 3(2x^2 + 3x - 5) = 6x^2 + 9x - 15.$$

It is straightforward to check that P is a vector space over $\mathbb{R}$.

Subspaces

Let V be a vector space over a field $\mathbb{F}$. A subset U of V is called a **subspace** of V, written $U \leq V$, if it is also a vector space with respect to the same operations of addition and scalar multiplication as they were defined in V.

Notes: (1) Recall from Note 2 following Example 3.3 that a **universal statement** is a statement that describes a property that is true for all elements without mentioning the existence of any new elements. A universal statement begins with the quantifier $\forall$ ("For all") and never includes the quantifier $\exists$ ("There exists" or "There is").

Properties defined by universal statements are **closed downwards**. This means that if a property defined by a universal statement is true in V and U is a subset of V, then the property is true in U as well.

For example, the statement for commutativity is $\forall v, w (v + w = w + v)$. This is read "For all v and w, $v + w = w + v$." The quantifier $\forall$ is referring to whichever set we are considering. If we are thinking about the set V, then we mean "For all v and w in V, $v + w = w + v$." If we are thinking about the set U, then we mean "For all v and w in U, $v + w = w + v$."

If we assume that $+$ is commutative in V and $U \subseteq V$, we can easily show that $+$ is also commutative in U. To see this, let $v, w \in U$. Since $U \subseteq V$, we have $v, w \in V$. Since $+$ is commutative in V, we have $v + w = w + v$. Since v and w were arbitrary elements in U, we see that $+$ is commutative in U.

(2) Associativity, commutativity, and distributivity are all defined by universal statements, and therefore, when checking if U is a subspace of V, we **do not** need to check any of these properties—they will always be satisfied in the subset U.

(3) The identity property for addition is **not** defined by a universal statement. It begins with the existential quantifier $\exists$ "There is." Therefore, we **do** need to check that the identity 0 is in a subset U of V when determining if U is a subspace of V. However, once we have checked that 0 is there, we **do not** need to check that it satisfies the property of being an identity. As long as $0 \in U$ (the same 0 from V), then it will behave as an identity because the defining property of 0 contains only the quantifier $\forall$.

(4) The inverse property for addition will always be true in a subset U of a vector space V that is closed under scalar multiplication. To see this, we use the fact that $-1v = -v$ for all v in a vector space (see Problem 4 (iv) below).

(5) Since the multiplicative identity 1 comes from the field $\mathbb{F}$ and not the vector space V, and we are using the same field for the subset U, we **do not** need to check the scalar multiplication identity when verifying that U is a subspace of V.

(6) The main issue when checking if a subset U of V is a subspace of V is closure. For example, we need to make sure that whenever we add 2 vectors in U, we get a vector that is also in U. If we were to take an arbitrary subset of V, then there is no reason this should happen. For example, let's consider the vector space $\mathbb{C}$ over the field $\mathbb{R}$. Let $A = \{2 + bi \mid b \in \mathbb{R}\}$. A is a subset of $\mathbb{C}$, but A is not a subspace of $\mathbb{C}$. To see this, we just need a single counterexample. $2 + i \in A$, but $(2 + i) + (2 + i) = 4 + 2i \notin A$ (because the real part is 4 and not 2).

(7) Notes 1 through 6 above tell us that to determine if a subset U of a vector space V is a subspace of V, we need only check that $0 \in U$, and U is closed under addition and scalar multiplication.

(8) The statements for closure, as we have written them do look a lot like universal statements. For example, the statement for closure under addition is "For all $v, w \in V$, $v + w \in V$." The issue here is that the set V is not allowed to be explicitly mentioned in the formula. It needs to be understood.

For example, we saw in Note 1 that the statement for commutativity can be written as "$\forall v, w(v + w = w + v)$." The quantifier $\forall$ (for all) can be applied to any set for which there is a notion of addition defined. We also saw that if the statement is true in V, and U is a subset of V, then the statement will be true in U.

With the statement of closure, to eliminate the set V from the formula, we would need to say something like, "For all x and y, $x + y$ exists." However, there is no way to say "exists" using just logical notation without talking about the set we wish to exist inside of.

We summarize these notes in the following theorem.

Theorem 8.1: Let V be a vector space over a field $\mathbb{F}$ and let $U \subseteq V$. Then $U \leq V$ if and only if (i) $0 \in U$, (ii) for all $v, w \in U$, $v + w \in U$, and (iii) for all $v \in U$ and $k \in \mathbb{F}$, $kv \in U$.

Proof: Let V be a vector space over a field $\mathbb{F}$, and $U \subseteq V$.

If U is a subspace of V, then by definition of U being a vector space, (i), (ii), and (iii) hold.

Now suppose that (i), (ii), and (iii) hold.

By (ii), $+$ is a binary operation on U.

Associativity and commutativity of $+$ are defined by universal statements, and therefore, since they hold in V and $U \subseteq V$, they hold in U.

We are given that $0 \in U$. If $v \in U$, then since $U \subseteq V$, $v \in V$. Since 0 is the additive identity for V, $0 + v = v + 0 = v$. Since $v \in U$ was arbitrary, the additive identity property holds in U.

Let $v \in U$. Since $U \subseteq V$, $v \in V$. Therefore, there is $-v \in V$ such that $v + (-v) = (-v) + v = 0$. By (iii), $-1v \in U$ and by Problem 4 (part (iv)), $-1v = -v$. Since $v \in U$ was arbitrary, the additive inverse property holds in U.

So, $(U, +)$ is a commutative group.

By (iii), U is closed under scalar multiplication.

Associativity of scalar multiplication and both types of distributivity are defined by universal statements, and therefore, since they hold in V and $U \subseteq V$, they hold in U.

Finally, if $v \in U$, then since $U \subseteq V$, $v \in V$. So, $1v = v$, and the scalar multiplication identity property holds in U.

Therefore, $U \leq V$.   □

Example 8.4:

1. Let $V = \mathbb{R}^2 = \{(a, b) \mid a, b \in \mathbb{R}\}$ be the vector space over $\mathbb{R}$ with the usual definitions of addition and scalar multiplication, and let $U = \{(a, 0) \mid a \in \mathbb{R}\}$. If $(a, 0) \in U$, then $a, 0 \in \mathbb{R}$, and so $(a, 0) \in V$. Thus, $U \subseteq V$. The 0 vector of V is $(0, 0)$ which is in U. If $(a, 0), (b, 0) \in U$ and $k \in \mathbb{R}$, then $(a, 0) + (b, 0) = (a + b, 0) \in U$ and $k(a, 0) = (ka, 0) \in U$. It follows from Theorem 8.1 that $U \leq V$.

   This subspace U of $\mathbb{R}^2$ looks and behaves just like $\mathbb{R}$, the set of real numbers. More specifically, we say that U is **isomorphic** to $\mathbb{R}$. Most mathematicians identify this subspace U of $\mathbb{R}^2$ with $\mathbb{R}$, and just call it $\mathbb{R}$. See Lesson 11 for a precise definition of "isomorphic."

   In general, it is common practice for mathematicians to call various isomorphic copies of certain structures by the same name. As a generalization of this example, if $m < n$, then we can say $\mathbb{R}^m \leq \mathbb{R}^n$ by identifying $(a_1, a_2, \ldots, a_m) \in \mathbb{R}^m$ with the vector $(a_1, a_2, \ldots, a_m, 0, 0, \ldots, 0) \in \mathbb{R}^n$ that has a tail end of $n - m$ zeros. For example, we may say that $(2, \sqrt{2}, 7, -\frac{1}{2}, 0, 0, 0)$ is in $\mathbb{R}^4$, even though it is technically in $\mathbb{R}^7$. With this type of identification, we have $\mathbb{R}^4 \leq \mathbb{R}^7$.

2. Let $V = \mathbb{Q}^3 = \{(a, b, c) \mid a, b, c \in \mathbb{Q}\}$ be the vector space over $\mathbb{Q}$ with the usual definitions of addition and scalar multiplication and let $U = \{(a, b, c) \in \mathbb{Q}^3 \mid c = a + 2b\}$. Let's check that $U \leq V$.

It's clear that $U \subseteq V$. Since $0 = 0 + 2 \cdot 0$, we see that the zero vector $(0,0,0)$ is in U. Let $(a,b,c), (d,e,f) \in U$ and $k \in \mathbb{Q}$. Then we have

$$(a,b,c) + (d,e,f) = (a,b,a+2b) + (d,e,d+2e) = \big(a+d, b+e, (a+d) + 2(b+e)\big).$$

$$k(a,b,c) = k(a,b,a+2b) = (ka, kb, ka + 2kb).$$

These vectors are both in U, and so, by Theorem 8.1, $U \leq V$.

3. Consider $V = \mathbb{C}$ as a vector space over $\mathbb{R}$ in the usual way and let $U = \{z \in \mathbb{C} \mid \text{Re } z = 1\}$. Then $U \subseteq V$, but $U \nleq V$ because the zero vector is not in U. After all, $0 = 0 + 0i$, and so, Re $0 = 0$.

4. Let $V = \{ax^2 + bx + c \mid a,b,c \in \mathbb{R}\}$ be the set of polynomials of degree 2 with real coefficients over $\mathbb{R}$, and let $U = \{p(x) \in V \mid p(5) = 0\}$. Let's check that $U \leq V$ (note that if $p(x) = ax^2 + bx + c$, then $p(5) = 25a + 5b + c$).

   It's clear that $U \subseteq V$. The zero polynomial $p(x) = 0$ satisfies $p(5) = 0$, and so, the zero vector is in U. Let $p(x), q(x) \in U$ and $k \in \mathbb{R}$. Then we have $p(5) + q(5) = 0 + 0 = 0$, so that $p(x) + q(x) \in U$, and we have $kp(5) = k \cdot 0 = 0$, so that $kp(x) \in U$. By Theorem 8.1, $U \leq V$.

5. Every vector space is a subspace of itself, and the vector space consisting of just the 0 vector from the vector space V is a subspace of V.

   In other words, for any vector space V, $V \leq V$ and $\{0\} \leq V$.

   The empty set, however, can never be a subspace of a vector space because it doesn't contain a zero vector.

Theorem 8.2: Let V be a vector space over a field $\mathbb{F}$ and let U and W be subspaces of V. Then $U \cap W$ is a subspace of V.

Proof: Let V be a vector space over a field $\mathbb{F}$ and let U and W be subspaces of V. Since $U \leq V$, $0 \in U$. Since $W \leq V$, $0 \in W$. So, $0 \in U \cap W$. Let $v, w \in U \cap W$. So, $v, w \in U$ and $v, w \in W$. Since $U \leq V$ and $W \leq V$, $v + w \in U$ and $v + w \in W$. Therefore, $v + w \in U \cap W$. Let $v \in U \cap W$ and $k \in \mathbb{F}$. Then $v \in U$ and $v \in W$. Since $U \leq V$ and $W \leq V$, $kv \in U$ and $kv \in W$. So, $kv \in U \cap W$. By Theorem 8.1, $U \cap W \leq V$. $\square$

Bases

Let V be a vector space over a field $\mathbb{F}$, let $v, w \in V$, and $j, k \in \mathbb{F}$. The expression $jv + kw$ is called a **linear combination** of the vectors v and w. We call the scalars j and k **weights**.

Example 8.5: Let $V = \mathbb{R}^2 = \{(a,b) \mid a,b \in \mathbb{R}\}$ be the vector space over $\mathbb{R}$ with the usual definitions of addition and scalar multiplication. Let $v = (1,0)$, $w = (0,1)$, $j = 4$, and $k = -2$. We have

$$jv + kw = 4(1,0) - 2(0,1) = (4,0) + (0,-2) = (4,-2).$$

It follows that the vector $(4,-2)$ is a linear combination of the vectors $(1,0)$ and $(0,1)$ with weights 4 and -2, respectively.

If $v, w \in V$, where V is a a vector space over a field $\mathbb{F}$, then the set of all linear combinations of v and w is called the **span** of v and w. Symbolically, we have span$\{v,w\} = \{jv + kw \mid j,k \in \mathbb{F}\}$.

Example 8.6: in Example 8.5, we saw that $(4, -2)$ can be written as a linear combination of the vectors $(1, 0)$ and $(0, 1)$. It follows that $(4, -2) \in \text{span}\{(1, 0), (0, 1)\}$.

Theorem 8.3: Let $V = \mathbb{R}^2 = \{(a, b) \mid a, b \in \mathbb{R}\}$ be the vector space over $\mathbb{R}$ with the usual definitions of addition and scalar multiplication. Then $\text{span}\{(1, 0), (0, 1)\} = \mathbb{R}^2$.

Proof: Let $v \in \text{span}\{(1, 0), (0, 1)\}$. Then there are weights $j, k \in \mathbb{R}$ with $v = j(1, 0) + k(0, 1)$. So, we have $v = j(1, 0) + k(0, 1) = (j, 0) + (0, k) = (j, k)$. Since $j, k \in \mathbb{R}$, we have $v = (j, k) \in \mathbb{R}^2$. Since $v \in \text{span}\{(1, 0), (0, 1)\}$ was arbitrary, $\text{span}\{(1, 0), (0, 1)\} \subseteq \mathbb{R}^2$.

Now, let $v \in \mathbb{R}^2$. Then there are $a, b \in \mathbb{R}$ with $v = (a, b) = (a, 0) + (0, b) = a(1, 0) + b(0, 1)$. Since we have expressed v as a linear combination of $(1, 0)$ and $(0, 1)$, we see that $v \in \text{span}\{(1, 0), (0, 1)\}$. Since $v \in \mathbb{R}^2$ was arbitrary, $\mathbb{R}^2 \subseteq \text{span}\{(1, 0), (0, 1)\}$.

Since $\text{span}\{(1, 0), (0, 1)\} \subseteq \mathbb{R}^2$ and $\mathbb{R}^2 \subseteq \text{span}\{(1, 0), (0, 1)\}$, we have $\text{span}\{(1, 0), (0, 1)\} = \mathbb{R}^2$. $\quad \square$

If $v, w \in V$, where V is a a vector space over a field $\mathbb{F}$, then we say that v and w are **linearly independent** if neither vector is a scalar multiple of the other one. Otherwise, we say that v and w are **linearly dependent**.

Example 8.7:

1. The vectors $(1, 0)$ and $(0, 1)$ are linearly independent in $\mathbb{R}^2$ because for any $k \in \mathbb{R}$, we have $k(1, 0) = (k, 0) \neq (0, 1)$ and $k(0, 1) = (0, k) \neq (1, 0)$.

2. The vectors $(1, 2)$ and $(-3, -6)$ are linearly dependent in $\mathbb{R}^2$ because $(-3, -6) = -3(1, 2)$.

If $v, w \in V$, where V is a vector space over a field $\mathbb{F}$, then we say that $\{v, w\}$ is a **basis** of V if v and w are linearly independent and $\text{span}\{v, w\} = V$.

Example 8.8:

1. In Example 8.7, we saw that the vectors $(1, 0)$ and $(0, 1)$ are linearly independent in $\mathbb{R}^2$. By Theorem 8.3, $\text{span}\{(1, 0), (0, 1)\} = \mathbb{R}^2$. It follows that $\{(1, 0), (0, 1)\}$ is a basis of $\mathbb{R}^2$.

2. In Example 8.7, we saw that the vectors $(1, 2)$ and $(-3, -6)$ are linearly dependent in $\mathbb{R}^2$. It follows that $\{(1, 2), (-3, -6)\}$ is **not** a basis of $\mathbb{R}^2$.

We would like to generalize the notion of linear dependence to more than two vectors. The definition of one vector being a scalar multiple of the other isn't quite good enough to do that. The following theorem gives us an alternative definition of linear dependence that generalizes nicely.

Theorem 8.4: Let V be a vector space over a field $\mathbb{F}$ and let $v, w \in V$. Then v and w are linearly dependent if and only if there are $j, k \in \mathbb{F}$, not both 0, such that $jv + kw = 0$.

Proof: Let $v, w \in V$, and suppose that v and w are linearly dependent. Then one vector is a scalar multiple of the other. Without loss of generality, we may assume that there is $c \in \mathbb{F}$ with $v = cw$. Then we have $1v + (-c)w = 0$. So, if we let $j = 1$ and $k = -c$, then $jv + kw = 0$, and $j = 1 \neq 0$.

Now suppose that there are $j, k \in \mathbb{F}$, not both 0, such that $jv + kw = 0$. Without loss of generality, assume that $j \neq 0$. Then we have $jv = -kw$, and so, $v = -\dfrac{k}{j}w$. So, v is a scalar multiple of w. Therefore, v and w are linearly dependent. $\qquad\square$

Note: See the Note following Theorem 6.6 in Lesson 6 for an explanation of the expression "Without loss of generality," and how to properly use it in a proof.

We will now extend the notions of linear dependence and independence to more than two vectors.

Let V be a vector space over a field $\mathbb{F}$, let $v_1, v_2, \ldots, v_n \in V$, and $k_1, k_2, \ldots, k_n \in \mathbb{F}$. The expression $k_1v_1 + k_2v_2 + \cdots + k_nv_n$ is called a **linear combination** of the vectors $v_1, v_2, \ldots, v_n$. We call the scalars $k_1, k_2, \ldots, k_n$ **weights**.

Example 8.9: Let $V = \mathbb{R}^3 = \{(a, b, c) \mid a, b, c \in \mathbb{R}\}$ be the vector space over $\mathbb{R}$ with the usual definitions of addition and scalar multiplication. Let $v_1 = (1, 0, 0)$, $v_2 = (0, 1, 0)$, $v_3 = (0, 0, 1)$, $k_1 = 3$, $k_2 = -5$, $k_3 = 6$ We have

$$k_1v_1 + k_2v_2 + k_3v_3 = 3(1, 0, 0) - 5(0, 1, 0) + 6(0, 0, 1).$$
$$= (3, 0, 0) + (0, -5, 0) + (0, 0, 6) = (3, -5, 6).$$

It follows that the vector $(3, -5, 6)$ is a linear combination of the vectors $(1, 0, 0)$, $(0, 1, 0)$, and $(0, 0, 1)$ with weights $3, -5,$ and 6, respectively.

If $v_1, v_2, \ldots, v_n \in V$, where V is a vector space over a field $\mathbb{F}$, then the set of all linear combinations of $v_1, v_2, \ldots, v_n \in V$ is called the **span** of $v_1, v_2, \ldots, v_n$. Symbolically, we have

$$\text{span}\{v_1, v_2, \ldots, v_n\} = \{k_1v_1 + k_2v_2 + \cdots + k_nv_n \mid k_1, k_2, \ldots, k_n \in \mathbb{F}\}.$$

Example 8.10: in Example 8.9, we saw that $(3, -5, 6)$ can be written as a linear combination of the vectors $(1, 0, 0)$, $(0, 1, 0)$, and $(0, 0, 1)$. It follows that $(3, -5, 6) \in \text{span}\{(1, 0, 0), (0, 1, 0), (0, 0, 1)\}$.

Theorem 8.5: Let $V = \mathbb{R}^n = \{(k_1, k_2, \ldots, k_n) \mid k_1, k_2, \ldots, k_n \in \mathbb{R}\}$ be the vector space over $\mathbb{R}$ with the usual definitions of addition and scalar multiplication. Then

$$\text{span}\{(1, 0, 0, \ldots, 0), (0, 1, 0, \ldots, 0), \ldots, (0, 0, 0, \ldots, 1)\} = \mathbb{R}^n.$$

Proof: Let $v \in \text{span}\{(1, 0, 0, \ldots, 0), (0, 1, 0, \ldots, 0), \ldots, (0, 0, 0, \ldots, 1)\}$. Then there are weights $k_1, k_2, \ldots, k_n \in \mathbb{R}$ with $v = k_1(1, 0, 0, \ldots, 0) + k_2(0, 1, 0, \ldots, 0) + \cdots + k_n(0, 0, 0, \ldots, 1)$. So, we have $v = (k_1, 0, 0, \ldots, 0) + (0, k_2, 0, \ldots, 0) + \cdots + (0, 0, 0, \ldots, k_n) = (k_1, k_2, \ldots, k_n)$. Since $k_1, k_2, \ldots, k_n \in \mathbb{R}$, we have $v = (k_1, k_2, \ldots, k_n) \in \mathbb{R}^n$. Since $v \in \text{span}\{(1, 0, 0, \ldots, 0), (0, 1, 0, \ldots, 0), \ldots, (0, 0, 0, \ldots, 1)\}$ was arbitrary, $\text{span}\{(1, 0, 0, \ldots, 0), (0, 1, 0, \ldots, 0), \ldots, (0, 0, 0, \ldots, 1)\} \subseteq \mathbb{R}^n$.

Now, let $v \in \mathbb{R}^n$. Then there are $k_1, k_2, \ldots, k_n \in \mathbb{R}$ with

$$v = (k_1, k_2, \ldots, k_n) = (k_1, 0, 0, \ldots, 0) + (0, k_2, 0, \ldots, 0) + \cdots + (0, 0, 0, \ldots, k_n)$$
$$= k_1(1, 0, 0, \ldots, 0) + k_2(0, 1, 0, \ldots, 0) + \cdots + k_n(0, 0, 0, \ldots, 1).$$

Since we have expressed v as a linear combination of $(1, 0, 0, \ldots, 0), (0, 1, 0, \ldots, 0), \ldots, (0, 0, 0, \ldots, 1)$, we see that $v \in \text{span}\{(1, 0, 0, \ldots, 0), (0, 1, 0, \ldots, 0), \ldots, (0, 0, 0, \ldots, 1)\}$. Since $v \in \mathbb{R}^n$ was arbitrary, we have $\mathbb{R}^n \subseteq \text{span}\{(1, 0, 0, \ldots, 0), (0, 1, 0, \ldots, 0), \ldots, (0, 0, 0, \ldots, 1)\}$.

Therefore, $\text{span}\{(1, 0, 0, \ldots, 0), (0, 1, 0, \ldots, 0), \ldots, (0, 0, 0, \ldots, 1)\} = \mathbb{R}^n$. $\qquad\square$

If $v_1, v_2, \ldots, v_n \in V$, where V is a vector space over a field $\mathbb{F}$, then we say that $v_1, v_2, \ldots, v_n$ are **linearly dependent** if there exist weights $k_1, k_2, \ldots, k_n \in \mathbb{F}$, with at least one weight nonzero, such that $k_1 v_1 + k_2 v_2 + \cdots + k_n v_n = 0$. Otherwise, we say that $v_1, v_2, \ldots, v_n$ are **linearly independent**.

Notes: (1) $v_1, v_2, \ldots, v_n$ are **linearly independent** if whenever we write $k_1 v_1 + k_2 v_2 + \cdots + k_n v_n = 0$, it follows that all the weights $k_1, k_2, \ldots, k_n$ are 0.

(2) We will sometimes call the expression $k_1 v_1 + k_2 v_2 + \cdots + k_n v_n = 0$ a **dependence relation**. If any of the weights $k_1, k_2, \ldots, k_n$ are nonzero, then we say that the dependence relation is **nontrivial**.

Example 8.11:

1. The three vectors $(1, 0, 0)$, $(0, 1, 0)$, and $(0, 0, 1)$ are linearly independent in $\mathbb{R}^3$. To see this, note that we have

    $$k_1(1, 0, 0) + k_2(0, 1, 0) + k_3(0, 0, 1) = (k_1, 0, 0) + (0, k_2, 0) + (0, 0, k_3) = (k_1, k_2, k_3).$$

    So, $k_1(1, 0, 0) + k_2(0, 1, 0) + k_3(0, 0, 1) = (0, 0, 0)$ if and only if $(k_1, k_2, k_3) = (0, 0, 0)$ if and only if $k_1 = 0$, $k_2 = 0$, and $k_3 = 0$.

2. A similar computation shows that the n vectors $(1, 0, 0, \ldots, 0), (0, 1, 0, \ldots, 0), \ldots, (0, 0, 0, \ldots, 1)$ are linearly independent in $\mathbb{R}^n$.

3. The vectors $(1, 2, 3)$, $(-2, 4, 3)$, and $(1, 10, 12)$ are linearly dependent in $\mathbb{R}^3$. To see this, note that $3(1, 2, 3) + (-2, 4, 3) = (3, 6, 9) + (-2, 4, 3) = (1, 10, 12)$, and therefore,

    $$3(1, 2, 3) + (-2, 4, 3) - (1, 10, 12) = 0.$$

    This gives us a nontrivial dependence relation because we have at least one nonzero weight (in fact, all three weights are nonzero). The weights are 3, 1, and -1.

If $v_1, v_2, \ldots, v_n \in V$, where V is a vector space over a field $\mathbb{F}$, then we say that $\{v_1, v_2, \ldots, v_n\}$ is a **basis** of V if $v_1, v_2, \ldots, v_n$ are linearly independent and $\text{span}\{v_1, v_2, \ldots, v_n\} = V$.

Example 8.12:

1. In Example 8.11, we saw that the vectors $(1, 0, 0)$, $(0, 1, 0)$, and $(0, 0, 1)$ are linearly independent in $\mathbb{R}^3$. By Theorem 8.5, $\text{span}\{(1, 0, 0), (0, 1, 0), (0, 0, 1)\} = \mathbb{R}^3$. It follows that $\{(1, 0, 0), (0, 1, 0), (0, 0, 1)\}$ is a basis of $\mathbb{R}^3$.

    Similarly, $\{(1, 0, 0, \ldots, 0), (0, 1, 0, \ldots, 0), \ldots, (0, 0, 0, \ldots, 1)\}$ is a basis of $\mathbb{R}^n$.

2. In Example 8.11, we saw that the vectors $(1, 2, 3)$, $(-2, 4, 3)$, and $(1, 10, 12)$ are linearly dependent in $\mathbb{R}^3$. It follows that $\{(1, 2, 3), (-2, 4, 3), (1, 10, 12)\}$ is **not** a basis of $\mathbb{R}^3$.

Problem Set 8

LEVEL 1

1. Determine if each of the following subsets of $\mathbb{R}^2$ is a subspace of $\mathbb{R}^2$:

   (i) $A = \{(x, y) \mid x + y = 0\}$

   (ii) $B = \{(x, y) \mid xy = 0\}$

   (iii) $C = \{(x, y) \mid 2x = 3y\}$

   (iv) $D = \{(x, y) \mid x \in \mathbb{Q}\}$

2. For each of the following, determine if the given pair of vectors v and w are linearly independent or linearly dependent in the given vector space V:

   (i) $V = \mathbb{Q}^4, v = (3, 2, 2, -1), w = \left(-1, -\frac{2}{3}, -\frac{2}{3}, -\frac{1}{3}\right)$

   (ii) $V = \mathbb{R}^3, v = \left(1, \sqrt{2}, 1\right), w = \left(\sqrt{2}, 2, \sqrt{2}\right)$

   (iii) $V = \mathbb{C}^5, v = (1, i, 2-i, 0, 3i), w = (-i, 1, -1 - 2i, 0, 3)$

   (iv) $V = M_{22}^{\mathbb{Q}}, v = \begin{bmatrix} a & b \\ \frac{a}{2} & 3b \end{bmatrix}, w = \begin{bmatrix} 1 & \frac{b}{a} \\ \frac{1}{2} & 3 \end{bmatrix} (a \neq 0, a \neq b)$

   (v) $V = \{ax^2 + bx + c \mid a, b, c \in \mathbb{R}\}, v = x, w = x^2$

LEVEL 2

3. Let $\mathbb{F}$ be a field. Prove that $\mathbb{F}^n$ is a vector space over $\mathbb{F}$.

4. Let V be a vector space over $\mathbb{F}$. Prove each of the following:

   (i) For every $v \in V, -(-v) = v$.

   (ii) For every $v \in V, 0v = 0$.

   (iii) For every $k \in \mathbb{F}, k \cdot 0 = 0$.

   (iv) For every $v \in V, -1v = -v$.

LEVEL 3

5. Let V be a vector space over a field $\mathbb{F}$ and let X be a set of subspaces of V. Prove that $\cap X$ is a subspace of V.

6. Prove that a finite set with at least two vectors is linearly dependent if and only if one of the vectors in the set can be written as a linear combination of the other vectors in the set.

LEVEL 4

7. Let U and W be subspaces of a vector space V. Determine necessary and sufficient conditions for $U \cup W$ to be a subspace of V.

8. Give an example of vector spaces U and V with $U \subseteq V$ such that U is closed under scalar multiplication, but U is not a subspace of V.

LEVEL 5

9. Let S be a set of two or more linearly dependent vectors in a vector space V. Prove that there is a vector v in the set so that span $S =$ span $S \setminus \{v\}$.

10. Prove that a finite set of vectors S in a vector space V is a basis of V if and only if every vector in V can be written uniquely as a linear combination of the vectors in S.

11. Let $S = \{v_1, v_2, \ldots, v_m\}$ be a set of linearly independent vectors in a vector space V and let $T = \{w_1, w_2, \ldots, w_n\}$ be a set of vectors in V such that span $T = V$. Prove that $m \leq n$.

12. Let B be a basis of a vector space V with n vectors. Prove that any other basis of V also has n vectors.

LESSON 9 – LOGIC
LOGICAL ARGUMENTS

Statements and Substatements

In Lesson 1, we introduced **propositional variables** such as p, q, and r to represent the building blocks of **statements** (or **propositions**).

We now define the set of statements a bit more formally as follows:

1. We have a list of symbols $p, q, r, \ldots$ called propositional variables, each of which is a statement (these are the **atomic statements**).

2. Whenever ϕ is a statement, $(\neg\phi)$ is a statement.

3. Whenever ϕ and ψ are statements, $(\phi \wedge \psi)$, $(\phi \vee \psi)$, $(\phi \rightarrow \psi)$, and $(\phi \leftrightarrow \psi)$ are statements.

Notes: (1) For easier readability, we will always drop the outermost pair of parentheses. For example, we will write $(p \wedge q)$ as $p \wedge q$, and we will write $\left(p \rightarrow (q \vee r)\right)$ as $p \rightarrow (q \vee r)$.

(2) Also, for easier readability, we will often drop the parentheses around $(\neg\phi)$ to get $\neg\phi$. For example, we will write $\left(p \wedge (\neg q)\right)$ as $p \wedge \neg q$. Notice that we dropped the outermost pair of parentheses to get $p \wedge (\neg q)$, and then we dropped the parentheses around $\neg q$.

(3) When we apply the negation symbol two or more times in a row, we will **not** drop parentheses. For example, $\left(\neg(\neg p)\right)$ will be written as $\neg(\neg p)$ and not as $\neg\neg p$.

(4) ϕ is called a **substatement** of $(\neg\phi)$. For example, p is a substatement of $\neg p$ ($\neg p$ is the abbreviated version of $(\neg p)$). Similarly, ϕ and ψ are substatements of $(\phi \wedge \psi)$, $(\phi \vee \psi)$, $(\phi \rightarrow \psi)$, and $(\phi \leftrightarrow \psi)$. For example, p and q are both substatements of $p \leftrightarrow q$. Also, if ϕ is a substatement of ψ and ψ is a substatement of τ, then we will consider ϕ to be a substatement of τ. For example, p is a substatement of $\neg(\neg p)$ because p is a substatement of $\neg p$ and $\neg p$ is a substatement of $\neg(\neg p)$.

(5) Although we are abbreviating statements by eliminating parentheses, it is important to realize that those parentheses are there. If we were to use $\wedge$ to form a new statement from $p \rightarrow q$ and r, it would be incorrect to write $p \rightarrow q \wedge r$. This expression is meaningless, as we do not know whether to apply $p \rightarrow q$ or $q \wedge r$ first. The correct expression is $(p \rightarrow q) \wedge r$. This is now an acceptable abbreviation for the statement $\left((p \rightarrow q) \wedge r\right)$.

Notice that p, q, r, and $p \rightarrow q$ are all substatements of $(p \rightarrow q) \wedge r$, whereas $q \wedge r$ is **not** a substatement of $(p \rightarrow q) \wedge r$.

Example 9.1: Let p, q, and r be propositional variables. Then we have the following:

1. p, q, and r are statements.

2. $(p \rightarrow q)$ is a statement (by 3 above). Using Note 1, we will abbreviate this statement as $p \rightarrow q$. p and q are both substatements of $p \rightarrow q$.

Example 9.2: Let's find the substatements of $\left((p \to q) \vee \neg r\right) \leftrightarrow \neg(q \wedge r)$.

Solution: The substatements are $p, q, r, \neg r, p \to q, (p \to q) \vee \neg r, q \wedge r$, and $\neg(q \wedge r)$.

Note: The given statement is an abbreviation for $\left(\left((p \to q) \vee (\neg r)\right) \leftrightarrow \left(\neg(q \wedge r)\right)\right)$. This is much harder to read, and shows why we like to use abbreviations.

Logical Equivalence

Let ϕ and ψ be statements. We say that ϕ and ψ are **logically equivalent**, written $\phi \equiv \psi$, if every truth assignment of the propositional variables appearing in either ϕ or ψ (or both) leads to the same truth value for both statements.

Example 9.3: Let p be a propositional variable, let $\phi = p$, and let $\psi = \neg(\neg p)$. If $p \equiv T$, then $\phi \equiv T$ and $\psi \equiv \neg(\neg T) \equiv \neg F \equiv T$. If $p \equiv F$, then $\phi \equiv F$ and $\psi \equiv \neg(\neg F) \equiv \neg T \equiv F$. So, both possible truth assignments of p lead to the same truth value for ϕ and ψ. It follows that $\phi \equiv \psi$ (ϕ and ψ are logically equivalent).

Notes: (1) One way to determine if two statements ϕ and ψ are logically equivalent is to draw the truth table for each statement. We would generally put all the information into a single table. If the columns corresponding to ϕ and ψ are a perfect match, then $\phi \equiv \psi$.

Here is a truth table with columns for $\phi = p$ and $\psi = \neg(\neg p)$.

p	$\neg p$	$\neg(\neg p)$
T	F	T
F	T	F

Observe that the first column gives the truth values for ϕ, the third column gives the truth values for ψ, and both these columns are identical. It follows that $\phi \equiv \psi$.

(2) The logical equivalence $p \equiv \neg(\neg p)$ is called the **law of double negation**.

Example 9.4: Let p and q be propositional variables, let $\phi = \neg(p \wedge q)$, and let $\psi = \neg p \vee \neg q$. If $p \equiv F$ or $q \equiv F$, then $\phi \equiv \neg F \equiv T$ and $\psi \equiv T$ (because $\neg p \equiv T$ or $\neg q \equiv T$). If $p \equiv T$ and $q \equiv T$, then $\phi \equiv \neg T \equiv F$ and $\psi \equiv F \vee F \equiv F$. So, all four possible truth assignments of p and q lead to the same truth value for ϕ and ψ. It follows that $\phi \equiv \psi$.

Notes: (1) Here is a truth table with columns for $\phi = \neg(p \wedge q)$ and $\psi = \neg p \vee \neg q$.

p	q	$\neg p$	$\neg q$	$p \wedge q$	$\neg(p \wedge q)$	$\neg p \vee \neg q$
T	T	F	F	T	F	F
T	F	F	T	F	T	T
F	T	T	F	F	T	T
F	F	T	T	F	T	T

Observe that the sixth column gives the truth values for ϕ, the seventh column gives the truth values for ψ, and both these columns are identical. It follows that $\phi \equiv \psi$.

(2) The logical equivalence $\neg(\boldsymbol{p} \wedge \boldsymbol{q}) \equiv \neg\boldsymbol{p} \vee \neg\boldsymbol{q}$ is one of **De Morgan's laws**.

(3) There are two De Morgan's laws. The second one is $\neg(\boldsymbol{p} \vee \boldsymbol{q}) \equiv \neg\boldsymbol{p} \wedge \neg\boldsymbol{q}$. I leave it to the reader to verify this equivalence.

List 9.1: Here is a list of some useful logical equivalences. The reader should verify each of these by drawing a truth table or by using arguments similar to those used in Examples 9.3 and 9.4 (see Problem 2 below).

1. **Law of double negation:** $p \equiv \neg(\neg p)$

2. **De Morgan's laws:** $\quad \neg(p \wedge q) \equiv \neg p \vee \neg q \qquad\qquad \neg(p \vee q) \equiv \neg p \wedge \neg q$

3. **Commutative laws:** $\quad p \wedge q \equiv q \wedge p \qquad\qquad\quad p \vee q \equiv q \vee p$

4. **Associative laws:** $\quad (p \wedge q) \wedge r \equiv p \wedge (q \wedge r) \qquad (p \vee q) \vee r \equiv p \vee (q \vee r)$

5. **Distributive laws:** $\quad p \wedge (q \vee r) \equiv (p \wedge q) \vee (p \wedge r) \quad p \vee (q \wedge r) \equiv (p \vee q) \wedge (p \vee r)$

6. **Identity laws:** $\quad p \wedge \mathrm{T} \equiv p \qquad p \wedge \mathrm{F} \equiv \mathrm{F} \qquad p \vee \mathrm{T} \equiv \mathrm{T} \qquad p \vee \mathrm{F} \equiv p$

7. **Negation laws:** $\quad p \wedge \neg p \equiv \mathrm{F} \qquad\qquad\qquad p \vee \neg p \equiv \mathrm{T}$

8. **Redundancy laws:** $\quad p \wedge p \equiv p \qquad\qquad\qquad p \vee p \equiv p$

9. **Absorption laws:** $\quad (p \vee q) \wedge p \equiv p \qquad\qquad (p \wedge q) \vee p \equiv p$

10. **Law of the conditional:** $\quad p \rightarrow q \equiv \neg p \vee q$

11. **Law of the contrapositive:** $p \rightarrow q \equiv \neg q \rightarrow \neg p$

12. **Law of the biconditional:** $\quad p \leftrightarrow q \equiv (p \rightarrow q) \wedge (q \rightarrow p)$

Notes: (1) Although this is a fairly long list of laws, a lot of it is quite intuitive. For example, in English the word "and" is commutative. If the statement "I have a cat and I have a dog" is true, then the statement "I have a dog and I have a cat" is also true. So, it's easy to see that $p \wedge q \equiv q \wedge p$ (the first law in 3 above). As another example, the statement "I have a cat and I do not have a cat" could never be true. So, it's easy to see that $p \wedge \neg p \equiv \mathrm{F}$ (the first law in 7 above).

(2) The law of the conditional allows us to replace the conditional statement $p \rightarrow q$ by the more intuitive statement $\neg p \vee q$. We can think of the conditional statement $p \rightarrow q$ as having the **hypothesis** (or **premise** or **assumption**) p and the **conclusion** q. The disjunctive form $\neg p \vee q$ tells us quite explicitly that a conditional statement is true if and only if the hypothesis p is false or the conclusion q is true.

(3) A statement that has truth value T for all truth assignments of the propositional variables is called a **tautology**. A statement that has truth value F for all truth assignments of the propositional variables is called a **contradiction**.

In laws 6 and 7 above, we can replace T by any tautology and F by any contradiction, and the law still holds. For example, since $q \leftrightarrow \neg q$ is a contradiction, by the fourth identity law, $p \vee (q \leftrightarrow \neg q) \equiv p$.

(4) It's worth observing that if ϕ and ψ are sentences, then $\phi \equiv \psi$ if and only if $\phi \leftrightarrow \psi$ is a tautology. This follows from the fact that $\phi \leftrightarrow \psi \equiv T$ if and only if ϕ and ψ have the same truth value.

For example, $(p \rightarrow q) \leftrightarrow (\neg q \rightarrow \neg p)$ is a tautology. This follows from the law of the contrapositive and the remark in the last paragraph. Let's look at the complete truth table for this example.

p	q	$\neg p$	$\neg q$	$p \rightarrow q$	$\neg q \rightarrow \neg p$	$(p \rightarrow q) \leftrightarrow (\neg p \rightarrow \neg q)$
T	T	F	F	T	T	T
T	F	F	T	F	F	T
F	T	T	F	T	T	T
F	F	T	T	T	T	T

Notice how the columns for $(p \rightarrow q)$ and $(\neg q \rightarrow \neg p)$ have the same truth values. So, it should be obvious that the column for $(p \rightarrow q) \leftrightarrow (\neg q \rightarrow \neg p)$ will have only T's.

The following three additional laws of logical equivalence will be used freely (often without mention):

1. **Law of transitivity of logical equivalence:** Let ϕ, ψ, and τ be statements such that $\phi \equiv \psi$ and $\psi \equiv \tau$. Then $\phi \equiv \tau$.

2. **Law of substitution of logical equivalents:** Let ϕ, ψ, and τ be statements such that $\phi \equiv \psi$ and ϕ is a substatement of τ. Let τ^* be the sentence formed by replacing ϕ by ψ inside of τ. Then $\tau^* \equiv \tau$.

3. **Law of substitution of sentences:** Let ϕ and ψ be statements such that $\phi \equiv \psi$, let p be a propositional variable, and let τ be a statement. Let ϕ^* and ψ^* be the sentences formed by replacing every instance of p with τ in ϕ and ψ, respectively. Then $\phi^* \equiv \psi^*$.

Example 9.5:

1. Since $q \equiv \neg(\neg q)$ (by the law of double negation), we have $p \wedge q \equiv p \wedge \neg(\neg q)$. Here we have used the law of substitution of logical equivalents with $\phi = q$, $\psi = \neg(\neg q)$, $\tau = p \wedge q$, and $\tau^* = p \wedge \neg(\neg q)$.

2. Let's show that the negation of the conditional statement $p \rightarrow q$ is logically equivalent to the statement $p \wedge \neg q$.

   We have $\neg(p \rightarrow q) \equiv \neg(\neg p \vee q) \equiv \neg(\neg p) \wedge \neg q \equiv p \wedge \neg q$. Here we have used the law of substitution of logical equivalents together with the law of the conditional, the second De Morgan's law, the law of double negation, and the law of transitivity of logical equivalence.

3. Since $p \rightarrow q \equiv \neg p \vee q$ (by the law of the conditional), $(p \wedge q) \rightarrow (p \vee q) \equiv \neg(p \wedge q) \vee (p \vee q)$. Here we have used the law of substitution of sentences twice. We replaced the propositional variable p by the statement $p \wedge q$, and then we replaced the propositional variable q by the statement $p \vee q$.

Notes: (1) If you think about the equivalence $\neg(p \rightarrow q) \equiv p \wedge \neg q$ from part 2 of Example 9.5 for a moment, you will realize that it makes perfect sense. Again, we can think of the conditional statement $p \rightarrow q$ as having the **hypothesis** p and the **conclusion** q. We know the only way to make a conditional statement **false** is to make the hypothesis true and the conclusion false.

So, to make the negation of the conditional statement **true**, we would do the same thing. In other words, the negation of the conditional is true if p is true and q is false, or equivalently, if $p \land \neg q$ is true.

In summary, the logical equivalence $\neg(p \rightarrow q) \equiv p \land \neg q$ says that a conditional statement is false if and only if the hypothesis is true and the conclusion is false.

(2) By the second associative law, $(p \lor q) \lor r \equiv p \lor (q \lor r)$. So, we can write $p \lor q \lor r$ because whichever way we choose to think about it ($p \lor q$ first or $q \lor r$ first), we get the same truth values.

In part 3 of Example 9.5, we saw that $(p \land q) \rightarrow (p \lor q) \equiv \neg(p \land q) \lor (p \lor q)$. By our remarks in the last paragraph, we can write $\neg(p \land q) \lor (p \lor q)$ as $\neg(p \land q) \lor p \lor q$ without causing any confusion.

Example 9.6: Let's show that the statement $p \land [(p \land \neg q) \lor q]$ is logically equivalent to the atomic statement p.

Solution:
$$p \land [(p \land \neg q) \lor q] \equiv p \land [q \lor (p \land \neg q)] \equiv p \land [(q \lor p) \land (q \lor \neg q)] \equiv p \land [(q \lor p) \land T]$$
$$\equiv p \land (q \lor p) \equiv (q \lor p) \land p \equiv (p \lor q) \land p \equiv p$$

So, we see that $p \land [(p \land \neg q) \lor q]$ is logically equivalent to the atomic statement p.

Notes: (1) For the first equivalence, we used the second commutative law.

(2) For the second equivalence, we used the second distributive law.

(3) For the third equivalence, we used the second negation law.

(4) For the fourth equivalence, we used the first identity law.

(5) For the fifth equivalence, we used the first commutative law.

(6) For the sixth equivalence, we used the second commutative law.

(7) For the last equivalence, we used the first absorption law.

(8) We also used the law of transitivity of logical equivalence and the law of substitution of logical equivalents several times.

Validity in Sentential Logic

A **logical argument** or **proof** consists of **premises** (statements that we are given) and **conclusions** (statements we are not given).

One way to write an argument is to list the premises and conclusions vertically with a horizontal line separating the premises from the conclusions. If there are two premises ϕ and ψ, and one conclusion τ, then the argument would look like this:

$$\phi$$
$$\psi$$
$$\overline{\tau}$$

Example 9.7: Let's take $p \rightarrow q$ and p to be premises and q to be a conclusion. Here is the argument.

$$p \rightarrow q$$
$$\underline{p }$$
$$q$$

A logical argument is **valid** if every truth assignment that makes all premises true also makes all the conclusions true. A logical argument that is not valid is called **invalid** or a **fallacy**.

There are several ways to determine if a logical argument is valid. We will give three methods in the next example.

Example 9.8: Let's show that the logical argument given in Example 9.7 is valid. The premises are $p \rightarrow q$ and p, and the conclusion is q.

$$p \rightarrow q$$
$$\underline{p }$$
$$q$$

Solution: Let's use a truth table to illustrate the three methods.

p	q	$p \rightarrow q$	$(p \rightarrow q) \wedge p$	$[(p \rightarrow q) \wedge p] \rightarrow q$
T	T	T	T	T
T	F	F	F	T
F	T	T	F	T
F	F	T	F	T

There are several ways to use this truth table to see that the logical argument is valid.

Method 1: We use only the first three columns. We look at each row where both premises (columns 1 and 3) are true. Only the first row satisfies this. Since the conclusion (column 2) is also true in the first row, the logical argument is valid. Symbolically, we write $p \rightarrow q, p \vdash q$, and we say that $\{p \rightarrow q, p\}$ **tautologically implies** q.

Method 2: We can take the conjunction of the premises, as we did in column 4. We look at each row where this conjunction is true. Again, only the first row satisfies this. Since the conclusion (column 2) is also true in the first row, the logical argument is valid. Symbolically, we write $(p \rightarrow q) \wedge p \vdash q$, and we say that $(p \rightarrow q) \wedge p$ **tautologically implies** q.

Method 3: We can use the conjunction of the premises as the hypothesis of the conditional with the appropriate conclusion, as we did in column 5. We now check that this statement is a tautology. Symbolically, we can write $\vdash [(p \rightarrow q) \wedge p] \rightarrow q$ (this can be read "$[(p \rightarrow q) \wedge p] \rightarrow q$ is a tautology").

Notes: (1) A valid argument is called a **rule of inference**. The rule of inference in this example is called **modus ponens**.

(2) We didn't need to draw a whole truth table to verify that the argument presented here was valid. For example, for Method 1, we could argue as follows: If $p \equiv$ T and $p \rightarrow q \equiv$ T, then we must have $q \equiv$ T because if q were false, we would have $p \rightarrow q \equiv$ T $\rightarrow$ F $\equiv$ F.

(3) p and q could be any statements here. For example, suppose p is the statement "Pigs have wings," and q is the statement "pigs can fly." Then the argument looks like this:

If pigs have wings, then they can fly
Pigs have wings
Pigs can fly

This seems like a good time to point out that just because a logical argument is valid, it does **not** mean that the conclusion is true. We have shown in the solution above that this argument is valid. However, I think we can all agree that pigs cannot fly!

(4) We say that a logical argument is **sound** if it is valid **and** all the premises are true. Note 3 above gives an example of an argument that is valid, but not sound.

Every tautology gives us at least one rule of inference.

Example 9.9: Recall the first De Morgan's law: $\neg(p \wedge q) \equiv \neg p \vee \neg q$. This law gives us the following two rules of inference.

$$\frac{\neg(p \wedge q)}{\neg p \vee \neg q} \qquad\qquad \frac{\neg p \vee \neg q}{\neg(p \wedge q)}$$

To show that an argument is invalid, we need only produce a single truth assignment that makes all the premises true and the conclusion (or one of the conclusions) false. Such a truth assignment is called a **counterexample**.

Example 9.10: The following invalid argument is called the **fallacy of the converse**.

$$\frac{p \to q}{q \to p}$$

To see that this argument is invalid, we will find a counterexample. Here we can use the truth assignment $p \equiv F$, $q \equiv T$. We then have that $p \to q \equiv F \to T \equiv T$ and $q \to p \equiv T \to F \equiv F$.

Notes: (1) Consider the conditional statement $p \to q$. The statement $q \to p$ is called the **converse** of the original conditional statement. The argument in this example shows that the converse of a conditional statement is **not** logically equivalent to the original conditional statement.

(2) The statement $\neg p \to \neg q$ is called the **inverse** of the original conditional statement. This statement is also **not** logically equivalent to the original conditional statement. The reader should write down the fallacy of the inverse and give a counterexample to show that it is invalid (as we did above for the converse).

(3) The statement $\neg q \to \neg p$ is called the **contrapositive** of the original conditional statement. By the law of the contrapositive, this statement **is** logically equivalent to the original conditional statement. The reader should write down the law of the contrapositive as a rule of inference, as was done for the first De Morgan's law in Example 9.9.

List 9.2: Here is a list of some useful rules of inference that **do not** come from tautologies. The reader should verify that each of the logical arguments given here is valid (see Problem 6 below).

Modus Ponens

$$\frac{\begin{array}{c} p \to q \\ p \end{array}}{q}$$

Modus Tollens

$$\frac{\begin{array}{c} p \to q \\ \neg q \end{array}}{\neg p}$$

Disjunctive Syllogism

$$\frac{\begin{array}{c} p \lor q \\ \neg p \end{array}}{q}$$

Hypothetical Syllogism

$$\frac{\begin{array}{c} p \to q \\ q \to r \end{array}}{p \to r}$$

Conjunctive Introduction

$$\frac{\begin{array}{c} p \\ q \end{array}}{p \land q}$$

Disjunctive Introduction

$$\frac{p}{p \lor q}$$

Biconditional Introduction

$$\frac{\begin{array}{c} p \to q \\ q \to p \end{array}}{p \leftrightarrow q}$$

Constructive Dilemma

$$\frac{\begin{array}{c} p \to q \\ r \to s \\ p \lor r \end{array}}{q \lor s}$$

Conjunctive Elimination

$$\frac{p \land q}{p}$$

Disjunctive Resolution

$$\frac{\begin{array}{c} p \lor q \\ \neg p \lor r \end{array}}{q \lor r}$$

Biconditional Elimination

$$\frac{p \leftrightarrow q}{p \to q}$$

Destructive Dilemma

$$\frac{\begin{array}{c} p \to q \\ r \to s \\ \neg q \lor \neg s \end{array}}{\neg p \lor \neg r}$$

A **derivation** is a valid logical argument such that each conclusion follows from the premises and conclusions above it using a rule of inference.

When creating a derivation, we will label each premise and conclusion with a number and state the rule of inference and numbers that are used to derive each conclusion.

Example 9.11: Let's give a derivation of the following logical argument.

$$\frac{\begin{array}{c} \neg p \\ \neg p \to \neg q \end{array}}{\neg q \lor p}$$

Solution:

1	$\neg p$	Premise
2	$\neg p \to \neg q$	Premise
3	$\neg q$	Modus ponens (2, 1)
4	$\neg q \lor p$	Disjunctive introduction (3)

Notes: (1) We started by listing the premises above the line.

(2) If we let $\phi = \neg p$ and $\psi = \neg q$, then by modus ponens, we have $\phi \to \psi, \phi \vdash \psi$. So, we can write $\psi \equiv \neg q$ as the third line of the derivation. We applied modus ponens to the sentences in lines 2 and 1 to derive $\neg q$.

(3) If we let $\phi = \neg q$, then by disjunctive introduction, we have $\phi \vee p = \neg q \vee p$. So, we can write $\neg q \vee p$ as the fourth line of the derivation. We applied disjunctive introduction to the sentence in line 3 to derive $\neg q \vee p$.

Example 9.12: Let's determine if the following logical argument is valid.

> If cats hiss and purr, then dogs can talk.
> Cats hiss.
> Dogs cannot talk.
> Therefore, cats do not purr.

Solution: Let h represent "Cats hiss," let p represent "Cats purr," and let t represent "Dogs can talk." We now give a derivation showing that the argument is valid.

1	$(h \wedge p) \rightarrow t$	Premise
2	h	Premise
3	$\neg t$	Premise
4	$\neg(h \wedge p)$	Modus tollens (1, 3)
5	$\neg h \vee \neg p$	De Morgan's law (4)
6	$\neg(\neg h)$	Law of double negation (2)
7	$\neg p$	Disjunctive syllogism (5, 6)

Note: The derivation in the solution above shows us that the logical argument is valid. However, notice that the statement we derived is **false**. After all, cats **do** purr. So, although the logical argument is valid, it is **not** sound (see Note 4 following Example 9.8). This means that one of the premises must be false. Which one is it? Well cats do hiss and dogs cannot talk. So, the false statement must be "If cats hiss and purr, then dogs can talk." If it's not clear to you that this statement is false, use the law of the conditional to rewrite it as "Neither cats hiss nor purr, or dogs can talk." Since cats do hiss and purr, the statement "Neither cats hiss nor purr" is false. Since dogs cannot talk, the statement "Dogs can talk" is also false. Therefore, the disjunction of those two statements is false.

Problem Set 9

Full solutions to these problems are available for free download here:

www.SATPrepGet800.com/PMFBXSG

LEVEL 1

1. Let ϕ be the following statement $(p \wedge \neg q) \leftrightarrow \neg[p \vee (\neg r \rightarrow q)]$.

   (i) The statement ϕ is abbreviated. Write ϕ in its unabbreviated form.

   (ii) Write down all the substatements of ϕ in both abbreviated and unabbreviated form.

2. Verify all the logical equivalences given in List 9.1.

LEVEL 2

3. Let ϕ, ψ, and τ be statements. Prove that $\phi \vdash \psi$ and $\psi \vdash \tau$ implies $\phi \vdash \tau$.

4. Let ϕ and ψ be statements. Prove that $\phi \vdash \psi$ if and only if $\phi \rightarrow \psi$ is a tautology.

LEVEL 3

5. Determine if each of the following statements is a tautology, a contradiction, or neither.

   (i) $p \wedge p$

   (ii) $p \wedge \neg p$

   (iii) $(p \vee \neg p) \rightarrow (p \wedge \neg p)$

   (iv) $\neg(p \vee q) \leftrightarrow (\neg p \wedge \neg q)$

   (v) $p \rightarrow (\neg q \wedge r)$

   (vi) $(p \leftrightarrow q) \rightarrow (p \rightarrow q)$

6. Verify all the rules of inference given in List 9.2.

LEVEL 4

7. Determine whether each of the following logical arguments is valid or invalid. If the argument is valid, provide a deduction. If the argument is invalid, provide a counterexample.

I	II	III	IV
$p \vee q$	$\neg(p \wedge q)$	$\neg p$	$p \rightarrow q$
q	q	$p \vee r$	$r \rightarrow \neg q$
p	$\neg p$	$q \rightarrow \neg r$	$p \rightarrow r$
		$\neg q$	

8. Simplify each statement.

    (i) $p \lor (p \land \lnot p)$

    (ii) $(p \land q) \lor \lnot p$

    (iii) $\lnot p \rightarrow (\lnot q \rightarrow p)$

    (iv) $(p \land \lnot q) \lor p$

    (v) $[(q \land p) \lor q] \land [(q \lor p) \land p]$

LEVEL 5

9. Determine if the following logical argument is valid. If the argument is valid, provide a deduction. If the argument is invalid, provide a counterexample.

> If a piano has 88 keys, then the box is empty.
> If a piano does not have 88 keys, then paintings are white.
> If we are in immediate danger, then the box is not empty.
> Therefore, paintings are white or we are not in immediate danger.

10. Determine if the following logical argument is valid. If the argument is valid, provide a deduction. If the argument is invalid, provide a counterexample.

> Tangs have fangs or tings have wings.
> It is not the case that tangs have fangs and tings do not have wings.
> It is not the case that tangs do not have fangs and tings have wings.
> Therefore, tangs have fangs and either tings have wings or tangs do not have fangs.

LESSON 10 – SET THEORY
RELATIONS AND FUNCTIONS

Relations

An **unordered pair** is a set with 2 elements. Recall, that a set doesn't change if we write the elements in a different order or if we write the same element multiple times. For example, $\{0, 1\} = \{1, 0\}$ and $\{0, 0\} = \{0\}$.

We now define the **ordered pair** (x, y) in such a way that (y, x) will **not** be the same as (x, y). The simplest way to define a set with this property is as follows:

$$(x, y) = \{\{x\}, \{x, y\}\}$$

We now show that with this definition, the ordered pair behaves as we would expect.

Theorem 10.1: $(x, y) = (z, w)$ if and only if $x = z$ and $y = w$.

Part of the proof of this theorem is a little trickier than expected. Assuming that $(x, y) = (z, w)$, there are actually two cases to consider: $x = y$ and $x \neq y$. If $x = y$, then (x, y) is a set with just one element. Indeed, $(x, x) = \{\{x\}, \{x, x\}\} = \{\{x\}, \{x\}\} = \{\{x\}\}$. So, the only element of (x, x) is $\{x\}$. Watch carefully how this plays out in the proof.

Proof of Theorem 10.1: First suppose that $x = z$ and $y = w$. Then by direct substitution, $\{x\} = \{z\}$ and $\{x, y\} = \{z, w\}$. So, $(x, y) = \{\{x\}, \{x, y\}\} = \{\{z\}, \{z, w\}\} = (z, w)$.

Conversely, suppose that $(x, y) = (z, w)$. Then $\{\{x\}, \{x, y\}\} = \{\{z\}, \{z, w\}\}$. There are two cases to consider.

Case 1: If $x = y$, then $\{\{x\}, \{x, y\}\} = \{\{x\}\}$. So, $\{\{x\}\} = \{\{z\}, \{z, w\}\}$. It follows that $\{z\} = \{x\}$ and $\{z, w\} = \{x\}$. Since $\{z, w\} = \{x\}$, we must have $z = x$ and $w = x$. Therefore, x, y, z, and w are all equal. In particular, $x = z$ and $y = w$.

Case 2: If $x \neq y$, then $\{x, y\}$ is a set with two elements. So, $\{x, y\}$ cannot be equal to $\{z\}$ (because $\{z\}$ has just one element). Therefore, we must have $\{x, y\} = \{z, w\}$. It then follows that $\{x\} = \{z\}$. So, we have $x = z$. Since $x = z$ and $\{x, y\} = \{z, w\}$, we must have $y = w$. $\square$

Note: (x, y) is an abbreviation for the set $\{\{x\}, \{x, y\}\}$. In the study of Set Theory, every object can be written as a set like this. It's often convenient to use abbreviations, but we should always be aware that if necessary, we can write any object in its unabbreviated form.

We can extend the idea of an ordered pair to an **ordered k-tuple**. An ordered 3-tuple (also called an **ordered triple)** is defined by $(x, y, z) = \big((x, y), z\big)$, an ordered 4-tuple is $(x, y, z, w) = \big((x, y, z), w\big)$, and so on.

Example 10.1: Let's write the ordered triple (x, y, z) in its unabbreviated form (take a deep breath!).

$$(x, y, z) = ((x, y), z) = \{\{(x, y)\}, \{(x, y), z\}\} = \left\{\left\{\{\{x\}, \{x, y\}\}\right\}, \left\{\{\{x\}, \{x, y\}\}, z\right\}\right\}$$

The **Cartesian product** of the sets A and B, written $A \times B$ is the set of ordered pairs (a, b) with $a \in A$ and $b \in B$. Symbolically, we have

$$A \times B = \{(a, b) \mid a \in A \wedge b \in B\}.$$

Example 10.2:

1. Let $A = \{0, 1, 2\}$ and $B = \{a, b\}$. Then $A \times B = \{(0, a), (0, b), (1, a), (1, b), (2, a), (2, b)\}$.

2. Let $C = \emptyset$ and $D = \{a, b, c, d\}$. Then $C \times D = \emptyset$.

3. Let $E = \{\emptyset\}$ and $F = \{\Delta, \ast\}$. Then $E \times F = \{(\emptyset, \Delta), (\emptyset, \ast)\}$.

We can extend the definition of the Cartesian product to more than two sets in the obvious way:

$$A \times B \times C = \{(a, b, c) \mid a \in A \wedge b \in B \wedge c \in C\}$$
$$A \times B \times C \times D = \{(a, b, c, d) \mid a \in A \wedge b \in B \wedge c \in C \wedge d \in D\}$$

Example 10.3:

1. $\{a\} \times \{1\} \times \{\Delta\} \times \{\propto\} = \{(a, 1, \Delta, \propto)\}$

2. $\{0\} \times \{0, 1\} \times \{1\} \times \{0, 1\} \times \{0\} = \{(0, 0, 1, 0, 0), (0, 0, 1, 1, 0), (0, 1, 1, 0, 0), (0, 1, 1, 1, 0)\}$

We abbreviate Cartesian products of sets with themselves using exponents.

$$A^2 = A \times A \qquad A^3 = A \times A \times A \qquad A^4 = A \times A \times A \times A$$

Example 10.4:

1. $\mathbb{R}^2 = \mathbb{R} \times \mathbb{R} = \{(x, y) \mid x, y \in \mathbb{R}\}$ is the set of ordered pairs of real numbers.

2. $\mathbb{N}^5 = \mathbb{N} \times \mathbb{N} \times \mathbb{N} \times \mathbb{N} \times \mathbb{N} = \{(a, b, c, d, e) \mid a, b, c, d, e \in \mathbb{N}\}$ is the set of ordered 5-tuples of natural numbers.

3. $\{0, 1\}^2 = \{0, 1\} \times \{0, 1\} = \{(0, 0), (0, 1), (1, 0), (1, 1)\}$.

A **binary relation** on a set A is a subset of $A^2 = A \times A$. Symbolically, we have

$$R \text{ is a binary relation on } A \text{ if and only if } R \subseteq A \times A.$$

We will usually abbreviate $(a, b) \in R$ as aRb.

Example 10.5:

1. Let $R = \{(a, b) \in \mathbb{N} \times \mathbb{N} \mid a < b\}$. For example, we have $(0, 1) \in R$ because $0 < 1$. However, $(1, 1) \notin R$ because $1 \not< 1$. We abbreviate $(0, 1) \in R$ by $0R1$.

   Observe that $R \subseteq \mathbb{N} \times \mathbb{N}$, and so, R is a binary relation on $\mathbb{N}$.

We would normally use the name $<$ for this relation R. So, we have $(0, 1) \in <$, which we abbreviate as $0 < 1$, and we have $(1, 1) \notin <$, which we abbreviate as $1 \not< 1$.

2. There are binary relations $<, \leq, >, \geq$ defined on $\mathbb{N}, \mathbb{Z}, \mathbb{Q}$, and $\mathbb{R}$. For example, if we consider $> \subseteq \mathbb{Q}^2$, we have $\left(\frac{17}{2}, -\frac{3}{5}\right) \in >$, or equivalently, $\frac{17}{2} > -\frac{3}{5}$.

3. Let $R = \{((a, b), (c, d)) \in (\mathbb{Z} \times \mathbb{Z}^*)^2 \mid ad = bc\}$. Then R is a binary relation on $\mathbb{Z} \times \mathbb{Z}^*$. For example, $(1, 2)R(2, 4)$ because $1 \cdot 4 = 2 \cdot 2$. However, $(1, 2)\not R(2, 5)$ because $1 \cdot 5 \neq 2 \cdot 2$. Compare this to the rational number system where we have $\frac{1}{2} = \frac{2}{4}$ because $1 \cdot 4 = 2 \cdot 2$, but $\frac{1}{2} \neq \frac{2}{5}$ because $1 \cdot 5 \neq 2 \cdot 2$.

We say that a binary relation R on A is

- **reflexive** if for all $a \in A$, $(a, a) \in R$.

- **symmetric** if for all $a, b \in A$, $(a, b) \in R$ implies $(b, a) \in R$.

- **transitive** if for all $a, b, c \in A$, $(a, b), (b, c) \in R$ implies $(a, c) \in R$.

- **antireflexive** if for all $a \in A$, $(a, a) \notin R$.

- **antisymmetric** if for all $a, b \in A$, $(a, b) \in R$ and $(b, a) \in R$ implies $a = b$.

Example 10.6:

1. Let A be any set, and let $R = \{(a, b) \in A^2 \mid a = b\}$. Then R is reflexive ($a = a$), symmetric (if $a = b$, then $b = a$), transitive (if $a = b$ and $b = c$, then $a = c$), and antisymmetric (trivially). If $A \neq \emptyset$, then this relation is not antireflexive because $a \neq a$ is false for any $a \in A$.

2. The binary relations $\leq$ and $\geq$ defined in the usual way on $\mathbb{Z}$ are transitive (if $a \leq b$ and $b \leq c$, then $a \leq c$, and similarly for $\geq$), reflexive ($a \leq a$ and $a \geq a$), and antisymmetric (if $a \leq b$ and $b \leq a$, then $a = b$, and similarly for $\geq$). These relations are not symmetric. For example, $1 \leq 2$, but $2 \not\leq 1$). These relations are not antireflexive. For example, $1 \leq 1$ is true.

   Any relation that is transitive, reflexive, and antisymmetric is called a **partial ordering**.

3. The binary relations $<$ and $>$ defined on $\mathbb{Z}$ are transitive (if $a < b$ and $b < c$, then $a < c$, and similarly for $>$), antireflexive ($a \not< a$ and $a \not> a$), and antisymmetric (this is vacuously true because $a < b$ and $b < a$ can never occur). These relations are not symmetric (for example, $1 < 2$, but $2 \not< 1$). These relations are not reflexive (for example, $1 < 1$ is false).

   Any relation that is transitive, antireflexive, and antisymmetric is called a **strict partial ordering**.

4. Let $R = \{(0, 0), (0, 2), (2, 0), (2, 2), (2, 3), (3, 2), (3, 3)\}$ be a relation on $\mathbb{R}$. Then it is easy to see that R is symmetric. R is not reflexive because $1 \in \mathbb{R}$, but $(1, 1) \notin R$ (however, if we were to consider R as a relation on $\{0, 2, 3\}$ instead of on $\mathbb{R}$, then R **would** be reflexive). R is not transitive because we have $(0, 2), (2, 3) \in R$, but $(0, 3) \notin R$. R is not antisymmetric because we have $(2, 3), (3, 2) \in R$ and $2 \neq 3$. R is not antireflexive because $(0, 0) \in R$.

We can extend the idea of a binary relation on a set A to an **n-ary relation** on A. For example, a 3-ary relation (or **ternary relation**) on A is a subset of $A^3 = A \times A \times A$. More generally, we have that R is an n-ary relation on A if and only if $R \subseteq A^n$. A **1-ary relation** (or **unary relation**) on A is just a subset of A.

Example 10.7: Let $R = \{(x, y, z) \in \mathbb{Z}^3 \mid x + y = z\}$. Then R is a ternary (or 3-ary) relation on $\mathbb{Z}$. We have, for example, $(1, 2, 3) \in R$ (because $1 + 2 = 3$) and $(1, 2, 4) \notin R$ (because $1 + 2 \neq 4$).

Equivalence Relations and Partitions

A binary relation R on a set A is an **equivalence relation** if R is reflexive, symmetric, and transitive.

Example 10.8:

1. The most basic equivalence relation on a set A is the relation $R = \{(a, b) \in A^2 \mid a = b\}$ (the **equality relation**). We already saw in part 1 of Example 10.6 that this relation is reflexive, symmetric and transitive.

2. Another trivial equivalence relation on a set A is the set A^2. Since every ordered pair (a, b) is in A^2, reflexivity, symmetry, and transitivity can never fail.

3. We say that integers a and b have the same **parity** if they are both even or both odd. Define $\equiv_2$ on $\mathbb{Z}$ by $\equiv_2 = \{(a, b) \in \mathbb{Z}^2 \mid a$ and b have the same parity$\}$. It is easy to see that $\equiv_2$ is reflexive ($a \equiv_2 a$ because every integer has the same parity as itself), $\equiv_2$ is symmetric (if $a \equiv_2 b$, then a has the same parity as b, so b has the same parity as a, and therefore, $b \equiv_2 a$), and $\equiv_2$ is transitive (if $a \equiv_2 b$ and $b \equiv_2 c$, then a, b, and c all have the same parity, and so, $a \equiv_2 c$). Therefore, $\equiv_2$ is an equivalence relation.

   Another way to say that a and b have the same parity is to say that $b - a$ is divisible by 2, or equivalently, $2 \mid b - a$ (see Lesson 4). This observation allows us to generalize the notion of having the same parity. For example, $\equiv_3 = \{(a, b) \in \mathbb{Z}^2 \mid 3 \mid b - a\}$ is an equivalence relation, and more generally, for each $n \in \mathbb{Z}^+$, $\equiv_n = \{(a, b) \in \mathbb{Z}^2 \mid n \mid b - a\}$ is an equivalence relation. I leave the proof that $\equiv_n$ is reflexive, symmetric, and transitive on $\mathbb{Z}$ as an exercise (see Problem 4 in the problem set below).

4. Consider the relation $R = \{((a, b), (c, d)) \in (\mathbb{Z} \times \mathbb{Z}^*)^2 \mid ad = bc\}$ defined in part 3 of Example 10.5. Since $ab = ba$, we see that $(a, b)R(a, b)$, and therefore, R is reflexive. If $(a, b)R(c, d)$, then $ad = bc$. Therefore, $cb = da$, and so, $(c, d)R(a, b)$. Thus, R is symmetric. Finally, suppose that $(a, b)R(c, d)$ and $(c, d)R(e, f)$. Then $ad = bc$ and $cf = de$. So, $adcf = bcde$. Using the fact that $(\mathbb{Z}, +, \cdot)$ is a commutative ring, we get $cd(af - be) = adcf - bcde = 0$. If $a = 0$, then $bc = 0$, and so, $c = 0$ (because $b \neq 0$). So, $de = 0$, and therefore, $e = 0$ (because $d \neq 0$). So, $af = be$ (because they're both 0). If $a \neq 0$, then $c \neq 0$. Therefore, $af - be = 0$, and so, $af = be$. Since $a = 0$ and $a \neq 0$ both lead to $af = be$, we have $(a, b)R(e, f)$. So, R is transitive. Since R is reflexive, symmetric, and transitive, it follows that R is an equivalence relation.

Recall: (1) If X is a nonempty set of sets, we say that X is **pairwise disjoint** if for all $A, B \in X$ with $A \neq B$, A and B are disjoint ($A \cap B = \emptyset$).

(2) If X is a nonempty set of sets, then **union** X is defined by $\bigcup X = \{y \mid$ there is $Y \in X$ with $y \in Y\}$.

A **partition** of a set S is a set of pairwise disjoint nonempty subsets of S whose union is S. Symbolically, X is a partition of S if and only if

$$\forall A \in X(A \neq \emptyset \wedge A \subseteq S) \wedge \forall A, B \in X(A \neq B \rightarrow A \cap B = \emptyset) \wedge \bigcup X = S.$$

Example 10.9:

1. Let $\mathbb{E} = \{2k \mid k \in \mathbb{Z}\}$ be the set of even integers and let $\mathbb{O} = \{2k + 1 \mid k \in \mathbb{Z}\}$ be the set of odd integers. Then $X = \{\mathbb{E}, \mathbb{O}\}$ is a partition of $\mathbb{Z}$. We can visualize this partition as follows:

$$\mathbb{Z} = \{\ldots, -4, -2, 0, 2, 4, \ldots\} \cup \{\ldots, -3, -1, 1, 3, 5, \ldots\}$$

2. Let $A = \{3k \mid k \in \mathbb{Z}\}$, $B = \{3k + 1 \mid k \in \mathbb{Z}\}$, and $C = \{3k + 2 \mid k \in \mathbb{Z}\}$. Then $X = \{A, B, C\}$ is a partition of $\mathbb{Z}$. A rigorous proof of this requires results similar to those given in Example 4.7 and the notes following (or you can wait for the Division Algorithm, which will be presented in Lesson 12). We can visualize this partition as follows:

$$\mathbb{Z} = \{\ldots, -6, -3, 0, 3, 6, \ldots\} \cup \{\ldots, -5, -2, 1, 4, 7, \ldots\} \cup \{\ldots, -4, -1, 2, 5, 8, \ldots\}$$

3. For each $n \in \mathbb{Z}$, let $A_n = (n, n + 1]$. Then $X = \{A_n \mid n \in \mathbb{Z}\}$ is a partition of $\mathbb{R}$. We can visualize this partition as follows:

$$\mathbb{R} = \cdots \cup (-2, -1] \cup (-1, 0] \cup (0, 1] \cup (1, 2] \cup (2, 3] \cup \cdots$$

4. For each $r \in \mathbb{R}$, let $A_r = \{r + bi \mid b \in \mathbb{R}\}$. Then $X = \{A_r \mid r \in \mathbb{R}\}$ is a partition of $\mathbb{C}$.

5. The only partition of $\emptyset$ is $\emptyset$.

6. The only partition of the one element set $\{a\}$ is $\{\{a\}\}$.

7. The partitions of the two element set $\{a, b\}$ with $a \neq b$ are $\{\{a\}, \{b\}\}$ and $\{\{a, b\}\}$.

We will now explore the relationship between equivalence relations and partitions. Let's begin with an example.

Example 10.10: Consider the equivalence relation $\equiv_2$ from part 3 of Example 10.8, defined by $a \equiv_2 b$ if and only if a and b have the same parity, and the partition $\{\mathbb{E}, \mathbb{O}\}$ of $\mathbb{Z}$ from part 1 of Example 10.9. For this partition, we are thinking of $\mathbb{Z}$ as the union of the even and odd integers:

$$\mathbb{Z} = \{\ldots, -4, -2, 0, 2, 4, \ldots\} \cup \{\ldots, -3, -1, 1, 3, 5, \ldots\}$$

Observe that a and b are in the same member of the partition if and only if $a \equiv_2 b$. For example, $-8 \equiv_2 4$ and $-8, 4 \in \mathbb{E}$, whereas $-8 \not\equiv_2 3$ and $-8 \in \mathbb{E}$, $3 \in \mathbb{O}$. In fact, $\mathbb{E} = \{n \in \mathbb{Z} \mid n \equiv_2 0\}$ and $\mathbb{O} = \{n \in \mathbb{Z} \mid n \equiv_2 1\}$. We call $\mathbb{E}$ the **equivalence class** of 0 and we call $\mathbb{O}$ the **equivalence class** of 1.

Let $\sim$ be an equivalence relation on a set S. If $x \in S$, the **equivalence class** of x, written $[x]$, is the set

$$[x] = \{y \in S \mid x \sim y\}.$$

Example 10.10 continued: We have $[0] = \{y \in \mathbb{Z} \mid 0 \equiv_2 y\} = \mathbb{E}$. Observe that $[2] = [0]$, and in fact, if n is any even integer, then $[n] = [0] = \mathbb{E}$. Similarly, if n is any odd integer, then $[n] = [1] = \mathbb{O}$.

Example 10.11: Recall that the **power set** of A, written $\mathcal{P}(A)$, is the set consisting of all subsets of A.

$$\mathcal{P}(A) = \{X \mid X \subseteq A\}$$

For example, if $A = \{a, b, c\}$, then $\mathcal{P}(A) = \{\emptyset, \{a\}, \{b\}, \{c\}, \{a, b\}, \{a, c\}, \{b, c\}, \{a, b, c\}\}$. We can define a binary relation $\sim$ on $\mathcal{P}(A)$ by $X \sim Y$ if and only if $|X| = |Y|$ (X and Y have the same number of elements). It is easy to see that $\sim$ is an equivalence relation on $\mathcal{P}(A)$. There are four equivalence classes.

$$[\emptyset] = \{\emptyset\}$$
$$[\{a\}] = \{\{a\}, \{b\}, \{c\}\}$$
$$[\{a, b\}] = \{\{a, b\}, \{a, c\}, \{b, c\}\}$$
$$[\{a, b, c\}] = \{\{a, b, c\}\}$$

Notes: (1) $\{a\} \sim \{b\} \sim \{c\}$ because each of these sets has one element. It follows that $\{a\}$, $\{b\}$, and $\{c\}$ are all in the same equivalence class. Above, we chose to use $\{a\}$ as the **representative** for this equivalence class. This is an arbitrary choice. In fact, $[\{a\}] = [\{b\}] = [\{c\}]$.

Similarly, $[\{a, b\}] = [\{a, c\}] = [\{b, c\}]$.

(2) The empty set is the only subset of A with 0 elements. Therefore, the equivalence class of $\emptyset$ contains only itself. Similarly, the equivalence class of $A = \{a, b, c\}$ contains only itself.

(3) Notice that the four equivalence classes are pairwise disjoint, nonempty, and their union is $\mathcal{P}(A)$. In other words, the equivalence classes form a partition of $\mathcal{P}(A)$.

Theorem 10.2: Let P be a partition of a set S. Then there is an equivalence relation $\sim$ on S for which the elements of P are the equivalence classes of $\sim$. Conversely, if $\sim$ is an equivalence relation on a set S, then the equivalence classes of $\sim$ form a partition of S.

You will be asked to prove Theorem 10.2 in Problem 17 below.

Important note: We will sometimes want to define relations or operations on equivalence classes. When we do this, we must be careful that what we are defining is **well-defined**. For example, consider the equivalence relation $\equiv_2$ on $\mathbb{Z}$, and let $X = \{[0], [1]\}$ be the set of equivalence classes.

Let's attempt to define a relation on X by $[x]R[y]$ if and only if $x < y$. Is $[0]R[1]$ true? It looks like it is because $0 < 1$. But this isn't the end of the story. Since $[0] = [2]$, if $[0]R[1]$, then we must also have $[2]R[1]$ (by a direct substitution). But $2 \not< 1$! So, $[2]R[1]$ is false. To summarize, $[0]R[1]$ should be true and $[2]R[1]$ should be false, but $[0]R[1]$ and $[2]R[1]$ represent the same statement. So, R is **not** a well-defined relation on X.

As another example, let's attempt to define an operation $+: X \times X \to X$ by $[x] + [y] = [x + y]$. This **is** a well-defined operation. We proved in Theorem 4.1 from Lesson 4 that the sum of two even integers is even. Similar arguments can be used to show that the sum of two odd integers is even and that the sum of an odd integer and an even integer is odd. These results can now be used to show that the operation $+$ is well-defined. For example, if $[x] = [0]$ and $[y] = [0]$, then x and y are even. By Theorem 4.1, it follows that $x + y$ is even. So, $[x + y] = [0]$. Since $[0 + 0] = [0]$, $[x] + [y] = [0] + [0]$. The reader should check the other three cases to finish verifying that $+$ is well-defined on X.

This principle applies whenever there are elements in a set that can be represented in more than one way. Let's take the set of rational numbers as an example. Each rational number has infinitely many representations. For example, $\frac{1}{2} = \frac{2}{4} = \frac{3}{6} = \cdots$ and so on. When verifying that $(\mathbb{Q}, +, \cdot)$ is a field (see Problems 9 and 11 from Lesson 3), were you careful to check that addition and multiplication are well-defined on $\mathbb{Q}$? If not, you may want to go back and do so now. Also take a look at Theorem 5.1.

Orderings

A binary relation $\leq$ on a set A is a **partial ordering** on A if $\leq$ is reflexive, antisymmetric, and transitive on A. If we replace "reflexive" by "antireflexive," then we call the relation a **strict partial ordering** on A (we would normally use the symbol $<$ instead of $\leq$ for a strict partial ordering).

A **partially ordered set** (or **poset**) is a pair $(A, \leq)$, where A is a set and $\leq$ is a partial ordering on A. Similarly, a **strict poset** is a pair $(A, <)$, where A is a set and $<$ is a strict partial ordering on A.

Example 10.12:

1. The usual ordering $\leq$ on $\mathbb{Z} = \{\dots, -3, -2, -1, 0, 1, 2, 3, \dots\}$ is a partial ordering, and the ordering $<$ on $\mathbb{Z}$ is a strict partial ordering. See Example 10.6 (parts 2 and 3).

2. If A is a set, then $(\mathcal{P}(A), \subseteq)$ is a poset. Since every set is a subset of itself, $\subseteq$ is reflexive. If $X, Y \in \mathcal{P}(A)$ with $X \subseteq Y$ and $Y \subseteq X$, then $X = Y$ by the Axiom of Extensionality (see the Technical note after Theorem 2.5 in Lesson 2). So, $\subseteq$ is antisymmetric. By Theorem 2.3, $\subseteq$ is transitive. The following tree diagrams give visual representations of this poset when $A = \{a, b\}$ and $A = \{a, b, c\}$. For a detailed explanation of these diagrams, see Example 2.8 in Lesson 2.

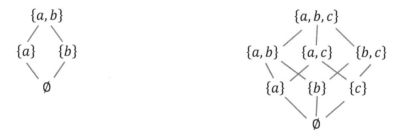

Let $(A, \leq)$ be a poset. We say that $a, b \in A$ are **comparable** if $a \leq b$ or $b \leq a$. The poset satisfies the **comparability condition** if every pair of elements in A are comparable. A poset that satisfies the comparability condition is called a **linearly ordered set** (or **totally ordered set**). Similarly, a **strict linearly ordered set** $(A, <)$ satisfies **trichotomy**: If $a, b \in A$, then $a < b$, $a = b$, or $b < a$.

Example 10.13:

1. $(\mathbb{N}, \leq)$, $(\mathbb{Z}, \leq)$, $(\mathbb{Q}, \leq)$, and $(\mathbb{R}, \leq)$ are linearly ordered sets. Problem 5 from Lesson 5 (parts (i), (ii), and (iv)) show that $(\mathbb{Q}, \leq)$ and $(\mathbb{R}, \leq)$ are linearly ordered.

   Similarly, $(\mathbb{N}, <)$, $(\mathbb{Z}, <)$, $(\mathbb{Q}, <)$, and $(\mathbb{R}, <)$ are strict linearly ordered sets.

2. If A has at least two elements, then $(\mathcal{P}(A), \subseteq)$ is not linearly ordered. Indeed, if $a, b \in A$ with $a \neq b$, then $\{a\} \nsubseteq \{b\}$ and $\{b\} \nsubseteq \{a\}$. See either of the tree diagrams above at the end of Example 10.12.

Functions

Let A and B be sets. f is a **function** from A to B, written $f: A \to B$, if the following two conditions hold.

1. $f \subseteq A \times B$.

2. For all $a \in A$, there is a unique $b \in B$ such that $(a, b) \in f$.

If $f: A \to B$, the **domain** of f, written dom f, is the set A, and the **range** of f, written ran f, is the set $\{f(a) \mid a \in A\}$. Observe that ran $f \subseteq B$. The set B is sometimes called the **codomain** of f. When we know that f is a function, we will abbreviate $(a, b) \in f$ by $f(a) = b$.

Example 10.14:

1. $f = \{(0, a), (1, a)\}$ is a function with dom $f = \{0, 1\}$ and ran $f = \{a\}$. Instead of $(0, a) \in f$, we will usually write $f(0) = a$. Similarly, instead of $(1, a) \in f$, we will write $f(1) = a$. Here is a visual representation of this function.

   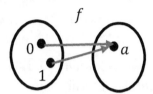

   This function $f: \{0, 1\} \to \{a\}$ is called a **constant function** because the range of f consists of a single element.

   Note also that f is a binary relation on the set $\{0, 1, a\}$. In general, a function $f: A \to B$ is a binary relation on $A \cup B$.

2. If $a \neq b$, then $g = \{(0, a), (0, b)\}$ is **not** a function because it violates the second condition in the definition of being a function. It is, however, a binary relation on $\{0, a, b\}$.

   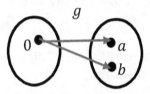

3. $h = \{(a, b) \mid a, b \in \mathbb{R} \land a > 0 \land a^2 + b^2 = 2\}$ is a relation on $\mathbb{R}$ that is **not** a function. $(1, 1)$ and $(1, -1)$ are both elements of h, violating the second condition in the definition of a function. See the figure below on the left. Notice how a vertical line hits the graph twice.

   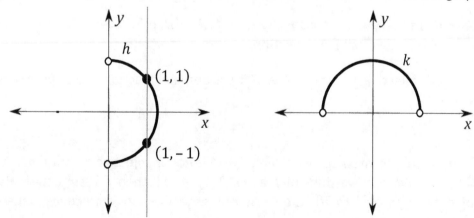

4. $k = \{(a, b) \mid a, b \in \mathbb{R} \land b > 0 \land a^2 + b^2 = 2\}$ **is** a function. See the figure above on the right. To see that the second condition in the definition of a function is satisfied, suppose that (a, b) and (a, c) are both in f. Then $a^2 + b^2 = 2$, $a^2 + c^2 = 2$, and b and c are both positive. It follows that $b^2 = c^2$, and since b and c are both positive, we have $b = c$.

We have dom $k = \left(-\sqrt{2}, \sqrt{2}\right)$ and ran $k = \left(0, \sqrt{2}\,\right]$. So, $k: \left(-\sqrt{2}, \sqrt{2}\right) \to \left(0, \sqrt{2}\,\right]$.

5. A function with domain $\mathbb{N}$ is called an **infinite sequence**. For example, let $f: \mathbb{N} \to \{0, 1\}$ be defined by $g(n) = \begin{cases} 0 & \text{if } n \text{ is even.} \\ 1 & \text{if } n \text{ is odd.} \end{cases}$ A nice way to visualize an infinite sequence is to list the "outputs" of the sequence in order in parentheses. So, we may write g as $(0, 1, 0, 1, 0, 1, \dots)$. In general, if A is a nonempty set and $f: \mathbb{N} \to A$ is a sequence, then we can write f as $(f(0), f(1), f(2), \dots)$.

Similarly, a **finite sequence** is a function with domain $\{0, 1, \dots, n-1\}$ for some n. For example, the sequence $(0, 2, 4, 6, 8, 10)$ is the function $h: \{0, 1, 2, 3, 4, 5\} \to \mathbb{N}$ defined by $f(k) = 2k$. If the domain of a finite sequence is $\{0, 1, \dots, n-1\}$, we say that the **length** of the sequence is n.

Observe how a finite sequence with domain $\{0, 1, \dots, n-1\}$ and range A looks just like an n-tuple in A^n. In fact, it's completely natural to identify a finite sequence of length n with the corresponding n-tuple. So, $(0, 2, 4, 6, 8, 10)$ can be thought of as a 6-tuple from $\mathbb{N}^6$, or as the function $h: \{0, 1, 2, 3, 4, 5\} \to \mathbb{N}$ defined by $f(k) = 2k$.

Informally, we can think of an infinite sequence as an infinite length tuple. As one more example, $(1, 2, 4, 8, 16, 32, \dots)$ represents the sequence $k: \mathbb{N} \to \mathbb{N}$ defined by $k(n) = 2^n$.

Note: In the study of set theory, we define the natural numbers by letting $0 = \emptyset$, $1 = \{0\}$, $2 = \{0, 1\}$, $3 = \{0, 1, 2\}$,... and so on. In general, the natural number n is the set of all its predecessors. Specifically, $n = \{0, 1, 2, \dots, n-1\}$. Using this notation, we can say that a finite sequence of length n is a function $f: n \to A$ for some set A. For example, the function h above has domain 6, so that $h: 6 \to \mathbb{N}$.

A function $f: A \to B$ is **injective** (or **one-to-one**), written $f: A \hookrightarrow B$, if for all $a, b \in A$, if $a \neq b$, then $f(a) \neq f(b)$. In this case, we call f an **injection**.

Note: The contrapositive of the statement "If $a \neq b$, then $f(a) \neq f(b)$" is "If $f(a) = f(b)$, then $a = b$." So, we can say that a function $f: A \to B$ is injective if for all $a, b \in A$, if $f(a) = f(b)$, then $a = b$.

A function $f: A \to B$ is **surjective** (or **onto B**), written $f: A \twoheadrightarrow B$, if for all $b \in B$, there is an $a \in A$ such that $f(a) = b$. In this case, we call f a **surjection**.

A function $f: A \to B$ is **bijective**, written $f: A \cong B$ if f is both an injection and a surjection. In this case, we call f a **bijection**.

Example 10.15:

1. $f = \{(0, a), (1, a)\}$ from part 1 of Example 10.14 is **not** an injective function because $f(0) = a$, $f(1) = a$, and $0 \neq 1$. If we think of f as $f: \{0, 1\} \to \{a\}$, then f is surjective. However, if we think of f as $f: \{0, 1\} \to \{a, b\}$, then f is **not** surjective. So, surjectivity depends upon the codomain of the function.

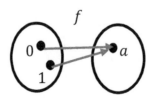

126

2. $k = \{(a, b) \mid a, b \in \mathbb{R} \wedge b > 0 \wedge a^2 + b^2 = 2\}$ from part 4 of Example 10.14 is **not** an injective function. For example, $(1, 1) \in k$ because $1^2 + 1^2 = 1 + 1 = 2$ and $(-1, 1) \in k$ because $(-1)^2 + 1^2 = 1 + 1 = 2$. Notice how a horizontal line hits the graph twice. If we think of k as a function from $\left(-\sqrt{2}, \sqrt{2}\right)$ to $\mathbb{R}^+$, then k is **not** surjective. For example, $2 \notin \operatorname{ran} k$ because for any $a \in \mathbb{R}$, $a^2 + 2^2 = a^2 + 4 \geq 4$, and so, $a^2 + 2^2$ cannot be equal to 2. However, if instead we consider k as a function with codomain $\left(0, \sqrt{2}\right]$, that is $k: \left(-\sqrt{2}, \sqrt{2}\right) \to \left(0, \sqrt{2}\right]$, then k **is** surjective. Indeed, if $0 < b \leq \sqrt{2}$, then $0 < b^2 \leq 2$, and so, $a^2 = 2 - b^2 \geq 0$. Therefore, $a = \sqrt{2 - b^2}$ is a real number such that $k(a) = b$.

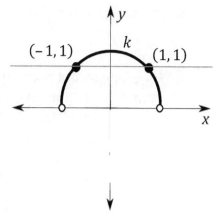

3. Define $g: \mathbb{R} \to \mathbb{R}$ by $g(x) = 7x - 3$. Then g is injective because if $g(a) = g(b)$, we then have $7a - 3 = 7b - 3$. Using the fact that $\mathbb{R}$ is a field, we get $7a = 7b$ (by the additive inverse property), and then $a = b$ (by the multiplicative inverse property). Also, g is surjective because if $b \in \mathbb{R}$, then $\frac{b+3}{7} \in \mathbb{R}$ (because $\mathbb{R}$ is a field) and

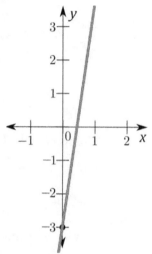

$$g\left(\frac{b+3}{7}\right) = 7\left(\frac{b+3}{7}\right) - 3 = (b + 3) - 3 = b + (3 - 3) = b + 0 = b$$

Therefore, g is bijective. See the image to the right for a visual representation of $\mathbb{R}^2$ and the graph of the function g.

Notice that any vertical line will hit the graph of g exactly once because g is a function with domain $\mathbb{R}$. Also, any horizontal line will hit the graph exactly once because g is bijective. Injectivity ensures that each horizontal line hits the graph *at most* once and surjectivity ensures that each horizontal line hits the graph *at least* once.

If $f: A \to B$ is bijective, we define $f^{-1}: B \to A$, the **inverse** of f, by $f^{-1} = \{(b, a) \mid (a, b) \in f\}$. In other words, for each $b \in B$, $f^{-1}(b) = $ "the unique $a \in A$ such that $f(a) = b$."

Notes: (1) Let $f: A \to B$ be bijective. Since f is surjective, for each $b \in B$, there is an $a \in A$ such that $f(a) = b$. Since f is injective, there is only one such value of a.

(2) The inverse of a bijective function is also bijective.

Example 10.16:

1. Define $f: \{0, 1\} \to \{a, b\}$ by $f = \{(0, a), (1, b)\}$. Then f is a bijection and $f^{-1}: \{a, b\} \to \{0, 1\}$ is defined by $f^{-1} = \{(a, 0), (b, 1)\}$. Observe that f^{-1} is also a bijection.

2. Let $\mathbb{E} = \{0, 2, 4, 6, 8, \dots\}$ be the set of even natural numbers and let $\mathbb{O} = \{1, 3, 5, 7, 9 \dots\}$ be the set of odd natural numbers. The function $f: \mathbb{E} \to \mathbb{O}$ defined by $f(n) = n + 1$ is a bijection with inverse $f^{-1}: \mathbb{O} \to \mathbb{E}$ defined by $f(n) = n - 1$.

3. If X and Y are sets, we define ^XY to be the set of functions from X to Y. Symbolically, we have
$$^XY = \{f \mid f: X \rightarrow Y\}$$

For example, if $A = \{a, b\}$ and $B = \{0, 1\}$, then ^AB has 4 elements (each element is a function from A to B). The elements are $f_1 = \{(a, 0), (b, 0)\}, f_2 = \{(a, 0), (b, 1)\}, f_3 = \{(a, 1), (b, 0)\}$, and $f_4 = \{(a, 1), (b, 1)\}$. Here is a visual representation of these four functions.

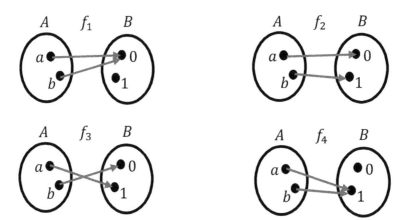

Define $F: {}^AB \rightarrow \mathcal{P}(A)$ by $F(f) = \{x \in A \mid f(x) = 1\}$.

So, $F(f_1) = \emptyset, F(f_2) = \{b\}, F(f_3) = \{a\}$, and $F(f_4) = \{a, b\}$.

Since $\mathcal{P}(A) = \{\emptyset, \{a\}, \{b\}, \{a, b\}\}$, we see that F is a bijection from ^AB to $\mathcal{P}(A)$.

The inverse of F is the function $F^{-1}: \mathcal{P}(A) \rightarrow {}^AB$ defined by $F^{-1}(C)(x) = \begin{cases} 0 & \text{if } x \notin C. \\ 1 & \text{if } x \in C. \end{cases}$

So, we see that $F^{-1}(\emptyset) = f_1, F^{-1}(\{b\}) = f_2, F^{-1}(\{a\}) = f_3$, and $F^{-1}(\{a, b\}) = f_4$.

4. For $A \neq \emptyset$ and $B = \{0, 1\}$, the function $F: {}^AB \rightarrow \mathcal{P}(A)$ defined by $F(f) = \{x \in A \mid f(x) = 1\}$ is always a bijection.

To see that F is injective, let $f, g \in {}^AB$ with $f \neq g$. Since f and g are different, there is some $a \in A$ such that either $f(a) = 0, g(a) = 1$ or $f(a) = 1, g(a) = 0$. Without loss of generality, assume that $f(a) = 0, g(a) = 1$. Since $f(a) = 0, a \notin F(f)$. Since $g(a) = 1, a \in F(g)$. So, $F(f) \neq F(g)$. Since $f \neq g$ implies $F(f) \neq F(g)$, F is injective.

To see that F is surjective, let $C \in \mathcal{P}(A)$, so that $C \subseteq A$. Define $f \in {}^AB$ by $f(x) = \begin{cases} 0 & \text{if } x \notin C. \\ 1 & \text{if } x \in C. \end{cases}$ Then $x \in F(f)$ if and only if $f(x) = 1$ if and only if $x \in C$. So, $F(f) = C$. Since $C \in \mathcal{P}(A)$ was arbitrary, F is surjective.

As in 3, the inverse of F is the function $F^{-1}: \mathcal{P}(A) \rightarrow {}^AB$ defined by $F^{-1}(C)(x) = \begin{cases} 0 & \text{if } x \notin C. \\ 1 & \text{if } x \in C. \end{cases}$

Notes: (1) See the Note following Theorem 6.6 in Lesson 6 for an explanation of the expression "Without loss of generality," and how to properly use it in a proof.

(2) As in the note following Example 10.14, using the notation $n = \{0, 1, 2, \ldots, n - 1\}$, we have just shown that for any nonempty set A, there is a bijection $f: {}^A2 \rightarrow \mathcal{P}(A)$.

Given functions $f: A \to B$ and $g: B \to C$, the **composite** of f and g, written $g \circ f: A \to C$, is defined by $(g \circ f)(a) = g(f(a))$ for all $a \in A$. Symbolically, we have

$$g \circ f = \{(a, c) \in A \times C \mid \text{There is a } b \in B \text{ such that } (a, b) \in f \text{ and } (b, c) \in g\}.$$

We can visualize the composition of two functions f and g as follows.

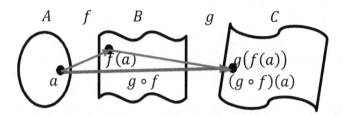

In the picture above, sets A, B, and C are drawn as different shapes simply to emphasize that they can all be different sets. Starting with an arbitrary element $a \in A$, we have an arrow showing a being mapped by f to $f(a) \in B$ and another arrow showing $f(a)$ being mapped by g to $g(f(a)) \in C$. There is also an arrow going directly from $a \in A$ to $(g \circ f)(a) = g(f(a))$ in C. Note that the only way we know how to get from a to $(g \circ f)(a)$ is to first travel from a to $f(a)$, and then to travel from $f(a)$ to $g(f(a))$.

Example 10.17: Define $f: \mathbb{Q} \to \mathbb{R}$ by $f(x) = x\sqrt{2}$ and define $g: \mathbb{R} \to \{0, 1\}$ by $g(x) = \begin{cases} 0 & \text{if } x \in \mathbb{Q} \\ 1 & \text{if } x \in \mathbb{R} \setminus \mathbb{Q} \end{cases}$
Then $g \circ f: \mathbb{Q} \to \{0, 1\}$ is defined by $(g \circ f)(x) = \begin{cases} 0 & \text{if } x = 0. \\ 1 & \text{if } x \in \mathbb{Q} \setminus \{0\}. \end{cases}$

To see this, observe that $(g \circ f)(0) = g(f(0)) = g(0\sqrt{2}) = g(0) = 0$ because $0 \in \mathbb{Q}$. If $x \in \mathbb{Q} \setminus \{0\}$, then $x\sqrt{2} \notin \mathbb{Q}$ because if $y = x\sqrt{2} \in \mathbb{Q}$, then since $\mathbb{Q}$ is a field, $\sqrt{2} = x^{-1}y \in \mathbb{Q}$, which we know to be false. So, $(g \circ f)(x) = g(f(x)) = g(x\sqrt{2}) = 1$.

It will be important to know that when we take the composition of bijective functions, we always get a bijective function. We will prove this in two steps. We will first show that the composition of injective functions is injective. We will then show that the composition of surjective functions is surjective.

Theorem 10.3: If $f: A \hookrightarrow B$ and $g: B \hookrightarrow C$, then $g \circ f: A \hookrightarrow C$.

Note: We are given that f and g are injections, and we want to show that $g \circ f$ is an injection. We can show this directly using the definition of injectivity, or we can use the contrapositive of the definition of injectivity. Let's do it both ways.

Direct proof of Theorem 10.3: Suppose that $f: A \hookrightarrow B$ and $g: B \hookrightarrow C$, and let $x, y \in A$ with $x \neq y$. Since f is injective, $f(x) \neq f(y)$. Since g is injective, $g(f(x)) \neq g(f(y))$. So, $(g \circ f)(x) \neq (g \circ f)(y)$. Since $x, y \in A$ were arbitrary, $g \circ f: A \hookrightarrow C$. $\qquad \square$

Contrapositive proof of Theorem 10.3: Suppose that $f: A \hookrightarrow B$ and $g: B \hookrightarrow C$, let $x, y \in A$ and suppose that $(g \circ f)(x) = (g \circ f)(y)$. Then $g(f(x)) = g(f(y))$. Since g is injective, $f(x) = f(y)$. Since f is injective, $x = y$. Since $x, y \in A$ were arbitrary, $g \circ f: A \hookrightarrow C$. $\qquad \square$

Theorem 10.4: If $f: A \mapsto B$ and $g: B \mapsto C$, then $g \circ f: A \mapsto C$.

Proof: Suppose that $f: A \mapsto B$ and $g: B \mapsto C$, and let $c \in C$. Since g surjective, there is $b \in B$ with $g(b) = c$. Since f is surjective, there is $a \in A$ with $f(a) = b$. So, $(g \circ f)(a) = g(f(a)) = g(b) = c$. Since $c \in C$ was arbitrary, $g \circ f$ is surjective. $\square$

Corollary 10.5: If $f: A \cong B$ and $g: B \cong C$, then $g \circ f: A \cong C$.

Proof: Suppose that $f: A \cong B$ and $g: B \cong C$. Then f and g are injective. By Theorem 10.3, $g \circ f$ is injective. Also, f and g are surjective. By Theorem 10.4, $g \circ f$ is surjective. Since $g \circ f$ is both injective and surjective, $g \circ f$ is bijective. $\square$

Note: A **corollary** is a theorem that follows easily from a theorem or theorems that have already been proved.

If A is any set, then we define the **identity function** on A, written $i_A: A \rightarrow A$ by $i_A(a) = a$ for all $a \in A$. Note that the identity function on A is a bijection from A to itself.

Theorem 10.6: If $f: A \cong B$, then $f^{-1} \circ f = i_A$ and $f \circ f^{-1} = i_B$.

Proof: Let $a \in A$ with $f(a) = b$. Then $f^{-1}(b) = a$, and so, $(f^{-1} \circ f)(a) = f^{-1}(f(a)) = f^{-1}(b) = a$. Since $i_A(a) = a$, we see that $(f^{-1} \circ f)(a) = i_A(a)$. Since $a \in A$ was arbitrary, $f^{-1} \circ f = i_A$.

Now, let $b \in B$. Since $f: A \cong B$, there is a unique $a \in A$ with $f(a) = b$. Equivalently, $f^{-1}(b) = a$. We have $(f \circ f^{-1})(b) = f(f^{-1}(b)) = f(a) = b$ Since $i_B(b) = b$, we see that $(f \circ f^{-1})(b) = i_B(b)$. Since $b \in B$ was arbitrary, $f \circ f^{-1} = i_B$. $\square$

Equinumerosity

We say that two sets A and B are **equinumerous**, written $A \sim B$ if there is a bijection $f: A \cong B$.

It is easy to see that $\sim$ **is an equivalence relation**. For any set A, the identity function $i_A: A \rightarrow A$ is a bijection, showing that $\sim$ is reflexive. For sets A and B, if $f: A \cong B$, then $f^{-1}: B \cong A$, showing that $\sim$ is symmetric. For sets $A, B,$ and C, if $f: A \cong B$ and $g: B \cong C$, then $g \circ f: A \cong C$ by Corollary 10.5, showing that $\sim$ is transitive.

Example 10.18:

1. Let $A = \{\text{anteater}, \text{elephant}, \text{giraffe}\}$ and $B = \{\text{apple}, \text{banana}, \text{orange}\}$. Then $A \sim B$. We can define a bijection $f: A \cong B$ by $f(\text{anteater}) = \text{apple}$, $f(\text{elephant}) = \text{banana}$, and $f(\text{giraffe}) = \text{orange}$. This is not the only bijection from A to B, but we need only find one (or prove one exists) to show that the sets are equinumerous.

2. At this point it should be easy to see that two finite sets are equinumerous if and only if they have the same number of elements. It should also be easy to see that a finite set can never be equinumerous with an infinite set.

3. Let $\mathbb{N} = \{0, 1, 2, 3, 4 \ldots\}$ be the set of natural numbers and $\mathbb{E} = \{0, 2, 4, 6, 8 \ldots\}$ the set of even natural numbers. Then $\mathbb{N} \sim \mathbb{E}$. We can actually see a bijection between these two sets just by looking at the sets themselves.

$$0 \quad 1 \quad 2 \quad 3 \quad 4 \quad 5 \quad 6 \ldots$$
$$0 \quad 2 \quad 4 \quad 6 \quad 8 \quad 10 \quad 12 \ldots$$

The function $f: \mathbb{N} \to \mathbb{E}$ defined by $f(n) = 2n$ is an explicit bijection. To see that f maps $\mathbb{N}$ into $\mathbb{E}$, just observe that if $n \in \mathbb{N}$, then $2n \in \mathbb{E}$ by the definition of an even integer (see Lesson 4). f is injective because if $f(n) = f(m)$, then $2n = 2m$, and so, $n = m$. Finally, f is surjective because if $n \in \mathbb{E}$, then there is $k \in \mathbb{N}$ such that $n = 2k$. So, $f(k) = 2k = n$.

4. $\mathbb{N} \sim \mathbb{Z}$ via the bijection $f: \mathbb{N} \cong \mathbb{Z}$ defined by $f(n) = \begin{cases} \dfrac{n}{2} & \text{if } n \text{ is even.} \\ -\dfrac{n+1}{2} & \text{if } n \text{ is odd.} \end{cases}$

Let's look at this correspondence visually:

$$0 \quad 1 \quad 2 \quad 3 \quad 4 \quad 5 \quad 6 \ldots$$
$$0 \quad -1 \quad 1 \quad -2 \quad 2 \quad -3 \quad 3 \ldots$$

Many students get confused here because they are under the misconception that the integers should be written "in order." However, when checking to see if two sets are equinumerous, we **do not** include any other structure. In other words, we are just trying to "pair up" elements—it does not matter how we do so.

You will be asked to verify that the function f defined above is a bijection in Problem 8 below.

5. For A any nonempty set, $^A\{0, 1\} \sim \mathcal{P}(A)$. We showed this in part 4 of Example 10.16.

We say that a set is **countable** if it is equinumerous with a subset of $\mathbb{N}$. It's easy to visualize a countable set because a bijection from a subset of $\mathbb{N}$ to a set A generates a list. For example, the set $\mathbb{E}$ can be listed as $0, 2, 4, 6, \ldots$ and the set $\mathbb{Z}$ can be listed as $0, -1, 1, -2, 2, \ldots$ (see Example 10.18 above).

There are two kinds of countable sets: finite sets and **denumerable** sets. We say that a set is denumerable if it is countably infinite.

At this point, you may be asking yourself if all infinite sets are denumerable. If this were the case, then we would simply have finite sets and infinite sets, and that would be the end of it. However, there are in fact infinite sets that are **not** denumerable. An infinite set that is not denumerable is **uncountable**.

Theorem 10.7 (Cantor's Theorem): If A is any set, then A is **not** equinumerous with $\mathcal{P}(A)$.

Analysis: How can we prove that A is not equinumerous with $\mathcal{P}(A)$? Well, we need to show that there **does not** exist a bijection from A to $\mathcal{P}(A)$. Recall that a bijection is a function which is both an injection and a surjection. So, we will attempt to show that there do not exist any surjections from A to $\mathcal{P}(A)$. To do this, we will take an arbitrary function $f: A \to \mathcal{P}(A)$, and then argue that f is not surjective. We will show that ran $f \neq \mathcal{P}(A)$ by finding a set $B \in \mathcal{P}(A) \setminus \text{ran } f$. In words, we will find a subset of A that is **not** in the range of f.

Let's begin by looking at $\mathbb{N}$, the set of natural numbers. Given a specific function $f: \mathbb{N} \to \mathcal{P}(\mathbb{N})$, it's not too hard to come up with a set $B \in \mathcal{P}(\mathbb{N}) \setminus \operatorname{ran} f$. Let's choose a specific such f and use this example to try to come up with a procedure for describing the set B.

$$f(0) = \{\mathbf{0}, 1, 2, 3, 4, 5, 6, 7, 8, 9, 10, \ldots\}$$
$$f(1) = \{0, \mathbf{1}, 3, 4, 5, 6, 7, 8, 9, 10, \ldots\}$$
$$f(2) = \{0, 1, 4, 5, 6, 7, 8, 9, 10, \ldots\}$$
$$f(3) = \{0, 1, 4, 6, 7, 8, 9, 10, \ldots\}$$
$$f(4) = \{0, 1, \mathbf{4}, 6, 8, 9, 10, \ldots\}$$

$$\ldots$$

Technical note: Recall that a **prime number** is a natural number with **exactly** two factors, 1 and itself. The set of prime numbers looks like this: $\{2, 3, 5, 7, 11, 13, 17, \ldots\}$. The function $f: \mathbb{N} \to \mathcal{P}(\mathbb{N})$ that we chose to use here is defined by $f(n) = \{k \in \mathbb{N} \mid k$ is not equal to one of the first n prime numbers$\}$. Notice how $f(0)$ is just the set $\mathbb{N}$ of all natural numbers, $f(1)$ is the set of all natural numbers except 2 (we left out the first prime), $f(2)$ is the set of all natural numbers except 2 and 3 (we left out the first two primes), and so on. Prime numbers will be covered in detail in Lesson 12.

Observe that the "inputs" of our function are natural numbers, and the "outputs" are sets of natural numbers. So, it's perfectly natural to ask the question "Is n in $f(n)$?"

For example, we see that $0 \in f(0)$, $1 \in f(1)$, and $4 \in f(4)$ (indicated in bold in the definition of the function above). However, we also see that $2 \notin f(2)$ and $3 \notin f(3)$.

Let's let B be the set of natural numbers n that are **not** inside their images. Symbolically, we have

$$B = \{n \in \mathbb{N} \mid n \notin f(n)\}.$$

Which natural numbers are in the set B? Well, we already said that $0 \in f(0)$. It follows that $0 \notin B$. Similarly, $1 \notin B$ and $4 \notin B$, but $2 \in B$ and $3 \in B$.

Why did we choose to define B this way? The reason is because we are trying to make sure that B cannot be equal to $f(n)$ for every n. Since $0 \in f(0)$, but $0 \notin B$, it follows that $f(0)$ and B are different sets because they differ by at least one element, namely 0. Similarly, since $1 \in f(1)$, but $1 \notin B$, B cannot be equal to $f(1)$. What about 2? Well $2 \notin f(2)$, but $2 \in B$. Therefore, $B \neq f(2)$ as well... and so on down the line. We intentionally chose to make B disagree with $f(n)$ for every natural number n, ensuring that B will not be in the range of f.

I think we are now ready to prove the theorem.

Proof of Theorem 10.7: Let $f: A \to \mathcal{P}(A)$, and let $B = \{a \in A \mid a \notin f(a)\}$. Suppose toward contradiction that $B \in \operatorname{ran} f$. Then there is $a \in A$ with $f(a) = B$. But then we have $a \in B$ if and only if $a \notin f(A)$ if and only if $a \notin B$. This contradiction tells us that $B \notin \operatorname{ran} f$, and so, f is not surjective. Since $f: A \to \mathcal{P}(A)$ was arbitrary, there does not exist a surjection from A to $\mathcal{P}(A)$, and therefore, there is no bijection from A to $\mathcal{P}(A)$. So, A is not equinumerous with $\mathcal{P}(A)$. $\qquad\square$

So, for example, $\mathbb{N}$ is not equinumerous with $\mathcal{P}(\mathbb{N})$. Which of these two sets is the "bigger" one? Let's consider the function $f: \mathbb{N} \to \mathcal{P}(\mathbb{N})$ defined by $f(n) = \{n\}$. This function looks like this:

$$0 \quad 1 \quad 2 \quad 3 \quad 4\ldots$$
$$\{0\} \quad \{1\} \quad \{2\} \quad \{3\} \quad \{4\}\ldots$$

Observe that we are matching up each natural number with a subset of natural numbers (a very simple subset consisting of just one natural number) in a way so that different natural numbers get matched with different subsets. In other words, we defined an injective function from $\mathbb{N}$ to $\mathcal{P}(\mathbb{N})$. It seems like there are lots of subsets of $\mathbb{N}$ that didn't get mapped to (for example, all infinite subsets of $\mathbb{N}$). So, it seems that $\mathbb{N}$ is a "smaller" set than $\mathcal{P}(\mathbb{N})$.

We use the notation $A \preccurlyeq B$ if there is an injective function from A to B.

$$A \preccurlyeq B \text{ if and only if } \exists f(f : A \hookrightarrow B)$$

We write $A \prec B$ if $A \preccurlyeq B$ and $A \nsim B$.

So, for example, $\mathbb{N} \prec \mathcal{P}(\mathbb{N})$.

Theorem 10.8: If A is any set, then $A \prec \mathcal{P}(A)$.

Proof: The function $f : A \to \mathcal{P}(A)$ defined by $f(a) = \{a\}$ is injective. So, $A \preccurlyeq \mathcal{P}(A)$. By Theorem 10.7, $A \nsim \mathcal{P}(A)$. It follows that $A \prec \mathcal{P}(A)$. $\qquad\square$

Example 10.19: If we let $A = \mathcal{P}(\mathbb{N})$, we can apply Theorem 10.8 to this set A to see that $\mathcal{P}(\mathbb{N}) \prec \mathcal{P}(\mathcal{P}(\mathbb{N}))$. Continuing in this fashion, we get a sequence of increasingly larger sets.

$$\mathbb{N} \prec \mathcal{P}(\mathbb{N}) \prec \mathcal{P}(\mathcal{P}(\mathbb{N})) \prec \mathcal{P}\left(\mathcal{P}(\mathcal{P}(\mathbb{N}))\right) \prec \cdots$$

If A and B are arbitrary sets, in general it can be difficult to determine if A and B are equinumerous by producing a bijection. Luckily, the next theorem provides an easier way.

Theorem 10.9 (The Cantor-Schroeder-Bernstein Theorem): If A and B are sets such that $A \preccurlyeq B$ and $B \preccurlyeq A$, then $A \sim B$.

Note: At first glance, many students think that Theorem 10.9 is obvious and that the proof must be trivial. This is not true. The theorem says that if there is an injective function from A to B and another injective function from B to A, then there is a bijective function from A to B. This is a deep result, which is far from obvious. Constructing a bijection from two arbitrary injections is not an easy thing to do. I suggest that the reader takes a few minutes to try to do it, if for no other reason than to convince themselves that the proof is difficult. I leave the proof itself as an optional exercise.

Example 10.20: Let's use Theorem 10.9 to prove that the open interval of real numbers $(0, 1)$ is equinumerous to the closed interval of real numbers $[0, 1]$.

Analysis: Since $(0, 1) \subseteq [0, 1]$, there is an obvious injective function $f : (0, 1) \to [0, 1]$ (just send each element to itself).

The harder direction is finding an injective function g from $[0, 1]$ into $(0, 1)$. We will do this by drawing a line segment with endpoints $\left(0, \frac{1}{4}\right)$ and $\left(1, \frac{3}{4}\right)$. This will give us a bijection from $[0, 1]$ to $\left[\frac{1}{4}, \frac{3}{4}\right]$. We can visualize this bijection using the graph to the right. We will write an equation for this line in the slope-intercept form $y = mx + b$. Here m is the slope of the line and b is the y-intercept of the line. We can use the graph to see that $b = \frac{1}{4}$ and

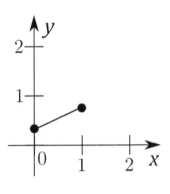

$m = \frac{\text{rise}}{\text{run}} = \frac{\frac{3}{4} - \frac{1}{4}}{1 - 0} = \frac{2}{4} = \frac{1}{2}$. So, we define $g : [0, 1] \to (0, 1)$ by $g(x) = \frac{1}{2}x + \frac{1}{4}$.

Let's write out the details of the proof.

Proof: Let $f : (0, 1) \to [0, 1]$ be defined by $f(x) = x$. Clearly, f is injective, so that $(0, 1) \preccurlyeq [0, 1]$.

Next, we define $g : [0, 1] \to \mathbb{R}$ by $g(x) = \frac{1}{2}x + \frac{1}{4}$. If $0 \le x \le 1$, then $0 \le \frac{1}{2}x \le \frac{1}{2}$, and therefore, $\frac{1}{4} \le \frac{1}{2}x + \frac{1}{4} \le \frac{3}{4}$. Since $0 < \frac{1}{4}$ and $\frac{3}{4} < 1$, we have $0 < g(x) < 1$. Therefore, $g : [0, 1] \to (0, 1)$. If $x \ne x'$, then $\frac{1}{2}x \ne \frac{1}{2}x'$, and so, $g(x) = \frac{1}{2}x + \frac{1}{4} \ne \frac{1}{2}x' + \frac{1}{4} = g(x')$. This shows that g is injective. It follows that $[0, 1] \preccurlyeq (0, 1)$.

Since $(0, 1) \preccurlyeq [0, 1]$ and $[0, 1] \preccurlyeq (0, 1)$, it follows from the Cantor-Schroeder-Bernstein Theorem that $(0, 1) \sim [0, 1]$. $\qquad\square$

Notes: (1) If $A \subseteq B$, then the function $f : A \to B$ defined by $f(a) = a$ for all $a \in A$ is always injective. It is called the **inclusion map**.

(2) It is unfortunate that the same notation is used for points and open intervals. Normally this isn't an issue, but in this particular example both usages of this notation appear. Take another look at the analysis above and make sure you can see when the notation (a, b) is being used for a point and when it is being used for an open interval.

(3) We could have used any interval $[a, b]$ with $0 < a < b < 1$ in place of $\left[\frac{1}{4}, \frac{3}{4}\right]$.

Problem Set 10

LEVEL 1

1. For each set A below, evaluate (i) A^2; (ii) $\mathcal{P}(A)$; (iii) ^AA.

    1. $A = \emptyset$ 2. $A = \{\emptyset\}$ 3. $A = \{0, 1\}$ 4. $A = \mathcal{P}(\{\emptyset\})$

2. Find all partitions of the three-element set $\{a, b, c\}$ and the four-element set $\{a, b, c, d\}$.

LEVEL 2

3. For $a, b \in \mathbb{N}$, we will say that a divides b, written $a|b$, if there is a natural number k such that $b = ak$. Notice that $|$ is a binary relation on $\mathbb{N}$. Prove that $(\mathbb{N}, |)$ is a partially ordered set, but it is not a linearly ordered set.

4. Prove that for each $n \in \mathbb{Z}^+$, $\equiv_n$ (see part 3 of Example 10.8) is an equivalence relation on $\mathbb{Z}$.

5. Let A, B, and C be sets. Prove the following:

    (i)   If $A \subseteq B$, then $A \preccurlyeq B$.

    (ii) $\preccurlyeq$ is transitive.

    (iii) $\prec$ is transitive.

    (iv)   If $A \preccurlyeq B$ and $B \prec C$, then $A \prec C$.

    (v)   If $A \prec B$ and $B \preccurlyeq C$, then $A \prec C$.

6. Let A and B be sets such that $A \subseteq B$. Prove that $\mathcal{P}(A) \preccurlyeq \mathcal{P}(B)$.

LEVEL 3

7. For $f, g \in {}^{\mathbb{R}}\mathbb{R}$, define $f \preccurlyeq g$ if and only if for all $x \in \mathbb{R}$, $f(x) \le g(x)$. Is $({}^{\mathbb{R}}\mathbb{R}, \preccurlyeq)$ a poset? Is it a linearly ordered set? What if we replace $\preccurlyeq$ by $\preccurlyeq^*$, where $f \preccurlyeq^* g$ if and only if there is an $x \in \mathbb{R}$ such that $f(x) \le g(x)$?

8. Prove that the function $f : \mathbb{N} \to \mathbb{Z}$ defined by $f(n) = \begin{cases} \dfrac{n}{2} & \text{if } n \text{ is even} \\ -\dfrac{n+1}{2} & \text{if } n \text{ is odd} \end{cases}$ is a bijection.

9. Define $\mathcal{P}_k(\mathbb{N})$ for each $k \in \mathbb{N}$ by $\mathcal{P}_0(\mathbb{N}) = \mathbb{N}$ and $\mathcal{P}_{k+1}(\mathbb{N}) = \mathcal{P}(\mathcal{P}_k(\mathbb{N}))$ for $k > 0$. Find a set B such that for all $k \in \mathbb{N}$, $\mathcal{P}_k(\mathbb{N}) \prec B$.

10. Prove that if $A \sim B$ and $C \sim D$, then $A \times C \sim B \times D$.

135

LEVEL 4

11. Define a partition P of $\mathbb{N}$ such that $P \sim \mathbb{N}$ and for each $X \in P$, $X \sim \mathbb{N}$.

12. Prove that a countable union of countable sets is countable.

13. Let A and B be sets such $A \sim B$. Prove that $\mathcal{P}(A) \sim \mathcal{P}(B)$.

14. Prove the following:

   (i) $\mathbb{N} \times \mathbb{N} \sim \mathbb{N}$.

   (ii) $\mathbb{Q} \sim \mathbb{N}$.

   (iii) Any two intervals of real numbers are equinumerous (including $\mathbb{R}$ itself).

   (iv) $^{\mathbb{N}}\mathbb{N} \sim \mathcal{P}(\mathbb{N})$.

15. Prove that $\{A \in \mathcal{P}(\mathbb{N}) \mid A \text{ is infinite}\}$ is uncountable.

16. For $f, g \in {}^{\mathbb{N}}\mathbb{N}$, define $f <^* g$ if and only if there is $n \in \mathbb{N}$ such that for all $m > n$, $f(m) < g(m)$.

   (i)   Is $({}^{\mathbb{N}}\mathbb{N}, <^*)$ a strict poset?

   (ii) Is $({}^{\mathbb{N}}\mathbb{N}, <^*)$ a strict linearly ordered set?

   (iii) Let $\mathcal{F} = \{f_n : \mathbb{N} \to \mathbb{N} \mid n \in \mathbb{N}\}$ be a countable set of functions. Must there be a function $g \in {}^{\mathbb{N}}\mathbb{N}$ such that for all $n \in \mathbb{N}$, $f_n <^* g$?

17. Let P be a partition of a set S. Prove that there is an equivalence relation $\sim$ on S for which the elements of P are the equivalence classes of $\sim$. Conversely, if $\sim$ is an equivalence relation on a set S, prove that the equivalence classes of $\sim$ form a partition of S.

LEVEL 5

18. Prove that if $A \sim B$ and $C \sim D$, then $^{A}C \sim {}^{B}D$.

19. Prove that for any sets A, B, and C, $^{B \times C}A \sim {}^{C}({}^{B}A)$.

20. Prove the following:

   (i) $\mathcal{P}(\mathbb{N}) \sim \{f \in {}^{\mathbb{N}}\mathbb{N} \mid f \text{ is a bijection}\}$.

   (ii) $^{\mathbb{N}}\mathbb{R} \nsim {}^{\mathbb{R}}\mathbb{N}$, given that $\mathbb{R} \sim \mathcal{P}(\mathbb{N})$.

CHALLENGE PROBLEM

21. Prove the Cantor-Schroeder-Bernstein Theorem.

Structures and Substructures

An **n-ary relation** on a set S is a subset of S^n. We usually use the expressions **unary**, **binary**, and **ternary** in place of 1-ary, 2-ary, and 3-ary. Note that a unary relation on S is simply a subset of S. We do not define a 0-ary relation.

Example 11.1: Let $\mathbb{Z} = \{\ldots, -3, -2, -1, 0, 1, 2, 3, \ldots\}$ be the set of integers. The set $\mathbb{N} = \{0, 1, 2, 3, \ldots\}$ of natural numbers is a unary relation on $\mathbb{Z}$. In other words, $\mathbb{N} \subseteq \mathbb{Z}$. Some examples of binary relations on $\mathbb{Z}$ are the linear orderings $<, \leq, >$, and $\geq$ (see Example 10.5 (part 2)) and the equivalence relations $\equiv_n = \{(a, b) \in \mathbb{Z}^2 \mid n \mid b - a\}$ (see Example 10.8 (part 3)). $R = \{(x, y, z) \in \mathbb{Z}^3 \mid x + y = z\}$ is an example of a ternary relation on $\mathbb{Z}$ (see Example 10.7).

An **n-ary operation** on a set S is a function from S^n to S. We also define a 0-ary operation to simply be an element of S. We will usually call a 0-ary operation a **constant** in S.

Example 11.2: Let $\mathbb{R}$ be the set of real numbers. Negation is an example of a unary operation on $\mathbb{R}$. This is the operation that maps each $x \in \mathbb{R}$ to $-x$. Addition, subtraction, and multiplication are examples of binary operations on $\mathbb{R}$. 0 is an example of a 0-ary operation on $\mathbb{R}$ or a constant in $\mathbb{R}$.

A **finitary relation** is an n-ary relation for some $n \in \mathbb{N}^*$. A **finitary operation** is an n-ary operation for some $n \in \mathbb{N}$.

A **structure** is a set together with a collection of finitary operations and relations defined on the set. The set is called the **domain** of the structure.

Example 11.3:

1. Semigroups, monoids, and groups are structures of the form $(S, \star)$, where S is a set and $\star$ is a binary operation on S.

   We may want to view a monoid as a structure of the form $(S, \star, e)$ and a group as a structure of the form $(S, \star, {}^{-1}, e)$, where e is a constant called the identity element of the monoid or group and ${}^{-1}$ is the unary inverse operator.

2. Rings and fields are structures of the form $(S, +, \cdot)$, where S is a set, and $+$ and $\cdot$ are binary operations on S. Again, we may want to include additional operations (see part 4 of Example 11.5 and also part 4 of Example 11.6 below).

3. Ordered rings and fields are structures of the form $(S, +, \cdot, \leq)$, where S is a set, $+$ and $\cdot$ are binary operations on S, and $\leq$ is a binary relation on S.

4. Every set without any operations and relations is a structure. For example, $\mathbb{N}, \mathbb{Z}, \mathbb{Q}, \mathbb{R}$, and $\mathbb{C}$ are structures. (Notice that we abbreviate the structure (S) as S.)

5. We can view a vector space $(V, \oplus)$ over the field $(F, +, \cdot)$ as $(V \cup F, V, F, R_\oplus, R_+, R_., R_\star)$, where V and F are unary relations, and $R_\oplus, R_+, R_., R_\star$ are the following ternary relations:

$$R_\oplus = \{(x,y,z) \in V^3 \mid x \oplus y = z\} \quad R_+ = \{(x,y,z) \in F^3 \mid x + y = z\}$$
$$R_\cdot = \{(x,y,z) \in F^3 \mid x \cdot y = z\} \qquad R_\star = \{(x,y,z) \in F \times V \times V \mid xy = z\}$$

Notice that we had to use ternary relations instead of binary functions for the four operations because the definition of a structure demands that functions be defined on $(V \cup F)^2$. However, none of the functions are defined on $(V \cup F)^2$. Indeed, $\oplus$ is defined only on V^2, $+$ and $\cdot$ are defined only on F^2, and scalar multiplication is defined on $F \times V$.

We will sometimes use a fraktur letter (such as $\mathfrak{A}$, $\mathfrak{B}$, $\mathfrak{C}$) for the name of a structure if we want to be clear that we are talking about the whole structure and not just the underlying set. For example, we might write $\mathfrak{G} = (G, \star)$ for a group $\mathfrak{G}$ with underlying set G and group operation $\star$.

Notes: (1) A finitary operation on a set S is a function $f: S^n \to S$ for some $n \in \mathbb{N}$. There are two important facts implied by this definition:

1. The operation f is defined for every n-tuple $(a_1, a_2, \ldots, a_n) \in S^n$.
2. The set S is closed under f.

(2) A finitary relation on a set S is a subset R of S^n for some $n \in \mathbb{N}$. We have more flexibility with relations than we do with operations. For example, an $(n+1)$-ary relation can be used to define a *partial* n-ary function. Suppose we want a structure that consists of the set of integers $\mathbb{Z}$ together with the partial function defined on only the even integers that divides each even integer by 2. We can define a relation $R = \{(2k, k) \mid k \in \mathbb{Z}\}$. The structure $(\mathbb{Z}, R)$ consists of the set of integers together with the function $f: 2\mathbb{Z} \to \mathbb{Z}$ defined by $f(n) = \frac{n}{2}$ ($2\mathbb{Z}$ is the set of even integers). Notice that we defined a *unary* partial function on $\mathbb{Z}$ by using a *binary* relation.

We say that structures $\mathfrak{A}$ and $\mathfrak{B}$ have the same **type** if they have the same number of n-ary operations for each $n \in \mathbb{N}$, and the same number of n-ary relations for each $n \in \mathbb{N}^*$ (recall that $\mathbb{N}^* = \mathbb{N} \setminus \{0\}$ is the set of nonzero natural numbers).

Example 11.4:

1. $(\mathbb{Q}, \leq)$, $(\mathcal{P}(\mathbb{N}), \subseteq)$, and for each $n \in \mathbb{N}^*$, $(\mathbb{Z}, \equiv_n)$ all have the same type because they each have exactly one binary relation.

2. $(\mathbb{Z}, +)$ and $(\mathbb{Z}, +, 0)$ have different types. The first structure has one binary operation and nothing else. The second structure has a binary operation and a constant (or a 0-ary operation). Both of these are different ways of describing the group of integers under addition. The second way is specifically mentioning the identity element, while the first is not. Another structure (of yet another type) that describes the same group is $(\mathbb{Z}, +, -, 0)$, where $-$ is the unary additive inverse operator.

Note: For structures with only finitely many operations and relations, the definition we gave of being of the same type is adequate. However, for structures with infinitely many operations and/or relations, we should be a little more careful with what we mean by "the same number." A better definition in this case is that for each $n \in \mathbb{N}$, the set of n-ary operations in $\mathfrak{A}$ is equinumerous with the set of n-ary operations in $\mathfrak{B}$, and for each $n \in \mathbb{N}^*$, the set of n-ary relations in $\mathfrak{A}$ is equinumerous with the set of n-ary relations in $\mathfrak{B}$. See Lesson 10 for more information on equinumerosity.

$\mathfrak{A}$ is a **substructure** of $\mathfrak{B}$, written $\mathfrak{A} \subseteq \mathfrak{B}$ if

1. $\mathfrak{A}$ and $\mathfrak{B}$ have the same type.

2. $A \subseteq B$.

3. If f is an n-ary operation, and $(a_1, a_2, \ldots, a_n) \in A^n$, then $f_A(a_1, a_2, \ldots, a_n) = f_B(a_1, a_2, \ldots, a_n)$.

4. If R is an n-ary relation, and $(a_1, a_2, \ldots, a_n) \in A^n$, then $R_A(a_1, a_2, \ldots, a_n)$ if and only if $R_B(a_1, a_2, \ldots, a_n)$

Notes: (1) Part 1 of the definition says that in order for $\mathfrak{A}$ to be a substructure of $\mathfrak{B}$, the two structures must have the same number of n-ary operations and n-ary relations for each n. For example, $(\mathbb{N}, +)$ is a substructure of $(\mathbb{Z}, +)$, written $(\mathbb{N}, +) \subseteq (\mathbb{Z}, +)$, but $(\mathbb{N}, +)$ is **not** a substructure of $(\mathbb{Z}, +, 0)$.

(2) The notation in 3 and 4 might look confusing at first. Let's clarify with an example of each. Suppose that f is addition, so that $f(a_1, a_2) = a_1 + a_2$. Then 3 says that if $\mathfrak{A} \subseteq \mathfrak{B}$ and we choose a_1 and a_2 from A, then we get the same result whether we add a_1 and a_2 in A or B. We might write this as $a_1 +_A a_2 = a_1 +_B a_2$. Now suppose that R is $<$, so that $R(a_1, a_2)$ means $a_1 < a_2$. Then 4 says that if $\mathfrak{A} \subseteq \mathfrak{B}$ and we choose a_1 and a_2 from A, then $a_1 <_A a_2$ if and only if $a_1 <_B a_2$.

Example 11.5:

1. Let $(S, \star)$ be a semigroup. A substructure $(T, \star)$ of $(S, \star)$ is called a **subsemigroup**. Notice that $T \subseteq S$ and the operation $\star$ must be the same for both structures. Also, $\star$ is a binary operation on T, which means that T is closed under $\star$. Is $\star$ associative in T? Recall from Note 2 following Example 3.3 in Lesson 3 that associativity is closed downwards. In other words, since $\star$ is associative in S and $T \subseteq S$, it follows that $\star$ is associative in T. We just showed that a subsemigroup of a semigroup is itself a semigroup.

   For example, let $\mathfrak{A} = (\mathbb{N}, +)$ and let $\mathfrak{B} = (\mathbb{E}, +)$, where $\mathbb{E} = \{2k \mid k \in \mathbb{N}\}$ is the set of even natural numbers. Then $\mathfrak{B} \subseteq \mathfrak{A}$. That is, $\mathfrak{B}$ is a subsemigroup of $\mathfrak{A}$.

   On the other hand, if we let $\mathbb{O} = \{2k + 1 | k \in \mathbb{N}\}$, then $(\mathbb{O}, +)$ is not even a structure because $+$ is **not** a binary operation on $\mathbb{O}$. For example, $3, 5 \in \mathbb{O}$, but $3 + 5 \notin \mathbb{O}$.

2. Let $(M, \star, e)$ be a monoid, where e is the identity of M. A substructure $(N, \star, e)$ of $(M, \star, e)$ is called a **submonoid**. Notice that the operation $\star$ and the identity e must be the same for both structures. As we saw in 1 above, N is closed under $\star$ and $\star$ is associative in N. We just showed that a submonoid of a monoid is itself a monoid.

   Note that a substructure $(N, \star)$ of a monoid $(M, \star)$ is a subsemigroup of $(M, \star)$, but may or may not be a submonoid of $(M, \star)$. For example, let $C = \mathbb{N} \setminus \{0, 1\} = \{2, 3, 4, \ldots\}$ be the set of natural numbers with 0 and 1 removed. Then $(C, \cdot)$ is a subsemigroup of the monoid $(\mathbb{N}, \cdot)$, but $(C, \cdot)$ is not a submonoid of $(\mathbb{N}, \cdot)$ because C is missing the multiplicative identity 1.

   If $(M, \star)$ is a monoid with identity e, we can define a submonoid to be a substructure $(N, \star)$ of $(M, \star)$ such that N contains e. In other words, if we wish to leave the identity out of the structure, we need to explicitly mention that the domain of the substructure contains the identity in order to guarantee that we get a submonoid. For example, if we let $\mathfrak{A} = (\mathbb{N}, +)$ and $\mathfrak{B} = (\mathbb{E}, +)$, we see that $\mathfrak{B}$ is a submonoid of $\mathfrak{A}$ because $\mathbb{E} \subseteq \mathbb{N}$ is closed under $+$ and $0 \in \mathbb{E}$.

3. Let $(G, \star, {}^{-1}, e)$ be a group, where ${}^{-1}$ is the unary inverse operator and e is the identity of G. A substructure $(H, \star, {}^{-1}, e)$ of $(G, \star, {}^{-1}, e)$ is called a **subgroup**. Notice that the operations $\star$ and ${}^{-1}$, and the identity e must be the same for both structures. As we saw in 1 and 2 above, H is closed under $\star$ and $\star$ is associative in N. By making the unary inverse operator part of the structure, we have guaranteed that the inverse property holds for the substructure. So, a subgroup of a group is itself a group.

Also note that if $\star$ is commutative in G, then $\star$ is commutative in H. Commutativity is closed downwards for the same reason that associativity is closed downwards (once again, see Note 2 following Example 3.3 in Lesson 3).

For example, let $\mathfrak{A} = (\mathbb{Z}, +, -, 0)$ and let $\mathfrak{B} = (2\mathbb{Z}, +, -, 0)$, where $2\mathbb{Z} = \{2k \mid k \in \mathbb{Z}\}$ is the set of even integers. Then $\mathfrak{B}$ is a subgroup of $\mathfrak{A}$. More generally, for any positive integer n, we can let $n\mathbb{Z} = \{nk \mid k \in \mathbb{Z}\}$. The structure $(n\mathbb{Z}, +, -, 0)$ is a subgroup of the group $(\mathbb{Z}, +, -, 0)$.

Note that a substructure $(H, \star)$ of a group $(G, \star)$ is a subsemigroup of $(G, \star)$, but may or may not be a subgroup of $(G, \star)$, as we saw in 2 above. Furthermore, a substructure $(H, \star, e)$ of a group $(G, \star, e)$ is a submonoid of $(G, \star, e)$ but still may not be a subgroup of $(G, \star, e)$. For example, $(\mathbb{N}, +, 0)$ is a substructure of the group $(\mathbb{Z}, +, 0)$ that is **not** a subgroup of $(\mathbb{Z}, +, 0)$ (it is a submonoid though). We need to include the unary inverse operator in the structure to guarantee that a substructure of a subgroup will be a subgroup.

If $(G, \star)$ is a group with identity e, we can define a subgroup to be a substructure $(H, \star)$ of $(G, \star)$ such that H contains e and for all $x \in H$, $x^{-1} \in H$ (in other words, we need to insist that H is closed under taking inverses). These conditions can be used in place of including symbols for inverse and identity in the structure itself. For example, if we let $\mathfrak{A} = (\mathbb{R}^*, \cdot)$ and $\mathfrak{B} = (\mathbb{Q}^*, \cdot)$, we see that $\mathfrak{B}$ is a subgroup of $\mathfrak{A}$ because $\mathbb{Q}^* \subseteq \mathbb{R}^*$, $1 \in \mathbb{Q}^*$, and $\mathbb{Q}^*$ is closed under taking multiplicative inverses.

If the operation is understood, we can simplify notation even further. We may write $H \leq G$ and say that H is a subgroup of G. What we mean by this is $(H, \star, {}^{-1}, e)$ is a substructure of $(G, \star, {}^{-1}, e)$, or equivalently, $(H, \star)$ is a substructure of $(G, \star)$ such that the identity of G is in H and H is closed under taking inverses.

We use the same notation for other structures as well. Just be careful about one thing. When we write $A \leq B$, we don't just mean that the structure $\mathfrak{A}$ is a substructure of the structure $\mathfrak{B}$. We also mean that the structure $\mathfrak{A}$ has all the properties we need for the type of structure under discussion. For example, if we are talking about groups under addition, then we would **not** write $\mathbb{N} \leq \mathbb{Z}$. However, if we are talking about monoids under addition, then we could write $\mathbb{N} \leq \mathbb{Z}$.

4. Let $(R, +, \cdot, -, 1)$ be a ring, where $-$ is the unary additive inverse operator and 1 is the multiplicative identity of R. A substructure $(S, +, \cdot, -, 1)$ of $(R, +, \cdot, -, 1)$ is called a **subring**. Notice that the operations $+$, $\cdot$, and $-$, and the multiplicative identity 1 must be the same for both structures. By the definition of a structure, S is closed under $+$, $\cdot$ and $-$.

You may be wondering why we didn't put a constant for 0 in the structure. The reason is because we don't need to. Since $1 \in S$ and S is closed under the additive inverse, we have $0 = 1 + (-1) \in S$. Associativity of addition and multiplication, commutativity of addition, and distributivity all hold in S because these operations are closed downwards (see Note 2 following Example 3.3 in Lesson 3). It follows that a subring is itself a ring.

Alternatively, we can say that $(S, +, \cdot)$ is a subring of $(R, +, \cdot)$ if $(S, +, \cdot)$ is a substructure of $(R, +, \cdot)$ such that S contains 1 and for all $x \in S$, $-x \in S$ (in other words, we need to insist that S is closed under taking additive inverses).

As we discussed above, we may write $S \leq R$ for S is a subring of R if it is clear that we are talking about the ring structures of S and R.

For example, $(\mathbb{Z}, +, \cdot)$ is a subring of the fields $(\mathbb{Q}, +, \cdot)$, $(\mathbb{R}, +, \cdot)$, and $(\mathbb{C}, +, \cdot)$.

$(\mathbb{Z}, +, \cdot)$ has no subring other than itself. To see this, let $A \leq \mathbb{Z}$. First note that the multiplicative identity $1 \in A$. Using closure of addition and the principle of mathematical induction, we can then show that each positive integer is in A (for example, $2 = 1 + 1$). Since A is closed under the additive inverse of $\mathbb{Z}$, for each positive integer n, $-n \in A$. It follows that $A = \mathbb{Z}$. (Note that we know that $0 \in A$ because we have already shown that 0 is in any subring of a ring.)

5. Let $(F, +, \cdot, -, \,^{-1}, 0, 1)$ be a field, where $-$ and $^{-1}$ are the unary additive inverse and multiplicative inverse operators, respectively, and 0 and 1 are the additive and multiplicative identities of R, respectively. Note that technically speaking, $^{-1}$ must be expressed as the binary relation $^{-1} = \{(x, y) \mid y = x^{-1}\}$ because $^{-1}$ isn't defined for $x = 0$. A substructure $(K, +, \cdot, -, \,^{-1}, 0, 1)$ of $(F, +, \cdot, -, \,^{-1}, 0, 1)$ is a **subfield** provided that the domain and range of the multiplicative inverse relation $^{-1}$ are both K^*. Notice that the operations $+, \cdot, -$, the relation $^{-1}$, and the identities 0 and 1 must be the same for both structures. By the definition of a structure, K is closed under $+$, $\cdot$, and $-$. Associativity and commutativity of addition and multiplication, and distributivity all hold in K because these operations are closed downwards (see Note 2 following Example 3.3 in Lesson 3). It follows that a subfield is itself a field.

Alternatively, we can say that $(K, +, \cdot)$ is a subfield of $(F, +, \cdot)$ if $(K, +, \cdot)$ is a substructure of $(F, +, \cdot)$ such that K contains 0 and 1, for all $x \in K$, $-x \in K$ and for all nonzero $x \in K$, $x^{-1} \in K$ (in other words, we need to insist that K is closed under taking additive inverses and K^* is closed under taking multiplicative inverses). We will write $K \leq F$ when K is a subfield of F and it is clear we are talking about the field structures of K and F.

For example, $(\mathbb{Q}, +, \cdot)$ is a subfield of both $(\mathbb{R}, +, \cdot)$ and $(\mathbb{C}, +, \cdot)$, and $(\mathbb{R}, +, \cdot)$ is a subfield of $(\mathbb{C}, +, \cdot)$.

6. If $(P, \leq)$ is a partially ordered set, then a substructure $(Q, \leq)$ of $(P, \leq)$ will also be a partially ordered set. This is because reflexivity, antisymmetry, and transitivity are all closed downwards. Once again, see Note 2 following Example 3.3 in Lesson 3 for an explanation of this. Similarly, any substructure of a linearly ordered set is linearly ordered, and similar results hold for strict partial and linear orders.

For example, we have $(\mathbb{N}, \leq) \subseteq (\mathbb{Z}, \leq) \subseteq (\mathbb{Q}, \leq) \subseteq (\mathbb{R}, \leq)$, and each of these structures are linearly ordered sets. Similarly, we have $(\mathbb{N}, <) \subseteq (\mathbb{Z}, <) \subseteq (\mathbb{Q}, <) \subseteq (\mathbb{R}, <)$.

Homomorphisms

A **homomorphism** is a function from one structure to another structure of the same type that preserves all the relations and functions of the structure (see the Note after Example 11.6 for a more rigorous definition).

Example 11.6:

1. Let $(S, \star)$ and $(T, \circ)$ be semigroups. A **semigroup homomorphism** is a function $f: S \to T$ such that for all $a, b \in S$, $f(a \star b) = f(a) \circ f(b)$.

    For example, let $\mathfrak{A} = (\mathbb{Z}^+, +)$, $\mathfrak{B} = (\mathbb{E}, \cdot)$, and let $f: \mathbb{Z}^+ \to \mathbb{E}$ be defined by $f(n) = 2^n$. For all $n, m \in \mathbb{Z}^+$, we have $f(n + m) = 2^{n+m} = 2^n \cdot 2^m = f(n) \cdot f(m)$. Therefore, f is a semigroup homomorphism.

    As another example, let $\mathfrak{A} = (\mathbb{N}, +)$, $\mathfrak{B} = (\{T, F\}, \vee)$, and let $g: \mathbb{N} \to \{T, F\}$ be defined by $g(n) = T$. For all $n, m \in \mathbb{Z}^+$, we have $g(n + m) = T = T \vee T = g(n) \vee g(m)$. Therefore, g is a semigroup homomorphism.

2. Let $(M, \star, e_M)$ and $(N, \circ, e_N)$ be monoids, where e_M and e_N are the identities of M and N, respectively. A **monoid homomorphism** is a function $f: M \to N$ such that for all $a, b \in M$, $f(a \star b) = f(a) \circ f(b)$ and $f(e_M) = e_N$.

    Note that we need to include the identity element of a monoid as part of the structure for a homomorphism to be a monoid homomorphism. Otherwise we get only a semigroup homomorphism. The second example in part 1 above is a semigroup homomorphism, but **not** a monoid homomorphism. Indeed, the identity of $(\mathbb{N}, +)$ is 0 and the identity of $(\{T, F\}, \vee)$ is F, but $g(0) = T \neq F$.

    On the other hand, if we change the domains of the structures in the first example from part 1 above slightly, we **do** get a monoid homomorphism. Let $\mathfrak{A} = (\mathbb{N}, +, 0)$, $\mathfrak{B} = (\mathbb{N}, \cdot, 1)$, and let $f: \mathbb{N} \to \mathbb{N}$ be defined by $f(n) = 2^n$. For all $n, m \in \mathbb{N}$, $f(n + m) = f(n) \cdot f(m)$, as we saw above, and $f(0) = 2^0 = 1$. Therefore, f is a monoid homomorphism.

3. Let $(G, \star)$ and $(H, \circ)$ be groups. A **group homomorphism** is a function $f: G \to H$ such that for all $a, b \in G$, $f(a \star b) = f(a) \circ f(b)$.

    You may be asking why we are not including constant symbols for the identity like we did for monoids. After all, we certainly want f to take the identity of G to the identity of H. And you may also be asking why we are not including a unary operator symbol for taking the inverse, as we certainly want $f(a^{-1}) = (f(a))^{-1}$. For structures $(G, \star, {}^{-1_G}, e_G)$ and $(H, \circ, {}^{-1_H}, e_H)$, we can define a group homomorphism to be a function $f: G \to H$ such that for all $a, b \in G$, $f(a \star b) = f(a) \circ f(b)$, for all $a \in G$, $f(a^{-1}) = (f(a))^{-1}$, and $f(e_G) = e_H$. However, it turns out that this more complicated definition is equivalent to our first simpler one. In other words, if $f: G \to H$ is a group homomorphism using the simpler definition, then f already maps the identity of G to the identity of H, and f already preserves inverses. We will prove these facts in Theorems 11.1 and 11.2 below.

As an example, let $\mathfrak{A} = (\mathbb{Z}, +)$, $\mathfrak{B} = (\{1, -1\}, \cdot)$, and let $f: \mathbb{Z} \to \{1, -1\}$ be defined by $f(n) = \begin{cases} 1 & \text{if } n \text{ is even.} \\ -1 & \text{if } n \text{ is odd.} \end{cases}$ There are four cases to consider. If n and m are both even, then $n + m$ is even, and so, $f(n + m) = 1$ and $f(n) \cdot f(m) = 1 \cdot 1 = 1$. If n and m are both odd, then $n + m$ is even, and so, $f(n + m) = 1$ and $f(n) \cdot f(m) = (-1) \cdot (-1) = 1$. If n is even and m is odd, then $n + m$ is odd, and so, $f(n + m) = -1$ and $f(n) \cdot f(m) = 1 \cdot (-1) = -1$. Finally, if n is odd and m is even, then $n + m$ is odd, and so, we have $f(n + m) = -1$ and $f(n) \cdot f(m) = -1 \cdot 1 = -1$. Therefore, f is a group homomorphism.

Let's look at another example. Let $\mathfrak{A} = (\mathbb{R}, +)$, $\mathfrak{B} = (\mathbb{R}, +)$, and let $g: \mathbb{R} \to \mathbb{R}$ be defined by $g(x) = x^2$. Then g is **not** a group homomorphism. To see this, we just need a single counterexample. We have $g(1) = 1^2 = 1$, $g(2) = 2^2 = 4$, $g(1 + 2) = g(3) = 3^2 = 9$, and $g(1) + g(2) = 1 + 4 = 5$. Since $g(1 + 2) \neq g(1) + g(2)$, g fails to be a homomorphism.

4. Let $(R, +_R, \cdot_R, 1_R)$ and $(S, +_S, \cdot_S, 1_S)$ be rings, where 1_R and 1_S are the multiplicative identities of R and S, respectively. A **ring homomorphism** is a function $f: R \to S$ such that for all $a, b \in R$, $f(a +_R b) = f(a) +_S f(b)$, $f(a \cdot_R b) = f(a) \cdot_S f(b)$, and $f(1_R) = 1_S$.

   Notice that we did not include constant symbols for the additive identities of the rings and we did not include unary operator symbols for taking the additive inverses of elements in the rings. We will see in Theorems 11.1 and 11.2 below that with f defined as above, it follows that for all $a \in R$, $f(-a) = -f(a)$, and $f(0_R) = 0_S$.

   Let's look at an example. First note that if R is a ring, then $R \times R$ with addition and multiplication defined componentwise is also a ring. That is, for $a, b, c, d \in R$, we define addition and multiplication by $(a, b) + (c, d) = (a + c, b + d)$ and $(a, b)(c, d) = (ac, bd)$. The verification that $R \times R$ is a ring with these definitions is straightforward (see Problem 5 below). Let $\mathfrak{A} = (\mathbb{Z} \times \mathbb{Z}, +, \cdot, (1, 1))$, $\mathfrak{B} = (\mathbb{Z}, +, \cdot, 1)$, and let $f: \mathbb{Z} \times \mathbb{Z} \to \mathbb{Z}$ be defined by $f((n, m)) = n$. Then for all $n, m, j, k \in \mathbb{Z}$, we have $f((n, m) + (j, k)) = f((n + j, m + k)) = n + j$ and $f((n, m)) + f((j, k)) = n + j$. We also have $f((n, m) \cdot (j, k)) = f((nj, mk)) = nj$ and $f((n, m)) \cdot f((j, k)) = nj$. Finally, $f((1, 1)) = 1$. Therefore, f is a ring homomorphism.

   Let's look at another example. Let $\mathfrak{A} = \mathfrak{B} = (\mathbb{Z}, +, \cdot, 1)$, and let $g: \mathbb{Z} \to \mathbb{Z}$ be defined by $g(n) = 2n$. Then g is **not** a ring homomorphism. To see this, we just need a single counterexample. $g(3) = 2 \cdot 3 = 6$, $g(5) = 2 \cdot 5 = 10$, $g(3 \cdot 5) = g(15) = 2 \cdot 15 = 30$, and $g(3) \cdot g(5) = 6 \cdot 10 = 60$. Since $g(3 \cdot 5) \neq g(3) \cdot g(5)$, g fails to be a ring homomorphism. Note, however, that g **is** a group homomorphism from $(\mathbb{Z}, +)$ to itself. Indeed, if $n, m \in \mathbb{Z}$, then $g(n + m) = 2(n + m) = 2n + 2m = g(n) + g(m)$.

5. A **field homomorphism** is the same as a ring homomorphism. The multiplicative inverse is automatically preserved (see Theorem 11.2 below), and so, nothing additional needs to be added to the definition.

6. Let $(A, \leq_A)$ and $(B, \leq_B)$ be partially ordered sets. An **order homomorphism** (also known as a **monotonic function**) is a function $f: A \to B$ such that for all $x, y \in A$, $x \leq_A y$ if and only if $f(x) \leq_B f(y)$.

   For example, let $\mathfrak{A} = \mathfrak{B} = (\mathbb{N}, \leq)$ and let $f: \mathbb{N} \to \mathbb{N}$ be defined by $f(n) = n + 3$. For all $n, m \in \mathbb{N}$, we have $n \leq m$ if and only if $n + 3 \leq m + 3$ if and only if $f(n) \leq f(m)$. Therefore, f is an order homomorphism.

As another example, let $\mathfrak{A} = (\mathbb{Z}, \geq)$, $\mathfrak{B} = (\mathcal{P}(\mathbb{Z}), \subseteq)$, and let $g: \mathbb{Z} \to \mathcal{P}(\mathbb{Z})$ be defined by $g(n) = \{k \in \mathbb{Z} \mid n \leq k\}$. Let $m, n \in \mathbb{Z}$. We will show that $m \geq n$ if and only if the relationship $\{k \in \mathbb{Z} \mid m \leq k\} \subseteq \{k \in \mathbb{Z} \mid n \leq k\}$ holds. Suppose that $m \geq n$ and let $j \in \{k \in \mathbb{Z} \mid m \leq k\}$. Then $j \geq m$. Since $m \geq n$, $j \geq n$, and so, $j \in \{k \in \mathbb{Z} \mid n \leq k\}$. Now, let $\{k \in \mathbb{Z} \mid m \leq k\} \subseteq \{k \in \mathbb{Z} \mid n \leq k\}$. Since $m \leq m$, we have $m \in \{k \in \mathbb{Z} \mid m \leq k\}$. So, $m \in \{k \in \mathbb{Z} \mid n \leq k\}$. Thus, $n \leq m$, or equivalently, $m \geq n$. Therefore, g is an order homomorphism.

Note: Here is a more rigorous definition of a homomorphism.

If $\mathfrak{A}$ and $\mathfrak{B}$ are structures of the same type with underlying domains A and B, then a homomorphism is a function $f: A \to B$ such that for each $n \in \mathbb{N}$,

1. if R is an n-ary relation, then $R_A(a_1, a_2, \ldots, a_n)$ if and only if $R_B(f(a_1), f(a_2), \ldots, f(a_n))$.

2. If F is an n-ary function, then $f(F_A(a_1, a_2, \ldots, a_n)) = F_B(f(a_1), f(a_2), \ldots, f(a_n))$.

In particular, 2 implies that if c is a constant, then $f(c_A) = c_B$.

Theorem 11.1: Let $(G, \star)$ and $(H, \circ)$ be groups with identities e_G and e_H, respectively, and let $f: G \to H$ be a group homomorphism. Then $f(e_G) = e_H$.

Proof: Since $e_G = e_G \star e_G$, we have $f(e_G) = f(e_G \star e_G) = f(e_G) \circ f(e_G)$. So,

$$f(e_G) = f(e_G) \circ e_H = f(e_G) \circ \left(f(e_G) \circ (f(e_G))^{-1} \right)$$
$$= (f(e_G) \circ f(e_G)) \circ (f(e_G))^{-1} = f(e_G) \circ (f(e_G))^{-1} = e_H. \qquad \square$$

Notes: (1) The computations in the proof take place in the group $(H, \circ)$. In particular, $f(e_G) \in H$ and $e_H \in H$. If the proof seems confusing because $f(e_G)$ appears so often, try making the substitutions $h = f(e_G)$ and $e = e_H$. Notice that $h, e \in H$ and by the first line of the proof, $h = h \circ h$. The rest of the proof then looks like this:

$$h = h \circ e = h \circ (h \circ h^{-1}) = (h \circ h) \circ h^{-1} = h \circ h^{-1} = e.$$

Remember that $h = f(e_G)$ and $e = e_H$. So, we have $f(e_G) = e_H$, as desired.

(2) $h = h \circ e$ because e is the identity for H.

(3) $e = h \circ h^{-1}$ by the definition of inverse and because e is the identity for H. From this equation, it follows that $h \circ e = h \circ (h \circ h^{-1})$.

(4) $h \circ (h \circ h^{-1}) = (h \circ h) \circ h^{-1}$ because $\circ$ is associative in H.

(5) $h \circ h = h$ from the first line of the proof (this is equivalent to $f(e_G) \circ f(e_G) = f(e_G)$). It follows that $(h \circ h) \circ h^{-1} = h \circ h^{-1}$.

(6) Finally, $h \circ h^{-1} = e$, again by the definition of inverse and because e is the identity for H.

(7) If the group operation is addition, then we usually use the symbols 0_G and 0_H for the identities.

Theorem 11.2: Let $(G, \star)$ and $(H, \circ)$ be groups and let $f: G \to H$ be a group homomorphism. Then for all $g \in G$, $f(g^{-1}) = \left(f(g)\right)^{-1}$.

Proof: By Theorem 11.1, we have $f(e_G) = e_H$. So, for $g \in G$, we have

$$e_H = f(e_G) = f(g \star g^{-1}) = f(g) \circ f(g^{-1}).$$

Since $f(g) \circ f(g^{-1}) = e_H$, $f(g^{-1}) = \left(f(g)\right)^{-1}$. $\qquad\square$

Notes: (1) $e_G = g \star g^{-1}$ by the definition of inverse and because e_G is the identity for G. From this equation, it follows that $f(e_G) = f(g \star g^{-1})$.

(2) $f(g \star g^{-1}) = f(g) \circ f(g^{-1})$ because f is a homomorphism.

(3) In a group with identity e, if $xy = e$ and $yx = e$, then $y = x^{-1}$. We actually need to verify only one of the equations $xy = e$ or $yx = e$ to determine that $y = x^{-1}$ (see Note 6 after the solution to Problem 7 in Problem Set 3 from Lesson 3). Letting $x = f(g)$, $y = f(g^{-1})$, and $e = e_H$, we showed in the proof that $xy = e$. It follows that $y = x^{-1}$. That is, $f(g^{-1}) = \left(f(g)\right)^{-1}$.

An **isomorphism** is a bijective homomorphism. If there is an isomorphism from a structure $\mathfrak{A}$ to a structure $\mathfrak{B}$, then we say that $\mathfrak{A}$ and $\mathfrak{B}$ are **isomorphic**, and we write $\mathfrak{A} \cong \mathfrak{B}$. Mathematicians generally consider isomorphic structures to be the same. Indeed, they behave identically. The only difference between them is the "names" of the elements.

Example 11.7:

1. For $n \in \mathbb{Z}^+$, the function $f: \mathbb{Z} \to n\mathbb{Z}$ defined by $f(k) = nk$ is an isomorphism between the groups $(\mathbb{Z}, +)$ and $(n\mathbb{Z}, +)$. It's easy to see that f is injective ($j \neq k \to nj \neq nk$) and surjective (if $nk \in n\mathbb{Z}$, then $f(k) = nk$). If $j, k \in \mathbb{Z}$, then $f(j + k) = n(j + k) = nj + nk = f(j) + f(k)$. It follows that $(\mathbb{Z}, +) \cong (n\mathbb{Z}, +)$.

   Note that this map is **not** a ring isomorphism for $n > 1$. First, $(n\mathbb{Z}, +, \cdot)$ is technically not even a ring for $n > 1$ because $1 \notin n\mathbb{Z}$. But it is "almost a ring." In fact, the multiplicative identity property is the only property that fails. See the notes following Theorem 11.4 for more details.

   Let's show that for $n > 1$, f is **not** an isomorphism between the "almost rings" $(\mathbb{Z}, +, \cdot)$ and $(n\mathbb{Z}, +, \cdot)$. Let's use $2, 3 \in \mathbb{Z}$ to provide a counterexample: $f(2 \cdot 3) = f(6) = n \cdot 6 = 6n$ and $f(2) \cdot f(3) = (n \cdot 2)(n \cdot 3) = 6n^2$. If $f(2 \cdot 3) = f(2) \cdot f(3)$, then $6n = 6n^2$, so that $n = n^2$. This equation is equivalent to $n^2 - n = 0$, or $n(n - 1) = 0$. So, $n = 0$ or $n = 1$.

   In fact, as "almost rings," $(\mathbb{Z}, +, \cdot)$ is **not** isomorphic to $(n\mathbb{Z}, +, \cdot)$ at all for $n > 1$. If $f: \mathbb{Z} \to n\mathbb{Z}$ were an isomorphism, then $f(1) = nm$ for some $m \in \mathbb{Z}$. But also, since f is a homomorphism, $f(1) = f(1 \cdot 1) = f(1)f(1) = (nm)(nm) = n^2m^2$. So, $nm = n^2m^2$, and thus, $m = 0, n = 0$, or $1 = nm$. If $m = 0$, then $f(1) = 0$, and so, $f(2) = f(1 + 1) = f(1) + f(1) = 0 + 0 = 0$. So, f is not injective. Since $n > 1$, $n \neq 0$ and $1 \neq nm$.

2. Recall that if $z = a + bi$ is a complex number, then the conjugate of z is the complex number $\bar{z} = a - bi$. The function $g: \mathbb{C} \to \mathbb{C}$ defined by $f(z) = \bar{z}$ is an isomorphism between the field $(\mathbb{C}, +, \cdot)$ and itself. By Problem 3 (parts (iii) and (iv)) from Problem Set 7 in Lesson 7, we have

$$f(z+w) = \overline{z+w} = \overline{z} + \overline{w} = f(z) + f(w) \quad f(zw) = \overline{zw} = \overline{z} \cdot \overline{w} = f(z)f(w) \quad f(1) = \overline{1} = 1$$

Thus, f is a homomorphism. Since for all $z \in \mathbb{C}$, $f(\overline{z}) = z$, f is surjective. Since $z \neq w$ implies that $\overline{z} \neq \overline{w}$, f is injective. Therefore, f is a bijective homomorphism, and so, f is an isomorphism.

An isomorphism from a structure to itself is called an **automorphism**. The identity function is always an automorphism from any structure to itself. In the previous example, we described a nontrivial automorphism from $\mathbb{C}$ to $\mathbb{C}$.

Images and Kernels

Let $f: A \rightarrow B$ be a homomorphism. The **image** of f is the set $f[A] = \{f(x) \mid x \in A\}$ and the **kernel** of f is the set $\ker(f) = \{x \in A \mid f(x) = e_B\}$. In the case where B has both an additive and multiplicative identity, then e_B will always be the additive identity (in other words, if $0, 1 \in B$, then the kernel of f is the set of all elements of A that map to 0).

Theorem 11.3: Let $f: R \rightarrow S$ be a ring homomorphism. Then $f[R]$ is a subring of S.

Proof: Since $f(x) + f(y) = f(x + y)$ and $f(x)f(y) = f(xy)$, we see that $f[R]$ is closed under addition and multiplication. Since $1_S = f(1_R)$, $1_S \in f[R]$. By Theorem 11.2, $-f(x) = f(-x)$ (this is the conclusion of Theorem 11.2 when additive notation is used). So, for each element $f(x) \in f[R]$, $-f(x) \in f[R]$. It follows that $f[R]$ is a subring of S. $\qquad\square$

Note: The same result holds if we replace "ring" by semigroup, monoid, group, or field. If $(S, \star)$ and $(T, \circ)$ are semigroups, and $f: S \rightarrow T$ is a semigroup homomorphism, then $f(x) \circ f(y) = f(x \star y)$ shows that $f[S]$ is closed under $\circ$, and therefore, $f[S]$ is a subsemigroup of T.

Furthermore, if $(M, \star)$ and $(N, \circ)$ are monoids, and $f: M \rightarrow N$ is a monoid homomorphism, then by definition, $f(e_M) = e_N$, and therefore, $f[M]$ is a submonoid of N.

If $(G, \star)$ and $(H, \circ)$ are groups, and $f: G \rightarrow H$ is a group homomorphism, then $f(e_G) = e_H$ by Theorem 11.1, and for all $g \in G$, $\left(f(g)\right)^{-1} = f(g^{-1})$ by Theorem 11.2. Therefore, $f[G]$ is a subgroup of H.

If $(F, +, \cdot)$ and $(K, +, \cdot)$ are fields, and $f: F \rightarrow K$ is a field homomorphism, then for all $x \in F^*$, $\left(f(x)\right)^{-1} = f(x^{-1})$ by Theorem 11.2 again. Therefore, $f[F]$ is a subfield of K.

Theorem 11.4: Let $f: G \rightarrow H$ be a group homomorphism. Then $\ker(f)$ is a subgroup of G.

Proof: Let $x, y \in \ker(f)$. Then $f(x) = e_H$ and $f(y) = e_H$. So $f(x \star y) = f(x) \circ f(y) = e_H \circ e_H = e_H$. Thus, $x \star y \in \ker(f)$. Since $f(e_G) = e_H$ (by Theorem 11.1), $e_G \in \ker(f)$. Suppose $x \in \ker(f)$. By Theorem 11.2, we have $f(x^{-1}) = \left(f(x)\right)^{-1} = e_H^{-1} = e_H$. So $x^{-1} \in \ker(f)$. Therefore, $\ker(f)$ is a subgroup of G. $\qquad\square$

Notes: (1) The same result holds for semigroups and monoids. This should be clear from the proof.

(2) Let's say that $(R, +, \cdot)$ is **almost a ring** if all the ring properties hold **except** the existence of a multiplicative identity. Similarly, we will say that $(S, +, \cdot)$ is **almost a subring** of the ring $(R, +, \cdot)$ if all the properties of being a subring hold **except** S does not contain the multiplicative identity.

In this case, some authors use the word "**rng.**" They intentionally leave out the "i" in ring to help remember that this structure has no multiplicative identity. In other words, 1 is missing from a rng.

(3) If $f: R \to S$ is a ring homomorphism, then unless S is the trivial ring $\{0\}$, $\ker(f)$ is not a ring because $f(1_R) = 1_S \neq 0_S$. So, $1_R \notin \ker(f)$. However, every other property holds and so $\ker(f)$ is almost a subring of R. Indeed, if $x, y \in \ker(f)$, then

$$f(x + y) = f(x) + f(y) = 0_S + 0_S = 0_S \text{ and } f(xy) = f(x)f(y) = 0_S \cdot 0_S = 0_S.$$

Also, $f(0_R) = 0_S$ by Theorem 11.1, and if $x \in \ker(f)$, then $f(-x) = -f(x) = -0_S = 0_S$ by Theorem 11.2 (this is the conclusion of Theorem 11.2 when additive notation is used).

(4) Some authors exclude the existence of a multiplicative identity from the definition of a ring. Note 3 gives a good justification for doing so. However, removing a property creates other complexities. So, there is no right or wrong answer here. For us, rings will always include a multiplicative identity. If we wish to exclude the multiplicative identity, we will call the structure "almost a ring."

Theorem 11.5: Let $f: G \to H$ be a group homomorphism. Then $\ker(f) = \{e_G\}$ if and only f is injective.

Proof: Suppose that $\ker(f) = \{e_G\}$, let $x, y \in G$, and let $f(x) = f(y)$. Then $f(x)\big(f(y)\big)^{-1} = e_H$. It follows from Theorem 11.2 that $f(xy^{-1}) = f(x)f(y^{-1}) = f(x)\big(f(y)\big)^{-1} = e_H$. So, $xy^{-1} \in \ker(f)$. Since $\ker(f) = \{e_G\}$, $xy^{-1} = e_G$. Therefore, $x = y$. Since $x, y \in G$ were arbitrary, f is injective.

Conversely, suppose that f is injective, and let $x \in \ker(f)$. Then $f(x) = e_H$. But also, by Theorem 11.1, $f(e_G) = e_H$. So, $f(x) = f(e_G)$. Since f is injective, $x = e_G$. Since $x \in G$ was arbitrary, $\ker(f) \subseteq \{e_G\}$. By Theorem 11.1, $f(e_G) = e_H$, so that $e_G \in \ker(f)$, and therefore, $\{e_G\} \subseteq \ker(f)$. It follows that $\ker(f) = \{e_G\}$. $\qquad \square$

Note: The theorem also holds for ring homomorphisms. Specifically, if $f: R \to S$ is a ring homomorphism, then $\ker(f) = \{0_R\}$ if and only if f is injective. The proof is the same, except additive notation should be used. Here is a sketch of the proof using additive notation:

If $\ker(f) = \{0_R\}$ and $f(x) = f(y)$, then $f\big(x + (-y)\big) = f(x) + f(-y) = f(x) - f(y) = 0_S$, so that $x + (-y) \in \ker(f)$, and thus, $x + (-y) = 0_R$, and so, $x = y$.

Conversely, if f is injective and $x \in \ker(f)$, then $f(x) = 0_S$. Since $f(0_R) = 0_S$ and f is injective, we have $x = 0_R$. So, $\ker(f) \subseteq \{0_R\}$. Also, $f(0_R) = 0_S$. So, $0_R \in \ker(f)$, and therefore, $\{0\}_R \subseteq \ker(f)$.

Normal Subgroups and Ring Ideals

Let $(G, \star)$ be a group and $h, k \in G$. We say that k is a **conjugate** of h if there is a $g \in G$ such that $k = ghg^{-1}$ (as usual, we abbreviate $g \star h \star g^{-1}$ as ghg^{-1}).

If $(G, \star)$ is a group, we say that a subgroup N of G is **normal**, and write $N \triangleleft G$, if whenever $h \in N$ and $k \in G$ is a conjugate of h, then $k \in N$. (In this case, we may say that N is **closed under conjugation**.)

Example 11.8:

1. If G is a commutative group, then every subgroup H of G is normal. Indeed, if $h \in H$ and $g \in G$, then $ghg^{-1} = hgg^{-1} = he = h \in H$.

2. If $f: G \to H$ is a group homomorphism, then $\ker(f)$ is a normal subgroup of G. We already showed in Theorem 11.4 that $\ker(f)$ is a subgroup of G. To see that $\ker(f) \triangleleft G$, let $h \in \ker(f)$ and let $g \in G$. Then $f(ghg^{-1}) = f(g)f(h)f(g^{-1}) = f(g)e(f(g))^{-1} = f(g)(f(g))^{-1} = e$.

3. Any group is a normal subgroup of itself. Indeed, if $h \in G$ and $g \in G$, then clearly $ghg^{-1} \in G$.

4. The trivial subgroup of a group G consisting of just the identity e is a normal subgroup of G. Indeed, if $h \in \{e\}$ and $g \in G$, then $ghg^{-1} = geg^{-1} = gg^{-1} = e \in \{e\}$.

5. Let A be a nonempty set. A bijection from A to itself is called a **permutation** of A. Let $S(A)$ be the set of permutations of A. Let's check that $(S(A), \circ)$ is a group, where $\circ$ is the operation of composition.

    By Corollary 10.5 from Lesson 10, $S(A)$ is closed under $\circ$.

    To see that $\circ$ is associative, let $f, g, h \in S(A)$ and let $a \in A$. Then

    $$((f \circ g) \circ h)(a) = (f \circ g)(h(a)) = f\big(g(h(a))\big) = f((g \circ h)(a)) = (f \circ (g \circ h))(a).$$

    Since $a \in A$ was arbitrary, $(f \circ g) \circ h = f \circ (g \circ h)$. So, $\circ$ is associative in $S(A)$.

    Recall that the identity permutation i_A is defined by $i_A(a) = a$ for all $a \in A$. If $a \in A$, then $(i_A \circ f)(a) = i_A(f(a)) = f(a) = f(i_A(a)) = (f \circ i_A)(a)$. Since $a \in A$ was arbitrary, we have $i_A \circ f = f$ and $f \circ i_A = f$.

    Recall that for any permutation f on A, there is an inverse permutation f^{-1} satisfying $f^{-1} \circ f = f \circ f^{-1} = i_A$ for each $f \in S(A)$ (by Theorem 10.6).

    So, we have verified that $(S(A), \circ)$ is a group.

    If $A = \{1, 2, \dots, n\}$, then we define S_n to be $S(A)$. For example, $S_3 = S(\{1, 2, 3\})$. We can visualize each element of S_3 with a **cycle diagram**. Here are the six elements of S_3 visualized this way.

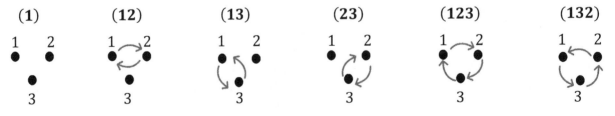

The first diagram represents the identity permutation $\{(1, 1), (2, 2), (3, 3)\}$, where each element is being mapped to itself. Technically, we should have an arrow from each point looping back to itself. However, to avoid unnecessary clutter, we leave out arrows for elements that are mapping to themselves. In **cycle notation**, we have $(1)(2)(3)$, which we abbreviate as (1).

The second diagram represents the permutation $\{(1,2),(2,1),(3,3)\}$, where 1 is being mapped to 2, 2 is being mapped to 1, and 3 is being mapped to itself. Again, we leave out the arrow from 3 to itself to avoid clutter, and we just put in the arrows from 1 to 2 and from 2 to 1. In cycle notation, we have $(12)(3)$, which we abbreviate as (12). In this notation, (12) represents a **cycle**. The cycle moves from left to right and the last element in the cycle connects to the first. So, 1 maps to 2 and 2 maps to 1. Any element that does not appear in the cycle notation maps to itself.

As one more example, in the cycle (123), 1 maps to 2, 2 maps to 3, and 3 maps to 1.

To compose two permutations in cycle notation, we write the one we want to apply first on the right (just as we do in function notation). For example, let's simplify $(12)(13)$. Starting with 1, we see that the rightmost cycle sends 1 to 3. The leftmost cycle sends 3 to itself, and so the composition sends 1 to 3. Let's do 2 next. The rightmost cycle sends 2 to itself, and then the leftmost cycle sends 2 to 1. So, the composition sends 2 to 1. And finally, let's look at 3. The rightmost cycle sends 3 to 1, and then the leftmost cycle sends 1 to 2. So, the composition sends 3 to 2. It follows that $(12)(13) = (132)$.

Observe that the group $(S_3, \circ)$ is not commutative. For example, $(12)(13) = (132)$, whereas $(13)(12) = (123)$.

Let's consider the subgroups $H = \{(1),(123),(132)\}$ and $K = \{(1),(12)\}$. One of these is a normal subgroup of S_3 and the other is not. You will be asked to verify that H and K are subgroups of S_3 and to determine which one is normal and which one is not in Problem 2 below.

Let $(R, +, \cdot)$ be a ring and let $A \subseteq R$. We say that A **absorbs** R if for every $a \in A$ and $x \in R$, $ax \in A$ and $xa \in A$.

Note: Since in a ring, multiplication is not necessarily commutative, both conditions $ax \in A$ and $xa \in A$ may be necessary. In a commutative ring, either condition follows from the other.

If $(R, +, \cdot)$ is a ring, we say that a subset I of R is an **ideal** of R, and write $I \lhd R$, if $(I, +)$ is a subgroup of $(R, +)$ and I absorbs R.

Example 11.9:

1. Consider the ring $(\mathbb{Z}, +, \cdot)$. Then $(2\mathbb{Z}, +, \cdot)$ is an ideal of $\mathbb{Z}$ because $(2\mathbb{Z}, +)$ is a subgroup of $(\mathbb{Z}, +)$ (see part 3 of Example 11.5) and when we multiply an even integer by **any** other integer, we get an even integer (so, $2\mathbb{Z}$ absorbs $\mathbb{Z}$).

   More generally, for each $n \in \mathbb{Z}^+$, $(n\mathbb{Z}, +, \cdot)$ is an ideal of $(\mathbb{Z}, +, \cdot)$.

2. If $f: R \to S$ is a ring homomorphism, then $\ker(f)$ is an ideal of G. We already showed in Note 3 following Theorem 11.4 that $(\ker(f), +)$ is a subgroup of $(R, +)$. To see that $\ker(f)$ absorbs R, let $a \in \ker(f)$ and let $x \in R$. Then $f(ax) = f(a)f(x) = 0_S \cdot f(x) = 0_S$, so that $ax \in \ker(f)$. Also, $f(xa) = f(x)f(a) = f(x) \cdot 0_S = 0_S$, so that $xa \in \ker(f)$.

3. Any ring is an ideal of itself. Indeed, if $a \in R$ and $x \in R$, then clearly $ax \in R$ and $xa \in R$.

4. $\{0_R\}$ is an ideal of R because for all $x \in R$, $0_R \cdot x = 0_R$ and $x \cdot 0_R = 0_R$.

Problem Set 11

LEVEL 1

1. Write the elements of S_4 in cycle notation.

2. Draw a group multiplication table for S_3. Let $H = \{(1), (123), (132)\}$ and $K = \{(1), (12)\}$. Show that H and K are subgroups of S_3 and determine which of these is a normal subgroup of S_3.

LEVEL 2

3. A **Gaussian integer** is a complex number of the form $a + bi$, where $a, b \in \mathbb{Z}$. Let $\mathbb{Z}[i]$ be the set of Gaussian integers. Prove that $(\mathbb{Z}[i], +, \cdot)$ is a subring of $(\mathbb{C}, +, \cdot)$.

4. Let $(G, \star)$ be a group with H a nonempty subset of G. Prove that $(H, \star)$ is a subgroup of $(G, \star)$ if and only if for all $g, h \in H$, $g \star h^{-1} \in H$.

5. Let $(R, +, \cdot)$ be a ring and define addition and multiplication on $R \times R$ componentwise, as was done in part 4 of Example 11.6. Prove that $(R \times R, +, \cdot)$ is a ring and that $(R, +, \cdot)$ is isomorphic to a subring of $(R \times R, +, \cdot)$.

LEVEL 3

6. Prove that there are exactly two ring homomorphisms from $\mathbb{Z}$ to itself.

7. Prove the following:

   (i)   Ring isomorphism is an equivalence relation.

   (ii) If we let $\mathrm{Aut}(R)$ be the set of automorphisms of a ring R, then $(\mathrm{Aut}(R), \circ)$ is a group, where $\circ$ is composition.

8. Let G be a group with H and K subgroups of G, and let $G = H \cup K$. Prove that $H = G$ or $K = G$.

9. Prove that a commutative ring R is a field if and only if the only ideals of R are $\{0\}$ and R.

10. Prove that if X is a nonempty set of normal subgroups of a group G then $\bigcap X$ is a normal subgroup of G. Similarly, prove that if X is a nonempty set of ideals of a ring R, then $\bigcap X$ is an ideal of R. Is the union of normal subgroups always a normal subgroup? Is the union of ideals always an ideal?

11. Let $\mathbb{Z}_n[x] = \{a_n x^n + a_{n-1} x^{n-1} + \cdots + a_1 x + a_0 \mid a_0, a_1, \ldots, a_n \in \mathbb{Z}\}$. In other words, $\mathbb{Z}_n[x]$ consists of all polynomials of degree at most n. Prove that $(\mathbb{Z}_n[x], +)$ is a commutative group for $n = 0, 1$, and 2, where addition is defined in the "usual way." Then prove that $\mathbb{Z}_0[x]$ is a subgroup of $\mathbb{Z}_1[x]$ and $\mathbb{Z}_1[x]$ is a subgroup of $\mathbb{Z}_2[x]$. What if we replace "all polynomials of degree at most n" with "all polynomials of degree n?"

LEVEL 4

12. Let N be a normal subgroup of a group G. For each $g \in G$, let $gN = \{gx \mid x \in N\}$. Prove that $gN = hN$ if and only if $gh^{-1} \in N$. Let $G/N = \{gN \mid g \in G\}$. Prove that $(G/N, \circ)$ is a group, where $\circ$ is defined by $gN \circ hN = (gh)N$.

13. Let I be an ideal of a ring R. For each $x \in R$, let $x + I = \{x + z \mid z \in I\}$. Prove that $x + I = y + I$ if and only if $x - y \in I$. Let $R/I = \{x + I \mid x \in R\}$. Prove that $(R/I, +, \cdot)$ is a ring, where addition and multiplication are defined by $(x + I) + (y + I) = (x + y) + I$ and $(x + I)(y + I) = xy + I$.

14. Let $\mathbb{Z}_n = \{[k] \mid k \in \mathbb{Z}\}$, where $[k]$ is the equivalence class of k under the equivalence $\equiv_n$. Prove that $(\mathbb{Z}_n, +, \cdot)$ is a ring, where addition and multiplication are defined by $[x] + [y] = [x + y]$ and $[xy] = [x] \cdot [y]$. Then prove that $\mathbb{Z}/n\mathbb{Z} \cong \mathbb{Z}_n$. Find the ideals of $\mathbb{Z}/15\mathbb{Z}$ and $\mathbb{Z}_{15}$ and show that there is a natural one-to-one correspondence between them.

LEVEL 5

15. Let $\mathbb{Z}[x] = \{a_k x^k + a_{k-1} x^{k-1} + \cdots + a_1 x + a_0 \mid k \in \mathbb{N} \wedge a_0, a_1, \ldots, a_k \in \mathbb{Z}\}$. $(\mathbb{Z}[x], +, \cdot)$ with addition and multiplication defined in the "usual way" is called the **polynomial ring over** $\mathbb{Z}$. Prove that $(\mathbb{Z}[x], +, \cdot)$ is a ring. Then prove that $(\mathbb{Z}_n[x], +, \cdot)$ is **not** a subring of $(\mathbb{Z}[x], +, \cdot)$ for any $n \in \mathbb{N}$. Let $R[x] = \{a_k x^k + a_{k-1} x^{k-1} + \cdots + a_1 x + a_0 \mid k \in \mathbb{N} \wedge a_0, a_1, \ldots, a_k \in R\}$ for an arbitrary ring R. Is $(R[x], +, \cdot)$ necessarily a ring?

16. Let N be a normal subgroup of the group G, and define $f: G \to G/N$ by $f(g) = gN$. Prove that f is a surjective group homomorphism with kernel N. Conversely, prove that if $f: G \to H$ is a group homomorphism, then $G/\ker(f) \cong f[G]$.

17. Let I be an ideal of a ring R, and define $f: R \to R/I$ by $f(x) = x + I$. Prove that f is a surjective ring homomorphism with kernel I. Conversely, prove that if $f: R \to S$ is a ring homomorphism, then $R/\ker(f) \cong f[R]$.

18. Prove that $(^{\mathbb{R}}\mathbb{R}, +, \cdot)$ is a ring, where addition and multiplication are defined pointwise. Then prove that for each $x \in \mathbb{R}$, $I_x = \{f \in {}^{\mathbb{R}}\mathbb{R} \mid f(x) = 0\}$ is an ideal of $^{\mathbb{R}}\mathbb{R}$ and the only ideal of $^{\mathbb{R}}\mathbb{R}$ containing I_x and not equal to I_x is $^{\mathbb{R}}\mathbb{R}$.

LESSON 12 – NUMBER THEORY
PRIMES, GCD, AND LCM

Prime Numbers

Recall that an integer a is **divisible** by an integer k, written $k|a$, if there is another integer b such that $a = kb$. We also say that k is a **factor** of a, k is a **divisor** of a, k **divides** a, or a is a **multiple** of k. For example, $7|21$ because $21 = 7 \cdot 3$. Also, see Examples 4.3 and 4.4 from Lesson 4.

Notes: (1) Every integer is divisible by 1. Indeed, if $n \in \mathbb{Z}$, then $n = 1 \cdot n$.

(2) Every integer is divisible by itself. Indeed, if $n \in \mathbb{Z}$, then $n = n \cdot 1$.

(3) It follows from Notes 1 and 2 above that every integer greater than 1 has at least 2 factors.

A **prime number** is a natural number with **exactly** two positive integer factors.

Notes: (1) An equivalent definition of a prime number is the following: A prime number is an integer greater than 1 that is divisible only by 1 and itself.

(2) An integer greater than 1 that is not prime is called **composite**.

Example 12.1:

1. 0 is **not** prime because every positive integer is a factor of 0. Indeed, if $n \in \mathbb{Z}^+$, then $0 = n \cdot 0$, so that $n|0$.

2. 1 is **not** prime because it has only one positive integer factor: if $1 = kb$ with $b > 0$, then $k = 1$ and $b = 1$.

3. The first ten prime numbers are $2, 3, 5, 7, 11, 13, 17, 19, 23$, and 29.

4. 4 is not prime because $4 = 2 \cdot 2$. In fact, the only even prime number is 2 because by definition, an even integer has 2 as a factor.

5. 9 is the first odd integer greater than 1 that is not prime. Indeed, 3, 5, and 7 are prime, but 9 is not because $9 = 3 \cdot 3$.

6. The first ten composite numbers are $4, 6, 8, 9, 10, 12, 14, 15, 16$, and 18.

Two very important facts about prime numbers (that we will prove in this Lesson) are the following.

1. There are infinitely many prime numbers.

2. Every integer greater than 1 can be written uniquely as a product of prime numbers, up to the order in which the factors are written.

The second fact is known as **The Fundamental Theorem of Arithmetic**. It is used often in many branches of mathematics.

When we write an integer n as a product of other integers, we call that product a **factorization** of n. If all the factors in the product are prime, we call the product a **prime factorization** of n.

Example 12.2:

1. $20 = 4 \cdot 5$ is a factorization of 20. This is **not** a prime factorization of 20 because 4 is **not** prime. $20 = 2 \cdot 10$ is another factorization of 20. This example shows that factorizations in general are **not** unique.

2. An example of a prime factorization of 20 is $20 = 2 \cdot 2 \cdot 5$. We can also write this prime factorization as $2 \cdot 5 \cdot 2$ or $5 \cdot 2 \cdot 2$. So, you can see that if we consider different orderings of the factors as different factorizations, then prime factorizations are **not** unique. This is why we say that prime factorizations are unique, **up to the order in which the factors are written**.

3. A prime number is equal to its own prime factorization. In other words, we consider a prime number to be a product of primes with just one factor in the product. For example, the prime factorization of 2 is 2.

Recall from Lesson 4 that the **Well Ordering Principle** says that every nonempty subset of natural numbers has a least element.

We will now use the Well Ordering Principle to prove half of the Fundamental Theorem of Arithmetic.

Theorem 12.1: Every integer greater than 1 can be written as a product of prime numbers.

Note that we left out the word "uniquely" here. The uniqueness is the second half of the Fundamental Theorem of Arithmetic, which we will prove later in this lesson.

Analysis: We will prove this theorem by contradiction using the Well Ordering Principle. The idea is simple. If an integer n greater than 1 is not prime, then it can be factored as kr with $1 < k < n$ and $1 < r < n$. If k and r can be written as a product of primes, then so can n because n is simply the product of all the factors of k and r. For example, $6 = 2 \cdot 3$ and $20 = 2 \cdot 2 \cdot 5$. Therefore, we have $120 = 6 \cdot 20 = (2 \cdot 3) \cdot (2 \cdot 2 \cdot 5)$. Let's write the proof.

Proof of Theorem 12.1: Suppose toward contradiction that there exists an integer greater than 1 that cannot be written as a product of prime numbers. By the Well Ordering Principle, there is a least such integer, let's call it n. Since n cannot be written as a product of prime numbers, then in particular, n is not prime. So, we can write $n = kr$ with $k, r \in \mathbb{N}$ and $1 < k < n$ and $1 < r < n$. Since n is the least integer greater than 1 that cannot be written as a product of prime numbers, k and r can both be written as products of prime numbers. But then $n = kr$ is also a product of prime numbers, contradicting our choice of n. This contradiction shows that every integer greater than 1 can be written as a product of prime numbers. $\qquad\square$

Notes: (1) Recall that a proof by contradiction works as follows:

1. We assume the negation of what we are trying to prove.

2. We use a logically valid argument to derive a statement which is false.

3. Since the argument was logically valid, the only possible error is our original assumption. Therefore, the negation of our original assumption must be true.

The negation of the statement "Every integer greater than 1 can be written as a product of prime numbers" is "There is an integer greater than 1 that **cannot** be written as a product of prime numbers." If we let $S = \{k \in \mathbb{N} \mid k > 1 \land k$ cannot be written as a product of prime numbers$\}$, then by our assumption, $S \neq \emptyset$. It follows from the Well Ordering Principle that S has a least element, which in the proof above, we name n.

The argument then proceeds to factor n as kr, where k and r are both greater than 1 and less than n. We can factor n this way because n in not prime.

Since n is the least element of S, it follows that k and r are not in S. Therefore, k and r **can** be written as a product of prime numbers. But this immediately gives us a prime factorization of n, contradicting our original assumption.

Since every step of our argument was logically valid, the only thing that could have been wrong was our original assumption. So, **every** integer greater than 1 **can** be written as a product of prime numbers.

(2) In general, if $P(x)$ is a property, then the negation of $\forall x(P(x))$ is $\exists x(\neg P(x))$. In other words, when we pass a negation symbol through a universal quantifier, the quantifier changes to an existential quantifier. So, $\neg\forall x(P(x)) \equiv \exists x(\neg P(x))$, where $\equiv$ is pronounced "is logically equivalent to." For Theorem 12.1, the property $P(x)$ is $q(x) \to r(x)$, where $q(x)$ is "$x > 1$" and $r(x)$ is "x can be written as a product of prime numbers." Recall from part 2 of Example 9.5 in Lesson 9 that $\neg(q(x) \to r(x))$ is logically equivalent to $q(x) \land \neg r(x)$. So $\exists x(\neg P(x))$ says, "There is an integer x such that $x > 1$ and x cannot be written as a product of prime numbers."

In general (although not needed here), we also have $\neg\exists x(P(x)) \equiv \forall x(\neg P(x))$.

Corollary 12.2: Every integer greater than 1 has a prime factor.

Proof: Let n be an integer greater than 1. By Theorem 12.1, n can be written as a product of prime numbers. Let p be any of the prime numbers in that product. Then p is a prime factor of n. $\qquad\square$

Theorem 12.3: There are infinitely many primes.

Analysis: Starting with a prime number $p > 1$, we want to find a prime number greater than p. This will prove that there infinitely many prime numbers, because if P is a finite set of prime numbers, then the previous statement implies that we can find a prime number greater than the biggest number in the set P.

Now recall that if n is a positive integer, then the number $n!$ (pronounced "**n factorial**") is defined by $n! = 1 \cdot 2 \cdots n$. For example, $3! = 1 \cdot 2 \cdot 3 = 6$ and $4! = 1 \cdot 2 \cdot 3 \cdot 4 = 24$.

If $n > 2$, then $n!$ is a number larger than n that is divisible by every positive integer less than or equal to n. For example, $3! = 6$ is divisible by $1, 2$, and 3, and $4! = 24$ is divisible by $1, 2, 3$, and 4.

Now, $n!$ Is certainly **not** prime. In fact, it has lots of factors! For example, $4! = 24$ has 8 factors (what are they?). Therefore, $n!$ itself won't work for us. So, we add 1 to this number to get the number $M = n! + 1$.

By adding 1 to $n!$ to produce M, we have destroyed almost all the divisibility that we had. Specifically, M is **not** divisible by any integer k with $1 < k \leq n$. To see this, let k be an integer satisfying $1 < k \leq n$. We know that there is an integer r such that $n! = kr$ (because $n!$ Is divisible by k). If M were divisible by k, then there would be an integer s such that $M = ks$. But then, by subtracting $n!$ from each side of the equation $M = n! + 1$, we get $1 = M - n! = ks - kr = k(s - r)$. Since $k > 1$ and $s - r$ is an integer, this is impossible! Therefore, M is not divisible by k.

It would be nice if we could prove that M is prime. Then M would be a prime number greater than n, thus completing the proof. Sometimes M does turn out to be prime. For example, if $n = 2$, then $M = 2! + 1 = 2 + 1 = 3$, which is prime. However, it is unfortunate for us that M is not always prime. In Problem 6 below you will find values for n for which M is not prime.

However, even if M is not prime, all is not lost. By Corollary 12.2, we know that M has a prime factor, let's call it p. We also know that M is **not** divisible by any integer k with $1 < k \leq n$. It follows that p is a prime number greater than n.

I think we're ready to write out the proof.

Proof of Theorem 12.3: Let P be a finite set of prime numbers with greatest member q and let $M = q! + 1$. By Corollary 12.2, M has a prime factor p. So, there is an integer k such that $M = pk$.

We show that $p > q$.

Suppose toward contradiction that $p \leq q$. Then $p|q!$. So, there is an integer r such that $q! = pr$. It follows that $1 = M - q! = pk - pr = p(k - r)$. So, $p = 1$, which contradicts that p is prime.

It follows that $p > q$ and so, p is greater than every prime number in P. Since P was an arbitrary finite set of prime numbers, we have shown that there are infinitely many prime numbers. □

The Division Algorithm

In Lesson 4 (Example 4.7 and the notes following), we showed that every integer is even or odd, and never both. In other words, if $n \in \mathbb{Z}$, there are unique integers k and r such that $n = 2k + r$, where $r = 0$ or $r = 1$. We sometimes say, "When n is divided by 2, k is the **quotient** and r is the **remainder**." Observe that when an integer n is divided by 2, the quotient can be any integer, but the remainder can be only 0 or 1.

Example 12.3:

1. When 11 is divided by 2, the quotient is 5 and the remainder is 1. That is, $11 = 2 \cdot 5 + 1$.

2. When 20 is divided by 2, the quotient is 10 and the remainder is 0. That is, $20 = 2 \cdot 10 + 0$, or equivalently, $20 = 2 \cdot 10$. Notice that in this case, 20 is divisible by 2.

3. When -11 is divided by 2, the quotient is -6 and the remainder is 1. That is $-11 = 2(-6) + 1$. Compare this to the first example. Based on that example, most students would probably guess that the quotient here would turn out to be -5. But as you can see, that is not the case.

The **Division Algorithm** generalizes the notion of an integer n being "even or odd" ($2k$ or $2k + 1$) to n being equal to $mk + r$, where $0 \leq r < m$.

For example, for $m = 3$, the Division Algorithm will tell us that every integer can be written uniquely in one of the three forms $3k$, $3k + 1$, or $3k + 2$. Observe that when an integer n is divided by 3, the quotient can be any integer, but the remainder can be only 0, 1, or 2.

As one more example, for $m = 4$, the Division Algorithm will tell us that every integer can be written uniquely in one of the four forms $4k$, $4k + 1$, $4k + 2$, or $4k + 3$. Observe that when an integer n is divided by 4, the quotient can be any integer, but the remainder can be only 0, 1, 2, or 3.

Example 12.4:

1. When 14 is divided by 3, the quotient is 4 and the remainder is 2. That is, $14 = 3 \cdot 4 + 2$.

2. When 36 is divided by 4, the quotient is 9 and the remainder is 0. That is, $36 = 4 \cdot 9 + 0$, or equivalently, $36 = 4 \cdot 9$. Notice that in this case, 36 is divisible by 4.

3. When 17 is divided by 5, the quotient is 3 and the remainder is 2. That is, $17 = 5 \cdot 3 + 2$.

4. When -17 is divided by 5, the quotient is -4 and the remainder is 3. That is $-17 = 5(-4) + 3$.

Theorem 12.4 (The Division Algorithm): Let n and m be integers with $m > 0$. Then there are unique integers k and r such that $n = mk + r$ with $0 \leq r < m$.

Many students find the standard proof of the Division Algorithm to be quite hard to follow. I know that when I read the proof for the first time, I found it quite confusing. To better understand the argument, let's first run a couple of simulations using specific examples that mimic the proof.

Simulation 1: Let's let $n = 7$ and $m = 2$. With these choices for n and m, the Division Algorithm says that there are unique integers k and r such that $7 = 2k + r$ and $0 \leq r < 2$ (in other words, $r = 0$ or $r = 1$).

Let's look at the equation $7 = 2k + r$ in the form $7 - 2k = r$. In particular, let's look at the possible values of $7 - 2k$ as k ranges over all possible integers. Let's do this by matching up each integer k with the corresponding value of $7 - 2k$:

	k	$\cdots$	-4	-3	-2	-1	0	1	2	3	4	$\cdots$
r?	$7 - 2k$	$\cdots$	15	13	11	9	7	5	3	1	-1	$\cdots$

Observe that the top row is simply "listing" all the integers. The "$\cdots$" to the left of -4 and to the right of 4 are there to indicate that this list keeps going infinitely in each direction. However, I did make sure to include the most important values in the visible part of our list.

We get each value in the bottom row by substituting the value above it for k in the expression $7 - 2k$. For example, for $k = -4$, we have $7 - 2k = 7 - 2(-4) = 7 + 8 = 15$.

Notice that the values in the bottom row decrease by 2 units for each 1 unit increase in k. This is because $m = 2$.

We highlighted the column where $k = 3$ and $r = 7 - 2k = 1$. This is the column where the smallest nonnegative number appears in the bottom row. In other words, we let r be the least positive value of $7 - 2t$, as t ranges over all the integers, and we let k be the corresponding t-value.

In general, how do we know that these values exist?

Well, since $n \geq 0$ ($n = 7$ in this example), the expression $n - mt \geq 0$ when $t = 0$. It follows that the set $\{n - mt \mid t \in \mathbb{Z} \land n - mt \geq 0\} = \{7 - 2t \mid t \in \mathbb{Z} \land 7 - 2t \geq 0\}$ is not empty ($7 - 2 \cdot 0 = 7$ is in this set). So, we can invoke the Well Ordering Principle to get a least element r. In this simulation, r will turn out to be 1 with a corresponding k-value of 3. (We will see what happens if $n < 0$ in the next simulation).

By taking r to be the least element from a set of natural numbers, we know that r will be nonnegative. But how do we know that r will be less than 2? We use the fact that the bottom row decreases by 2 units for each 1 unit increase in the top row.

Suppose we accidentally chose $r = 3$. Then we have $7 - 2k = 3$. If we subtract 2 from each side of this equation, we get $7 - 2k - 2 = 1$. Using distributivity, we have that $7 - 2k - 2$ is equal to $7 - 2(k + 1)$. So, $7 - 2(k + 1) = 1$. Looks like we chose the wrong value for r. What we just showed is that if we increase k by 1 (from 2 to 3), we decrease r by 2 (from 3 to 1).

In general, if $r \geq 2$, then we have $n - 2k \geq 2$, so that $n - 2k - 2 \geq 0$. Thus, $n - 2(k + 1) \geq 0$. But $n - 2(k + 1) = n - 2k - 2 < n - 2k$. This contradicts that r was the least possible value of $n - 2t$ with $n - 2t \geq 0$. It follows that $r < 2$.

Now let's check uniqueness. So, we have $7 = 2 \cdot 3 + 1$. How do we know that there aren't two other numbers k' and r' with $0 \leq r' < 1$ such that $7 = 2k' + r'$?

Well, if there were, then we would have $2 \cdot 3 + 1 = 2k' + r'$. Subtracting $2k'$ from each side of the equation and subtracting 1 from each side of the equation gives us $2 \cdot 3 - 2k' = r' - 1$. We now use the distributive property on the left to get $2(3 - k') = r' - 1$. This equation shows that 2 is a factor of $r' - 1$. r' can't be 0 because 2 is not a factor of -1. Therefore, $r' = 1$ (remember that 0 and 1 are the only two choices for r'). So, $2(3 - k') = 0$, and therefore, $3 - k' = 0$. So, $k' = 3$. Oh, look at that! r' and k' are the same as r and k.

So, we just proved that there is exactly one way to write 7 in the form $2k + r$ with k and r integers and $0 \leq r < 2$. We showed that $7 = 2 \cdot 3 + 1$ is the only way to do it.

Simulation 2: This time, let's let $n = -4$ and $m = 3$. With these choices for n and m, the Division Algorithm says that there are unique integers k and r such that $-4 = 3k + r$ and $0 \leq r < 3$ (in other words, $r = 0$, $r = 1$, or $r = 2$).

Let's look at the equation $-4 = 3k + r$ in the form $-4 - 3k = r$, and as we did in Simulation 1, let's match up each integer k with the corresponding value of $-4 - 3k$:

157

k	$\cdots$	-4	-3	-2	-1	0	1	2	3	4	$\cdots$
$r?$ $\quad -4-3k$	$\cdots$	8	5	2	-1	-4	-7	-10	-13	-16	$\cdots$

This time, since $m = 3$, the values in the bottom row decrease by 3 units for each 1 unit increase in k.

We highlighted the column where $k = -2$ and $r = -4 - 3(-2) = -4 + 6 = 2$ because it is the column where the smallest nonnegative number appears in the bottom row. This time 2 is the smallest possible value of r, and this r-value corresponds to a k-value of -2.

Since $n < 0$ this time ($n = -4$ in this example), setting $t = 0$ in the expression $n - mt$ does **not** produce a nonnegative value. This time, we let $t = n$ to get $n - m \cdot n$ (specifically, for this simulation we set $t = -4$ to get $-4 - 3(-4) = -4 + 12 = 8$, which is greater than 0). It follows that the set $\{n - mt \mid t \in \mathbb{Z} \land n - mt \geq 0\} = \{-4 - 3t \mid t \in \mathbb{Z} \land -4 - 3t \geq 0\}$ is not empty. So, once again, we can invoke the Well Ordering Principle to get a least element r. In this simulation, r will turn out to be 2 with a corresponding k-value of -2.

As in Simulation 1, it is clear that $r \geq 0$, and we use the fact that the bottom row decreases by 3 units for each 1 unit increase in the top row to show that $r < 3$.

Suppose we accidentally chose $r = 5$. Then we have $-4 - 3k = 5$. If we subtract 3 from each side of this equation, we get $-4 - 3k - 3 = 2$. But using distributivity, we have that $-4 - 3k - 3$ is equal to $-4 - 3(k + 1)$. So, $-4 - 3(k + 1) = 2$. We just showed is that if we increase k by 1 (from -3 to -2), we decrease r by 3 (from 5 to 2).

In general, if $r \geq 3$, then we have $n - 3k \geq 3$, so that $n - 3k - 3 \geq 0$. Thus, $n - 3(k + 1) \geq 0$. But $n - 3(k + 1) = n - 3k - 3 < n - 3k$. This contradicts that r was the least possible value of $n - 3t$ with $n - 3t \geq 0$. It follows that $r < 3$.

I leave it as an exercise for the reader to check uniqueness for this special case.

Let's move on to the proof of the Theorem.

Proof of Theorem 12.4: Let $n, m \in \mathbb{Z}$ with $m > 0$, and let $S = \{n - mt \mid t \in \mathbb{Z} \land n - mt \geq 0\}$. To see that $S \neq \emptyset$, we consider two cases. If $n \geq 0$, then let $t = 0$, and we have $n - mt = n \in S$. If $n < 0$, then let $t = n$, so that we have $n - mt = n - mn = n(1 - m)$. Since $m \geq 1$, we have $1 - m \leq 0$. It follows that $n(1 - m) \geq 0$, and so, $n - mt \in S$. In both cases, we have shown that $S \neq \emptyset$.

Since S is a nonempty subset of natural numbers, by the Well Ordering Principle, S has a least element $r = n - mk$, where $k \in \mathbb{Z}$. Since $S \subseteq \mathbb{N}$, $r \geq 0$. By adding mk to each side of the equation, we have $n = mk + r$.

We need to show that $r < m$. Suppose toward contradiction that $r \geq m$. Substituting $n - mk$ for r gives us $n - mk \geq m$. Subtracting m from each side of this last equation gives $(n - mk) - m \geq 0$. Now, since $m > 0$, $r > r - m = (n - mk) - m$. But $(n - mk) - m = n - mk - m = n - m(k + 1)$, and so, $(n - mk) - m$ is an element of S smaller than r, contradicting r being the least element of S. This contradiction tells us that we must have $r < m$.

We still need to prove that k and r are unique. Suppose that $n = mk_1 + r_1$ and $n = mk_2 + r_2$ with both $0 \leq r_1 < m$ and $0 \leq r_2 < m$. Without loss of generality, we may assume that $r_2 \geq r_1$.

By a simple substitution, $mk_1 + r_1 = mk_2 + r_2$. Subtracting mk_2 from each side of the equation and simultaneously subtracting r_1 from each side of the equation, we get $mk_1 - mk_2 = r_2 - r_1$. Factoring m on the left gives $m(k_1 - k_2) = r_2 - r_1$, and we see that $m | r_2 - r_1$.

Since $r_2 \geq r_1$, we have $r_2 - r_1 \geq 0$. Since we have $r_1 \geq 0$ and $r_2 < m$, we have $r_2 - r_1 < m - 0 = m$. So, $m | r_2 - r_1$ and $0 \leq r_2 - r_1 < m$. It follows that $r_2 - r_1 = 0$. So, $r_2 = r_1$. Finally, $r_2 = r_1$ and $mk_1 + r_1 = mk_2 + r_2$ together imply that $mk_1 = mk_2$, and so, $k_1 = k_2$. □

GCD and LCM

Let a and b be two integers. An integer j is a **common divisor** (or **common factor**) of a and b if j is a factor of both a and b. An integer k is a **common multiple** of a and b if k is a multiple of both a and b.

Example 12.5: Let $a = 6$ and $b = 15$. The positive divisors of a are $1, 2, 3$, and 6. The positive divisors of b are $1, 3, 5$, and 15. Therefore, the positive common divisors of a and b are **1 and 3**.

For each positive divisor there is a corresponding negative divisor. So, a complete list of the divisors of a are $1, 2, 3, 6, -1, -2, -3$, and -6 and a complete list of the divisors of b are $1, 3, 5, 15, -1, -3, -5$, and -15. Therefore, a complete list of the common divisors of a and b are **1, 3, -1, and -3**.

If both a and $-a$ are in a list, we will sometimes use the notation $\pm a$ instead of listing a and $-a$ separately. In this example, we can say that the complete list of common divisors of a and b is $\pm 1, \pm 3$.

The multiples of a are $\pm 6, \pm 12, \pm 18, \pm 24, \pm 30, \pm 36, \ldots$ and so on. The multiples of 15 are $\pm 15, \pm 30, \pm 45, \pm 60, \ldots$ and so on. Therefore, the common multiples of a and b are $\pm 30, \pm 60, \pm 90, \pm 120, \ldots$ **and so on**.

Again, let a and b be distinct integers. The **greatest common divisor** (or **greatest common factor**) of a and b, written $\gcd(a, b)$, is the largest common divisor of a and b. The **least common multiple** of a and b, written $\mathrm{lcm}(a, b)$, is the smallest positive common multiple of a and b.

Example 12.6:

1. From Example 12.5, it's easy to see that $\gcd(6, 15) = 3$ and $\mathrm{lcm}(6, 15) = 30$.

2. $\gcd(2, 3) = 1$ and $\mathrm{lcm}(2, 3) = 6$. More generally, if p and q are prime numbers with $p \neq q$, then $\gcd(p, q) = 1$ and $\mathrm{lcm}(p, q) = pq$.

3. $\gcd(4, 15) = 1$ and $\mathrm{lcm}(4, 15) = 60$. Observe that neither 4 nor 15 is prime, and yet their gcd is 1 and their lcm is the product of 4 and 15. This is because 4 and 15 have no common factors except for 1 and -1. We say that 4 and 15 are **relatively prime**.

   Note that if p and q are prime numbers with $p \neq q$, then p and q are relatively prime.

   We have the following more general result: if a and b are relatively prime integers, then $\gcd(a, b) = 1$ and $\mathrm{lcm}(a, b) = ab$ (see Theorem 12.10 below).

We can extend all these ideas to larger sets of numbers. Specifically, let X be a finite set of integers containing at least one nonzero integer. Then the **greatest common divisor** of the integers in X, written $\gcd(X)$ (or $\gcd(a_1, a_2, \ldots, a_n)$, where $X = \{a_1, a_2, \ldots, a_n\}$) is the largest integer that divides every integer in the set X, and the **least common multiple** of the integers in X, written $\text{lcm}(X)$ (or $\text{lcm}(a_1, a_2, \ldots, a_n)$) is the smallest positive integer that each integer in the set X divides.

For convenience, if X contains only 0, we define $\gcd(X) = 0$.

Also, the integers in the set X are said to be **mutually relatively prime** if $\gcd(X) = 1$. The integers in the set X are said to be **pairwise relatively prime** if for each pair $a, b \in X$ with $a \neq b$, $\gcd(a, b) = 1$.

Example 12.7:

1. $\gcd(10, 15, 35) = 5$ and $\text{lcm}(10, 15, 35) = 210$.

2. $\gcd(2, 3, 12) = 1$ and $\text{lcm}(2, 3, 12) = 12$. Notice that here 2, 3, and 12 are mutually relatively prime, but **not** pairwise relatively prime because for example, $\gcd(2, 12) = 2 \neq 1$.

3. $\gcd(10, 21, 143) = 1$ and $\text{lcm}(10, 21, 143) = 30{,}030$. In this case, we have 10, 21, and 143 are pairwise relatively prime.

   We have the following result: if $X = \{a_1, a_2, \ldots, a_n\}$ is a set of pairwise relatively prime integers, then $\gcd(X) = 1$ and $\text{lcm}(X) = a_1 a_2 \cdots a_n$. The proof of this is left as an optional exercise for the reader. Also note that pairwise relatively prime implies mutually relatively prime.

4. For a set X with just one element a, $\gcd(a) = a$ and $\text{lcm}(a) = a$. In particular, $\gcd(0) = 0$ and $\text{lcm}(0) = 0$.

Let $a, b \in \mathbb{Z}$. A **linear combination** of a and b is an expression of the form $ma + nb$ with $m, n \in \mathbb{Z}$. We call the integers m and n **weights**.

Example 12.8:

1. Since $5 \cdot 10 - 2 \cdot 15 = 50 - 30 = 20$, we see that 20 is a linear combination of 10 and 15. When we write 20 as $5 \cdot 10 - 2 \cdot 15$, the weights are 5 and -2.

   This is not the only way to write 20 as a linear combination of 10 and 15. For example, we also have $-1 \cdot 10 + 2 \cdot 15 = -10 + 30 = 20$. When we write 20 as $-1 \cdot 10 + 2 \cdot 15$, the weights are -1 and 2.

2. Any number that is a multiple of either 10 or 15 is a linear combination of 10 and 15 because we can allow weights to be 0. For example, 80 is a linear combination of 10 and 15 because $80 = 8 \cdot 10 + 0 \cdot 15$.

   Also, 45 is a linear combination of 10 and 15 because $45 = 0 \cdot 10 + 3 \cdot 15$.

3. We will see in Theorem 12.5 below that $\gcd(a, b)$ can always be written as a linear combination of a and b. For example, $\gcd(10, 15) = 5$, and we have $5 = -1 \cdot 10 + 1 \cdot 15$.

4. Using the same theorem mentioned in 3, if a and b are relatively prime, then 1 can be written as a linear combination of a and b. For example, 4 and 15 are relatively prime and we have $1 = 4 \cdot 4 - 1 \cdot 15$.

Theorem 12.5: Let a and b be integers, at least one of which is not 0. Then $\gcd(a, b)$ is the least positive integer k such that there exist $m, n \in \mathbb{Z}$ with $k = ma + nb$.

This theorem says two things. First, it says that $\gcd(a, b)$ can be written as a linear combination of a and b. Second, it says that any positive integer smaller than $\gcd(a, b)$ **cannot** be written as a linear combination of a and b.

Proof: We first prove the theorem for $a, b \in \mathbb{Z}^+$. So, let a, b be positive integers and let S be the set of all positive linear combinations of a and b with weights in $\mathbb{Z}$.

$$S = \{ma + nb \mid m, n \in \mathbb{Z} \wedge ma + nb > 0\}$$

Notice that $a, b \in S$ because $a = 1a + 0b$ and $b = 0a + 1b$. In particular, $S \neq \emptyset$. By the Well Ordering Principle, S has a least element k. By the definition of S, there exist $m, n \in \mathbb{Z}$ with $k = ma + nb$.

By the Division Algorithm, there are $s, r \in \mathbb{Z}$ with $a = ks + r$ and $0 \leq r < k$.

So, $r = a - ks = a - (ma + nb)s = a - mas - nbs = (1 - ms)a - (ns)b$. We see that r is a linear combination of a and b. Since $r < k$ and r is a linear combination of a and b, r cannot be in S (because k is the least element of S). So, r must be 0. It follows that $a = ks$. Therefore, $k|a$.

Replacing a by b in the last two paragraphs shows that $k|b$ as well. So, k is a common divisor of a and b. Now, if c is another common divisor of a and b, then by Problem 7 from Problem Set 4 in Lesson 4, c is a divisor of any linear combination of a and b. Since k is a linear combination of a and b, c is a divisor of k. Since every common divisor of a and b is also a divisor of k, it follows that $k = \gcd(a, b)$.

Since $ma = (-m)(-a)$ and $nb = (-n)(-b)$, the result holds whenever a and b are both nonzero.

Finally, suppose $a = 0$ or $b = 0$. Without loss of generality, let $a = 0$. Then $b \neq 0$. So, $\gcd(a, b) = b$ (or $-b$ if $b < 0$). We also have for any $m, n \in \mathbb{Z}$, $ma + nb = m \cdot 0 + nb = nb$. The least positive integer of the form nb is $1 \cdot b = b$ (or $-1 \cdot b$ if $b < 0$). So, the result holds in this case as well. □

We're almost ready to finish proving the Fundamental Theorem of Arithmetic. We will first prove two preliminary results that will make the proof easier.

Theorem 12.6: Let $a, b, c \in \mathbb{Z}^+$ with a and b relatively prime and $a|bc$. Then $a|c$.

Proof: Let $a, b, c \in \mathbb{Z}^+$ with a and b relatively prime and let $a|bc$. Since $\gcd(a, b) = 1$, by Theorem 12.5, there are integers m and n with $1 = ma + nb$. Since $a|bc$, there is an integer k such that $bc = ak$. Multiplying each side of the equation $1 = ma + nb$ by c and using the distributive property, $c = c(ma + nb) = cma + cnb = cma + nbc = cma + nak = a(cm + nk)$. Since $c, m, n, k \in \mathbb{Z}$ and $\mathbb{Z}$ is closed under addition and multiplication, $cm + nk \in \mathbb{Z}$. Therefore, $a|c$. □

Theorem 12.7: Let p be prime and let $a_1, a_2, \ldots, a_n$ be positive integers such that $p|a_1 a_2 \cdots a_n$. Then there is an integer j with $1 \leq j \leq n$ such that $p|a_j$.

Proof: We will prove this theorem by induction on $n \geq 1$.

Base Case $(n = 1)$**:** We are given that p is prime, $a_1 \in \mathbb{Z}^+$, and $p|a_1$. Wait a sec... $p|a_1$ is the conclusion we were looking for. So, the theorem holds for $n = 1$.

Inductive Step: Let $k \in \mathbb{N}$ and assume that the result holds for $n = k$.

Let p be prime and let $a_1, a_2, \ldots a_k, a_{k+1}$ be positive integers such that $p|a_1 a_2 \cdots a_k a_{k+1}$. Since p is prime, its only positive factors are 1 and p. Therefore, $\gcd(p, a_1 a_2 \cdots a_k)$ is either 1 or p.

If $\gcd(p, a_1 a_2 \cdots a_k) = 1$, then by Theorem 12.6, $p|a_{k+1}$. If $\gcd(p, a_1 a_2 \cdots a_k) = p$, then $p|a_1 a_2 \cdots a_k$, and by our inductive assumption, there is an integer j with $1 \leq j \leq k$ such that $p|a_k$.

Therefore, the result holds for $n = k + 1$.

By the Principle of Mathematical Induction, the result holds for all $n \in \mathbb{N}$ with $n \geq 1$. $\square$

We are finally ready to finish the proof of the Fundamental Theorem of Arithmetic.

Theorem 12.8 (The Fundamental Theorem of Arithmetic): Every integer greater than 1 can be written uniquely as a product of prime numbers, up to the order in which the factors are written.

Proof: By Theorem 12.1, every integer greater than 1 can be written as a product of prime numbers. We need to show that any two such prime factorizations are equal. Assume toward contradiction that n can be written in the following two different ways: $n = p_1 p_2 \cdots p_k = q_1 q_2 \cdots q_r$, where $p_1, p_2, \ldots, p_k, q_1, q_2, \ldots, q_r$ are prime numbers. Without loss of generality, assume $p_1 \leq p_2 \leq \cdots \leq p_k$ and $q_1 \leq q_2 \leq \cdots \leq q_r$. Also, by cancelling common primes on the left with common primes on the right, we may assume that for all $i \leq k$ and $j \leq r$, $p_i \neq q_j$. Suppose $1 \leq i \leq k$. Then $p_i|p_1 p_2 \cdots p_k$. Since $p_1 p_2 \cdots p_k = q_1 q_2 \cdots q_r$, we have $p_i|q_1 q_2 \cdots q_r$. By Theorem 12.7, there is j with $1 \leq j \leq r$ such that $p_i|q_j$. This is a contradiction. So, there cannot exist two different prime factorizations of n. $\square$

Since prime factorizations are unique only up to the order in which the factors are written, there can be many ways to write a prime factorization. For example, 10 can be written as $2 \cdot 5$ or $5 \cdot 2$. To make things as simple as possible we always agree to use the **canonical representation** (or **canonical form**). The word "canonical" is just a fancy name for "natural," and the most natural way to write a prime factorization is in increasing order of primes. So, the canonical representation of 10 is $2 \cdot 5$.

As another example, the canonical representation of 18 is $2 \cdot 3 \cdot 3$. We can tidy this up a bit by rewriting $3 \cdot 3$ as 3^2. So, the canonical representation of 18 is $2 \cdot 3^2$.

If you are new to factoring, you may find it helpful to draw a factor tree.

For example, here is a factor tree for 18:

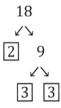

To draw this tree, we started by writing 18 as the product $2 \cdot 9$. We put a box around 2 because 2 is prime and does not need to be factored any more. We then proceeded to factor 9 as $3 \cdot 3$. We put a box around each 3 because 3 is prime. We now see that we are done, and the prime factorization can be found by multiplying all the boxed numbers together. Remember that we will usually want the canonical representation, and so, we write the final product in increasing order of primes.

By the Fundamental Theorem of Arithmetic above it does not matter how we factor the number—we will always get the same canonical form. For example, here is a different factor tree for 18:

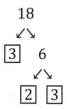

Now, to prove that a positive integer n is composite, we simply need to produce a factor of n that is different from 1 and n itself. This may sound easy, but in practice, as we look at larger and larger values of n it can become very difficult to find factors of n. For example, the largest prime number that we are currently aware of (at the time I am writing this book) is $2^{77,232,917} - 1$. This is an enormous number with 23,249,425 digits. By Theorem 12.3, we know that there are prime numbers larger than this, but we have not yet found one.

The following theorem provides a couple of tricks to help us (or a computer) determine if a positive integer is prime more quickly.

Theorem 12.9: If n is composite, then n has a prime factor $p \leq \sqrt{n}$.

Proof: Let n be composite, so that there are integers a, b with $1 < a, b < n$ and $n = ab$. If both a and b are greater than $\sqrt{n}$, then we would have $n = ab > \sqrt{n} \cdot \sqrt{n} = n$, a contradiction. So, either $a \leq \sqrt{n}$ or $b \leq \sqrt{n}$. Without loss of generality, suppose that $a \leq \sqrt{n}$. By Corollary 12.2, a has a prime factor p. Since p is a factor of a and a is a factor n, it follows that p is a factor of n. Also, since p is a factor of a and $a \leq \sqrt{n}$, we have $p \leq \sqrt{n}$. $\qquad\square$

Example 12.9:

1. Let's determine if 187 is prime or composite. Since $\sqrt{187} < \sqrt{196} = 14$, by Theorem 12.9, we need only check to see if 187 is divisible by $2, 3, 5, 7, 11$, and 13. Checking each of these, we see that $187 = 11 \cdot 17$. So, 187 is composite.

2. Let's determine if 359 is prime or composite. Since $\sqrt{359} < \sqrt{361} = 19$, by Theorem 12.9, we need only check to see if 359 is divisible by $2, 3, 5, 7, 11\ 13$, and 17. A quick check shows that 359 is **not** divisible by any of these numbers, and so, 359 is prime.

Sometimes in a prime factorization we will want to make sure that we do not "skip" any primes, and that each prime has a power.

For example, the canonical representation of 50 is $2 \cdot 5^2$. Note that we "skipped over" the prime 3 and there is no exponent written for 2. We can easily give 2 an exponent by rewriting it as 2^1, and since $x^0 = 1$ for any nonzero x (by definition), we can write $1 = 3^0$. Therefore, the prime factorization of 50 can be written as $2^1 \cdot 3^0 \cdot 5^2$.

This convention can be especially useful when comparing two or more positive integers or performing an operation on two or more integers. We will say that $p_0^{a_0} p_1^{a_1} \cdots p_n^{a_n}$ is a **complete prime factorization** if $p_0, p_1, \ldots, p_n$ are the first n primes ($p_0 = 2, p_1 = 3$, and so on) and $a_0, a_1, \ldots, a_n \in \mathbb{N}$.

Example 12.10:

1. The prime factorization of 364 in canonical form is $2^2 \cdot 7 \cdot 13$. However, this is **not** a complete factorization.

   A complete factorization of 364 is $2^2 \cdot 3^0 \cdot 5^0 \cdot 7^1 \cdot 11^0 \cdot 13^1$. This is not the only complete factorization of 364. Another one is $2^2 \cdot 3^0 \cdot 5^0 \cdot 7^1 \cdot 11^0 \cdot 13^1 \cdot 17^0$.

   Given a complete factorization $p_0^{a_0} p_1^{a_1} \cdots p_n^{a_n}$ of a positive integer, $p_0^{a_0} p_1^{a_1} \cdots p_n^{a_n} p_{n+1}^0$ is another complete factorization, and in fact, for any $k \in \mathbb{N}$, $p_0^{a_0} p_1^{a_1} \cdots p_n^{a_n} p_{n+1}^0 p_{n+2}^0 \cdots p_{n+k}^0$ is also a complete factorization of that same positive integer. In words, we can include finitely many additional prime factors at the tail end of the original factorization all with exponent 0. Just be careful not to skip any primes!

2. $2^0 \cdot 3^5 \cdot 5^0 \cdot 7^2 \cdot 11^0 \cdot 13^0 \cdot 17^2$ and $2^3 \cdot 3^1 \cdot 5^0 \cdot 7^0 \cdot 11^6$ are complete prime factorizations. In many cases, it is useful to rewrite the second factorization as $2^3 \cdot 3^1 \cdot 5^0 \cdot 7^0 \cdot 11^6 \cdot 13^0 \cdot 17^0$. This is also a complete prime factorization. However, this one has all the same prime factors as the first number given.

Complete prime factorizations give us an easy way to compute greatest common divisors and least common multiples of positive integers.

Suppose that $a = p_0^{a_0} p_1^{a_1} \cdots p_n^{a_n}$ and $b = p_0^{b_0} p_1^{b_1} \cdots p_n^{b_n}$ are complete prime factorizations of a and b. Then we have

$$\gcd(a, b) = p_0^{\min\{a_0, b_0\}} p_1^{\min\{a_1, b_1\}} \cdots p_n^{\min\{a_n, b_n\}} \qquad \text{lcm}(a, b) = p_0^{\max\{a_0, b_0\}} p_1^{\max\{a_1, b_1\}} \cdots p_n^{\max\{a_n, b_n\}}.$$

Example 12.11: Let $a = 2 \cdot 5^2 \cdot 7$ and $b = 3 \cdot 5 \cdot 11^2$. We can rewrite a and b with the following complete prime factorizations: $a = 2^1 \cdot 3^0 \cdot 5^2 \cdot 7^1 \cdot 11^0$ and $b = 2^0 \cdot 3^1 \cdot 5^1 \cdot 7^0 \cdot 11^2$. From these factorizations, it is easy to compute $\gcd(a, b)$ and $\text{lcm}(a, b)$.

$\gcd(a, b) = 2^0 \cdot 3^0 \cdot 5^1 \cdot 7^0 \cdot 11^0 = 5$ and $\text{lcm}(a, b) = 2^1 \cdot 3^1 \cdot 5^2 \cdot 7^1 \cdot 11^2 = 127{,}050$.

Observe that in this example, $ab = 350 \cdot 1815 = 635{,}250 = 5 \cdot 127{,}050 = \gcd(a, b) \cdot \text{lcm}(a, b)$.

We will now show that the equation $ab = \gcd(a, b) \cdot \text{lcm}(a, b)$ is true for all positive integers a and b.

Before we state and prove the theorem, note that $\min\{x, y\} + \max\{x, y\} = x + y$ (check this!).

Theorem 12.10: Let $a, b \in \mathbb{Z}^+$. Then $\gcd(a, b) \cdot \text{lcm}(a, b) = ab$.

Proof: Let $a = p_0^{a_0} p_1^{a_1} \cdots p_n^{a_n}$ and $b = p_0^{b_0} p_1^{b_1} \cdots p_n^{b_n}$ be complete prime factorizations of a and b. Then

$$\gcd(a,b) \cdot \text{lcm}(a,b)$$

$$= p_0^{\min\{a_0,b_0\}} p_1^{\min\{a_1,b_1\}} \cdots p_n^{\min\{a_n,b_n\}} \cdot p_0^{\max\{a_0,b_0\}} p_1^{\max\{a_1,b_1\}} \cdots p_n^{\max\{a_n,b_n\}}$$

$$= p_0^{\min\{a_0,b_0\}} p_0^{\max\{a_0,b_0\}} p_1^{\min\{a_1,b_1\}} p_1^{\max\{a_1,b_1\}} \cdots p_n^{\min\{a_n,b_n\}} p_n^{\max\{a_n,b_n\}}$$

$$= p_0^{\min\{a_0,b_0\}+\max\{a_0,b_0\}} p_1^{\min\{a_1,b_1\}+\max\{a_1,b_1\}} \cdots p_n^{\min\{a_n,b_n\}+\max\{a_n,b_n\}}$$

$$= p_0^{a_0+b_0} p_1^{a_1+b_1} \cdots p_n^{a_n+b_n}$$

$$= p_0^{a_0} p_0^{b_0} p_1^{a_1} p_1^{b_1} \cdots p_n^{a_n} p_n^{b_n}$$

$$= p_0^{a_0} p_1^{a_1} \cdots p_n^{a_n} \cdot p_0^{b_0} p_1^{b_1} \cdots p_n^{b_n}$$

$$= ab \qquad \square$$

We will finish this lesson with the Euclidean Algorithm. This is an algorithm for computing the gcd of two positive integers. It also provides a method for expressing the gcd as a linear combination of the two integers.

Theorem 12.11 (The Euclidean Algorithm): Let $a, b \in \mathbb{Z}^+$ with $a \geq b$. Let $r_0 = a$, $r_1 = b$. Apply the division algorithm to r_0 and r_1 to find $k_1, r_2 \in \mathbb{Z}^+$ such that $r_0 = r_1 k_1 + r_2$, where $0 \leq r_2 < r_1$. If we iterate this process to get $r_j = r_{j+1} k_{j+1} + r_{j+2}$, where $0 \leq r_{j+2} < r_{j+1}$ for $j = 0, 1, \dots, n-1$ so that $r_{n+1} = 0$. Then $\gcd(a,b) = r_n$.

You will be asked to prove the Euclidean Algorithm in Problem 12 below.

Example 12.12: Let's use the Euclidean Algorithm to find $\gcd(305, 1040)$.

$$1040 = 305 \cdot 3 + 125$$
$$305 = 125 \cdot 2 + 55$$
$$125 = 55 \cdot 2 + 15$$
$$55 = 15 \cdot 3 + 10$$
$$15 = 10 \cdot 1 + \mathbf{5}$$
$$10 = 5 \cdot 2 + \mathbf{0}$$

So, $\gcd(305, 1040) = \mathbf{5}$.

Notes: (1) In this example, we have $a = r_0 = 1040$ and $b = r_1 = 305$. By the Division Algorithm we can write $1040 = 305 k_1 + r_2$, where $0 < r_2 < 305$. To find k_1, we are simply looking for the largest integer k such that $305k \leq 1040$. Well, $305 \cdot 3 = 915$ and $305 \cdot 4 = 1220$. So, 4 is too big and therefore, we let $k_1 = 3$. It follows that $r_2 = 1040 - 305 \cdot 3 = 1040 - 915 = 125$.

We now repeat the procedure using $r_1 = 305$ and $r_2 = 125$ to get $305 = 125 \cdot 2 + 55$. Notice that $125 \cdot 3 = 375$, which is too big because $375 > 305$. This is why we let $k_2 = 2$. It follows that $r_3 = 305 - 125 \cdot 2 = 305 - 250 = 55$.

Continuing this process, we eventually wind up with $10 = 5 \cdot 2 + 0$, so that $r_7 = 0$. By Theorem 12.11, $\gcd(305, 1040) = r_6 = 5$.

(2) As we go through the algorithm, we get $r_0 = 1040, r_1 = 305, r_2 = 125, r_3 = 55, r_4 = 15$, $r_5 = 10, r_6 = 5$, and $r_7 = 0$.

We also get $k_1 = 3, k_2 = 2, k_3 = 2, k_4 = 3, k_5 = 1$, and $k_6 = 2$.

(3) We can now go backwards through the algorithm to express $\gcd(305, 1040)$ as a linear combination of 305 and 1040.

We start with the second to last line (line 5): $15 = 10 \cdot 1 + 5$. We solve this equation for 5 to get $5 = 15 - 1 \cdot 10$.

Working backwards, we next look at line 4: $55 = 15 \cdot 3 + 10$. We solve this equation for 10 and then substitute into the previous equation: $10 = 55 - 15 \cdot 3$. After substituting, we get

$$5 = 15 - 1 \cdot 10 = 15 - 1(55 - 15 \cdot 3)$$

We then distribute and group all the 15's together and all the 55's together. So, we have

$$5 = 15 - 1 \cdot 10 = 15 - 1(55 - 15 \cdot 3) = 15 - 1 \cdot 55 + 3 \cdot 15 = 4 \cdot 15 - 1 \cdot 55.$$

Line 3 is next: $125 = 55 \cdot 2 + 15$. We solve this equation for 15 to get $15 = 125 - 2 \cdot 55$. And once again we now substitute into the previous equation to get

$$5 = 4 \cdot 15 - 1 \cdot 55 = 4(125 - 2 \cdot 55) - 1 \cdot 55 = 4 \cdot 125 - 8 \cdot 55 - 1 \cdot 55 = 4 \cdot 125 - 9 \cdot 55.$$

Let's go to line 2: $305 = 125 \cdot 2 + 55$. We solve this equation for 55 to get $55 = 305 - 2 \cdot 125$. Substituting into the previous equation gives us

$$5 = 4 \cdot 125 - 9 \cdot 55 = 4 \cdot 125 - 9(305 - 2 \cdot 125)$$
$$= 4 \cdot 125 - 9 \cdot 305 + 18 \cdot 125 = 22 \cdot 125 - 9 \cdot 305.$$

And finally line 1: $1040 = 305 \cdot 3 + 125$. Solving this equation for 125 gives us $125 = 1040 - 3 \cdot 305$. Substituting into the previous equation gives

$$5 = 22 \cdot 125 - 9 \cdot 305 = 22(1040 - 3 \cdot 305) - 9 \cdot 305$$
$$= 22 \cdot 1040 - 66 \cdot 305 - 9 \cdot 305 = 22 \cdot 1040 - 75 \cdot 305.$$

So, we see that $\gcd(305, 1040) = 5 = 22 \cdot 1040 - 75 \cdot 305 = -75 \cdot 305 + 22 \cdot 1040$.

(4) With a little practice, the computations done in Note 3 can be done fairly quickly. Here is what the quicker computation might look like:

$$5 = 15 - 1 \cdot 10 = 15 - 1 \cdot (55 - 15 \cdot 3) = 4 \cdot 15 - 1 \cdot 55 = 4(125 - 55 \cdot 2) - 1 \cdot 55 = 4 \cdot 125 - 9 \cdot 55$$
$$= 4 \cdot 125 - 9(305 - 125 \cdot 2) = 22 \cdot 125 - 9 \cdot 305 = 22(1040 - 305 \cdot 3) - 9 \cdot 305 = 22 \cdot 1040 - 75 \cdot 305$$

So, $5 = \gcd(305, 1040) = -75 \cdot 305 + 22 \cdot 1040$.

Problem Set 12

LEVEL 1

1. Write each of the following positive integers as a product of prime factors in canonical form:

    (i)   9

    (ii) 13

    (iii) 21

    (iv) 30

    (v)   44

    (vi) 693

    (vii) 67,500

    (viii) 384,659

    (ix) 9,699,690

2. List all prime numbers less than 100.

3. Find the gcd and lcm of each of the following sets of numbers:

    (i) $\{4, 6\}$

    (ii) $\{12, 180\}$

    (iii) $\{2, 3, 5\}$

    (iv) $\{14, 21, 77\}$

    (v) $\{720, 2448, 5400\}$

    (vi) $\{2^{17}5^4 11^9 23, 2^5 3^2 7^4 11^3 13\}$

LEVEL 2

4. Determine if each of the following numbers is prime:

    (i)   101

    (ii) 399

    (iii) 1829

    (iv) 1933

    (v)   8051

    (vi) 13,873

    (vii) 65,623

5. Use the division algorithm to find the quotient and remainder when 723 is divided by 17.

6. For $n \in \mathbb{Z}^+$, let $M_n = n! + 1$. Determine if M_n is prime for $n = 1, 2, 3, 4, 5, 6$, and 7.

LEVEL 3

7. Use the Euclidean Algorithm to find $\gcd(825, 2205)$. Then express $\gcd(825, 2205)$ as a linear combination of 825 and 2205.

8. Prove that if $k \in \mathbb{Z}$ with $k > 1$, then $k^3 + 1$ is not prime.

9. Prove that $\gcd(a, b) \mid \text{lcm}(a, b)$.

10. Let $a, b, c \in \mathbb{Z}$. Prove that $\gcd(a, b) = \gcd(a + bc, b)$.

11. Let $a, b, k, r \in \mathbb{Z}$ with $a = bk + r$. Prove that $\gcd(a, b) = \gcd(r, b)$.

LEVEL 4

12. Prove the Euclidean Algorithm: Let $a, b \in \mathbb{Z}^+$ with $a \geq b$. Let $r_0 = a, r_1 = b$. Apply the division algorithm to r_0 and r_1 to find $k_1, r_2 \in \mathbb{Z}^+$ such that $r_0 = r_1 k_1 + r_2$, where $0 \leq r_2 < r_1$. If we iterate this process to get $r_j = r_{j+1} k_{j+1} + r_{j+2}$, where $0 \leq r_{j+2} < r_{j+1}$ for $j = 0, 1, \ldots, n - 1$ so that $r_{n+1} = 0$. Then $\gcd(a, b) = r_n$.

13. Prove that if $a \mid c$ and $b \mid c$, then $\text{lcm}(a, b) \mid c$.

14. Suppose that $a, b \in \mathbb{Z}^+$, $\gcd(a, b) = 1$, and $c \mid ab$. Prove that there are integers d and e such that $c = de$, $d \mid a$, and $e \mid b$.

15. A **prime triple** is a sequence of three prime numbers of the form p, $p + 2$, and $p + 4$. For example, $3, 5, 7$ is a prime triple. Prove that there are no other prime triples.

LEVEL 5

16. If $a, b \in \mathbb{Z}^+$ and $\gcd(a, b) = 1$, find the following:

   (i) $\gcd(a, a + 1)$

   (ii) $\gcd(a, a + 2)$

   (iii) $\gcd(3a + 2, 5a + 3)$

   (iv) $\gcd(a + b, a - b)$

   (v) $\gcd(a + 2b, 2a + b)$

17. Find the smallest ideal of $\mathbb{Z}$ containing 6 and 15. Find the smallest ideal of $\mathbb{Z}$ containing 2 and 3. In general, find the smallest ideal of $\mathbb{Z}$ containing j and k, where $j, k \in \mathbb{Z}$.

18. Find all subgroups of $(\mathbb{Z}, +)$ and all submonoids of $(\mathbb{Z}, +)$.

Strips and Rectangles

A **horizontal strip** in $\mathbb{R} \times \mathbb{R}$ is a set of the form $\mathbb{R} \times (c, d) = \{(x, y) \mid c < y < d\}$.

Example 13.1: The horizontal strips $\mathbb{R} \times (-2, 1)$ and $\mathbb{R} \times (2.25, 2.75)$ can be visualized in the xy-**plane** as follows:

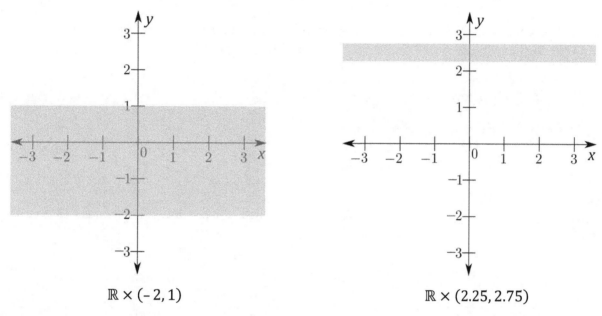

$$\mathbb{R} \times (-2, 1) \qquad\qquad \mathbb{R} \times (2.25, 2.75)$$

Similarly, a **vertical strip** in $\mathbb{R} \times \mathbb{R}$ is a set of the form $(a, b) \times \mathbb{R} = \{(x, y) \mid a < x < b\}$.

Example 13.2: The vertical strips $(-3, 0) \times \mathbb{R}$ and $(0.8, 1) \times \mathbb{R}$ can be visualized in the xy-**plane** as follows:

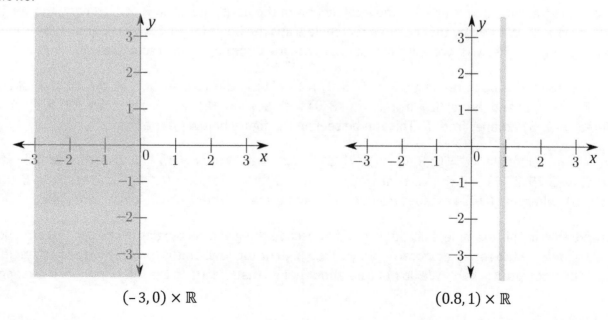

$$(-3, 0) \times \mathbb{R} \qquad\qquad (0.8, 1) \times \mathbb{R}$$

We will say that the horizontal strip $\mathbb{R} \times (c, d)$ **contains** y if $y \in \mathbb{R}$ and $c < y < d$. Otherwise, we will say that the horizontal strip **excludes** y.

Similarly, we will say that the vertical strip $(a, b) \times \mathbb{R}$ **contains** x if $x \in \mathbb{R}$ and $a < x < b$. Otherwise, we will say that the vertical strip **excludes** x.

Example 13.3: The horizontal strip $\mathbb{R} \times (2.25, 2.75)$ contains 2.5 and excludes 3. One way to visualize this is to draw the horizontal lines $y = 2.5$ and $y = 3$. Below in the figure on the left, we used a solid line for the line $y = 2.5$ because it is contained in the horizontal strip and we used a dashed line for the line $y = 3$ because it is not contained in the horizontal strip.

Similarly, the vertical strip $(0.8, 1) \times \mathbb{R}$ contains 0.9 and excludes 2. Again, we can visualize this by drawing the vertical lines $x = 0.9$ and $x = 2$. These vertical lines are shown below in the figure on the right.

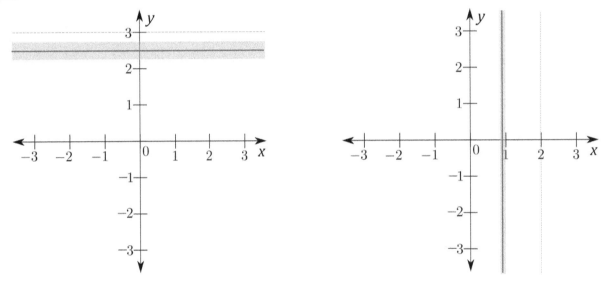

An **open rectangle** is a set of the form $(a, b) \times (c, d) = \{(x, y) \mid a < x < b \wedge c < y < d\}$. Note that the open rectangle $(a, b) \times (c, d)$ is the intersection of the horizontal strip $\mathbb{R} \times (c, d)$ and the vertical strip $(a, b) \times \mathbb{R}$. We will say that an open rectangle **traps** the point (x, y) if $x, y \in \mathbb{R}$ and (x, y) is in the open rectangle. Otherwise, we will say that (x, y) **escapes** from the open rectangle.

Example 13.4: The open rectangle $R = (-3, 0) \times (-2, 1)$ is the intersection of the horizontal strip $H = \mathbb{R} \times (-2, 1)$ and the vertical strip $V = (-3, 0) \times \mathbb{R}$. So, $R = H \cap V$. The rectangle R traps $(-1, 0)$, whereas $(-2, 3)$ escapes from R. This can be seen in the figure below on the left.

The open rectangle $R = (0.8, 1) \times (2.25, 2.75)$ is the intersection of the horizontal strip $H = \mathbb{R} \times (2.25, 2.75)$ and the vertical strip $V = (0.8, 1) \times \mathbb{R}$. So, $R = H \cap V$. The rectangle R traps $(0.9, 2.5)$, whereas $(0.9, 2)$ escapes from R. This can be seen in the figure below on the right.

Observe that in this example, I chose points that escape the given rectangles in the vertical direction. They fall outside the rectangle because they're too high or too low. This is the only type of escape that we will be interested in here. We do not care about points that escape to the left or right of a rectangle.

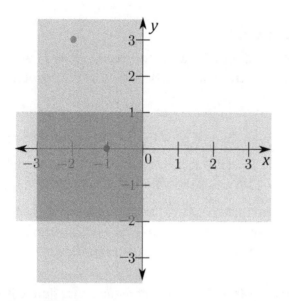 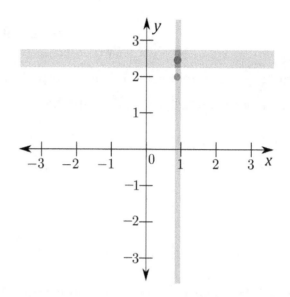

Let $A \subseteq \mathbb{R}$, let $f \colon A \to \mathbb{R}$, and let $R = (a, b) \times (c, d)$ be an open rectangle. We say that R **traps** f if for all $x \in (a, b)$, R traps $(x, f(x))$. Otherwise we say that f **escapes** from R.

Example 13.5: Let $f \colon \mathbb{R} \to \mathbb{R}$ be defined by $f(x) = x + 1$. Consider the open rectangles $R = (0, 2) \times (1, 3)$ and $S = (0, 2) \times (0, 2)$. Then R traps f, as can be seen in the figure below on the left, whereas f escapes from S, as can be seen in the figure below on the right. I put a box around the points of the form $(x, f(x))$ that escape from S. For example, the point $(1.2, f(1.2)) = (1.2, 2.2)$ escapes from S because $0 < 1.2 < 2$, but $f(1.2) = 2.2 \geq 2$.

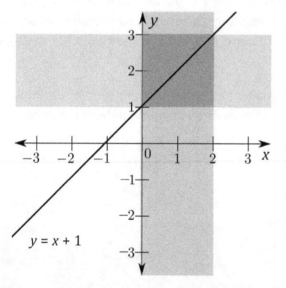 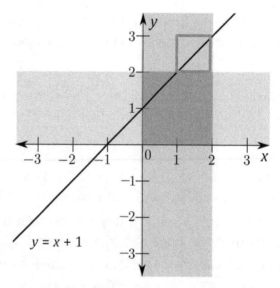

When we are checking the limiting behavior near a real number r, we don't care if the point $(r, f(r))$ escapes. Therefore, before we define a limit, we need to modify our definitions of "traps" and "escapes" slightly to account for this.

Let $A \subseteq \mathbb{R}$, let $f \colon A \to \mathbb{R}$, and let $R = (a, b) \times (c, d)$ be an open rectangle. We say that **R traps f around r** if for all $x \in (a, b) \setminus \{r\}$, R traps $(x, f(x))$. Otherwise, we say **f escapes from R around r**.

Limits and Continuity

Let $A \subseteq \mathbb{R}$, let $f\colon A \to \mathbb{R}$, and let $r, L \in \mathbb{R}$. We say that the **limit of f as x approaches r is L**, written $\lim_{x \to r} f(x) = L$, if for every horizontal strip H that contains L there is a vertical strip V that contains r such that the rectangle $H \cap V$ traps f around r.

Technical note: According to the definition of limit just given, in order for $\lim_{x \to r} f(x)$ to exist, the set A needs to contain a deleted neighborhood of r, say $N_\epsilon^\odot(r) = (r - \epsilon, r) \cup (r, r + \epsilon)$. As an example, suppose that $A = \{0\}$ and $f\colon A \to \mathbb{R}$ is defined by $f(0) = 1$. What is the value of $\lim_{x \to 0} f(x)$? Well, any rectangle of the form $H \cap V$ does not trap any points of the form $(x, f(x))$ with $x \neq 0$ simply because $f(x)$ is not defined when $x \neq 0$. Therefore, given a horizontal strip H, there is no vertical strip V such that $H \cap V$ traps f around r, and so, $\lim_{x \to r} f(x)$ does not exist. This agrees with our intuition.

As a less extreme example, suppose that $A = \mathbb{Q}$ and $g\colon \mathbb{Q} \to \mathbb{R}$ is the constant function where $g(x) = 1$ for all $x \in \mathbb{Q}$. Then for any $r \in \mathbb{Q}$, we should probably have $\lim_{x \to r} g(x) = 1$. But if we use our current definition of limit, then $\lim_{x \to r} g(x)$ does not exist. A more general definition of limit would yield finite values for limits defined on certain sets (like $\mathbb{Q}$) that do not contain a neighborhood of r.

Specifically, we really should insist only that for each $j \in \mathbb{R}^+$, $A \cap \left((r - j, r + j) \setminus \{r\}\right) \neq \emptyset$. The definition of limit given above could be modified slightly to accommodate this more general situation. For example, we could change "R traps f around r" to "for all $x \in A \cap \left((a, b) \setminus \{r\}\right)$, R traps $(x, f(x))$." If we were to use this more general definition, it is very important that we also insist that the set A has the property given at the beginning of this paragraph. Otherwise, we would have an issue with the function f defined at the beginning of this note. The interested reader may want to investigate this.

In this lesson, we will avoid these more complicated domains and stick with the simpler definition of limit. Let's just always assume that if $\lim_{x \to r} f(x)$ exists, then f is defined on some deleted neighborhood of r.

Example 13.6: Let $f\colon \mathbb{R} \to \mathbb{R}$ be defined by $f(x) = x + 1$, let $r = 1.5$, and let $L = 1$. Let's show that $\lim_{x \to 1.5} f(x) \neq 1$.

If $H = \mathbb{R} \times (0, 2)$ and V is any vertical strip that contains 1.5, then $H \cap V$ does **not** trap f around 1.5. Indeed, if $V = (a, b) \times \mathbb{R}$, then if we let $x = \frac{1}{2}(1.5 + b)$, we will show that $x \in (a, b)$ and $f(x) = \frac{1}{2}(1.5 + b) + 1 > 2$ (see the figure to the right).

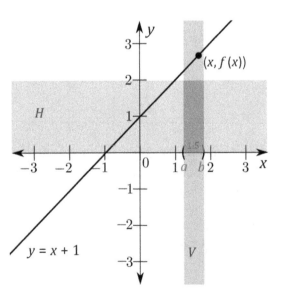

To see that $x \in (a, b)$, note that since $b > 1.5$, we have $x = \frac{1}{2}(1.5 + b) > \frac{1}{2}(1.5 + 1.5) = \frac{1}{2} \cdot 3 = 1.5 > a$, and we have $x = \frac{1}{2}(1.5 + b) < \frac{1}{2}(b + b) = \frac{1}{2} \cdot 2b = b$.

To see that $f(x) > 2$, note that

$$f(x) = \tfrac{1}{2}(1.5 + b) + 1 > \tfrac{1}{2}(1.5 + 1.5) + 1 = \tfrac{1}{2} \cdot 3 + 1 = 1.5 + 1 = 2.5 > 2.$$

So, what is $\lim\limits_{x \to 1.5} f(x)$ equal to? From the picture above, a good guess would be 2.5. To verify that this is true, let $H = \mathbb{R} \times (c, d)$ be a horizontal strip that contains 2.5. Next, let $V = (c - 1, d - 1) \times \mathbb{R}$. We will show that $H \cap V = (c - 1, d - 1) \times (c, d)$ traps f around 1.5. Let $x \in (c - 1, d - 1) \setminus \{1.5\}$, so that $c - 1 < x < d - 1$ and $x \neq 1.5$. Adding 1 to each part of this sequence of inequalities gives $c < x + 1 < d$, so that $c < f(x) < d$, or equivalently, $f(x) \in (c, d)$. Since $x \in (c - 1, d - 1) \setminus \{1.5\}$ and $f(x) \in (c, d)$, it follows that $(x, f(x)) \in (c - 1, d - 1) \times (c, d) = H \cap V$. Therefore, $H \cap V$ traps f around 1.5.

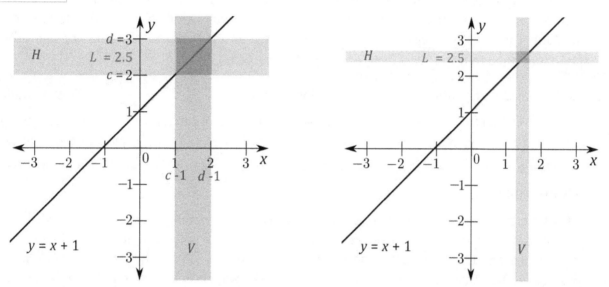

Notes: (1) The figures above give a visual representation of the argument just presented. In the figure on the left, we let $c = 2$ and $d = 3$, so that $H = \mathbb{R} \times (2, 3)$. Our choice of V is then $(1, 2) \times \mathbb{R}$, and therefore, $H \cap V = (1, 2) \times (2, 3)$. Now, if $1 < x < 2$, then $2 < x + 1 < 3$. So, $(x, f(x)) \in H \cap V$.

In the figure on the right, we started with a thinner horizontal strip without being specific about its exact definition. Notice that we then need to use a thinner vertical strip to prevent f from escaping. If the vertical strip were just a little wider on the right, then some points of the form $(x, f(x))$ would escape the rectangle because they would be too high. If the vertical strip were just a little wider on the left, then some points of the form $(x, f(x))$ would escape the rectangle because they would be too low.

(2) Notice that in this example, the point $(1.5, f(1.5))$ itself always stays in the rectangle. In the argument given, we excluded this point from consideration. Even if $(1.5, f(1.5))$ were to escape the rectangle, it would not change the result here. We would still have $\lim\limits_{x \to 1.5} f(x) = 2.5$. I indicated the parts of the argument where $(1.5, f(1.5))$ was being excluded from consideration in Example 13.6 above by placing rectangles around that part of the text. If we delete all the parts of the argument inside those rectangles, the resulting argument would still be correct. We will examine this situation more carefully in the next example.

If we modify the definition of limit by getting rid of "around r," insisting that $r \in A$, and replacing L by $f(r)$, we get the definition of continuity. Specifically, we have the following definition.

Let $A \subseteq \mathbb{R}$, let $f: A \to \mathbb{R}$, and let $r \in A$. We say that the function f is **continuous** at r if for every horizontal strip H that contains $f(r)$ there is a vertical strip V that contains r such that the rectangle $H \cap V$ traps f.

Example 13.7:

1. If we delete all the text that I placed in rectangles in Example 13.6 above, then the resulting argument shows that the function f defined by $f(x) = x + 1$ is continuous at $x = 1.5$.

   To summarize, given a horizontal strip H containing $f(1.5) = 2.5$, we found a vertical strip V containing 1.5 such that $H \cap V$ traps f. Notice once again that in this example we do not exclude $x = 1.5$ from consideration, and when we mention trapping f, we do not say "around 1.5." We need to trap $(1.5, f(1.5)) = (1.5, 2.5)$ as well.

2. Let's consider the function $g: \mathbb{R} \to \mathbb{R}$ defined by $g(x) = \begin{cases} x + 1 & \text{if } x \neq 1.5 \\ -2 & \text{if } x = 1.5 \end{cases}$. This function is nearly identical to the function f we have been discussing. It differs from the previous function only at $x = 1.5$. It should follow that $\lim_{x \to 1.5} g(x) = \lim_{x \to 1.5} f(x)$. And, in fact it does. The same exact argument that we gave in Example 13.6 shows that $\lim_{x \to 1.5} g(x) = 2.5$. The figures below illustrate the situation.

   This time however, we cannot delete the text inside the rectangles in Example 13.6. $x = 1.5$ needs to be excluded from consideration for the argument to go through. In the leftmost figure below, we see that if H is the horizontal strip $H = \mathbb{R} \times (2, 3)$, then for any vertical strip $V = (a, b) \times \mathbb{R}$ that contains 1.5, the point $(1.5, -2)$ will escape the rectangle $H \cap V$. Indeed, $H \cap V = (a, b) \times (2, 3)$, and $(1.5, g(1.5)) = (1.5, -2) \notin (a, b) \times (2, 3)$ because $-2 < 2$. This shows that g is **not** continuous at $x = 1.5$.

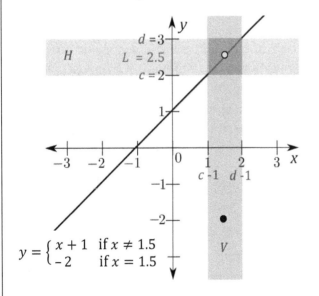 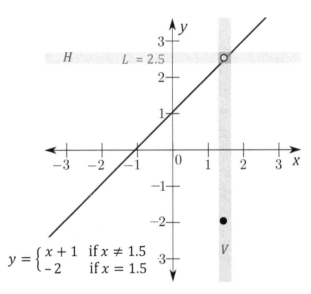

The strip game: Suppose we want to determine if $\lim\limits_{x \to r} f(x) = L$. Consider the following game between two players: Player 1 "attacks" by choosing a horizontal strip H_0 containing L. Player 2 then tries to "defend" by choosing a vertical strip V_0 containing r such that $H_0 \cap V_0$ traps f around r. If Player 2 cannot find such a vertical strip, then Player 1 wins and $\lim\limits_{x \to r} f(x) \neq L$. If Player 2 defends successfully, then Player 1 chooses a new horizontal strip H_1 containing L. If Player 1 is smart, then he/she will choose a "much thinner" horizontal strip that is contained in H_0 (compare the two figures above). The thinner the strip, the harder it will be for Player 2 to defend. Player 2 once again tries to choose a vertical strip V_1 such that $H_1 \cap V_1$ traps f around r. This process continues indefinitely. Player 1 wins the strip game if at some stage, Player 2 cannot defend successfully. Player 2 wins the strip game if he or she defends successfully at every stage.

Player 1 has a winning strategy for the strip game if and only if $\lim\limits_{x \to r} f(x) \neq L$, while Player 2 has a winning strategy for the strip game if and only if $\lim\limits_{x \to r} f(x) = L$.

Note that if it's possible for Player 1 to win the strip game, then Player 1 can win with a single move—just choose the horizontal strip immediately that Player 2 cannot defend against.

For example, if $f(x) = x + 1$, then $\lim\limits_{x \to 1.5} f(x) \neq 1$. Player 1 can win the appropriate strip game immediately by choosing the horizontal strip $H = \mathbb{R} \times (0, 2)$. Indeed, if Player 2 chooses any vertical strip $V = (a, b) \times \mathbb{R}$ that contains 1.5, let $x \in (a, b)$ with $x > 1.5$. Then we have

$$f(x) = x + 1 > 1.5 + 1 = 2.5 > 2.$$

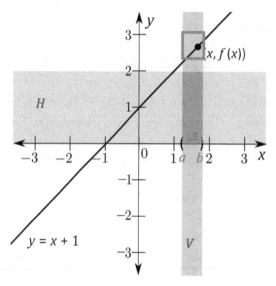

So, $(x, f(x))$ escapes $H \cap V$. In the figure to the right, we see that Player 1 has chosen $H = \mathbb{R} \times (0, 2)$ and Player 2 chose $V = (a, b) \times \mathbb{R}$ for some $a, b \in \mathbb{R}$ with $a < 1.5 < b$. The part of the line inside the square is an illustration of where f escapes $H \cap V$ between a and b. Observe that no matter how much thinner we try to make that vertical strip, if it contains 1.5, then it will contain a portion of the line that is inside the square.

Now, if it's possible for Player 2 to win the game, then we need to describe how Player 2 defends against an arbitrary attack from Player 1. Suppose again that $f(x) = x + 1$ and we are trying to show that $\lim\limits_{x \to 1.5} f(x) = 2.5$. We have already seen how Player 2 can defend against an arbitrary attack from Player 1 in Example 13.6. If at stage n, Player 1 attacks with the horizontal strip $H_n = \mathbb{R} \times (a, b)$, then Player 2 can successfully defend with the vertical strip $V_n = (a - 1, b - 1) \times \mathbb{R}$.

Equivalent Definitions of Limits and Continuity

The definitions of limit and continuity can be written using open intervals instead of strips. Specifically, we have the following:

Theorem 13.1: Let $A \subseteq \mathbb{R}$, let $f: A \to \mathbb{R}$, and let $r, L \in \mathbb{R}$. The following are equivalent:

1. $\lim_{x \to r} f(x) = L$.

2. For every open interval (c, d) with $L \in (c, d)$, there is an open interval (a, b) with $r \in (a, b)$ such that whenever $x \in (a, b)$ and $x \neq r$, $f(x) \in (c, d)$.

3. For every positive real number ϵ, there is a positive real number δ such that whenever $x \in (r - \delta, r + \delta)$ and $x \neq r$, $f(x) \in (L - \epsilon, L + \epsilon)$.

This is the first Theorem where we want to prove more than two statements equivalent. We will do this with the following chain: $1 \to 2 \to 3 \to 1$. In other words, we will assume statement 1 and use it to prove statement 2. We will then assume statement 2 and use it to prove statement 3. Finally, we will assume statement 3 and use it to prove statement 1.

Proof of Theorem 13.1: $(1 \to 2)$ Suppose that $\lim_{x \to r} f(x) = L$ and let $L \in (c, d)$. Then the horizontal strip $\mathbb{R} \times (c, d)$ contains L. Since $\lim_{x \to r} f(x) = L$, there is a vertical strip $(a, b) \times \mathbb{R}$ that contains r such that the rectangle $R = (a, b) \times (c, d)$ traps f around r. Since the vertical strip $(a, b) \times \mathbb{R}$ contains r, $r \in (a, b)$. Since the rectangle R traps f around r, for all $x \in (a, b) \setminus \{r\}$, R traps $(x, f(x))$. In other words, whenever $x \in (a, b)$ and $x \neq r$, we have $(x, f(x)) \in (a, b) \times (c, d)$, and thus, $f(x) \in (c, d)$.

$(2 \to 3)$ Suppose 2 holds and let ϵ be a positive real number. Then $L - \epsilon < L < L + \epsilon$, or equivalently, $L \in (L - \epsilon, L + \epsilon)$. By 2, there is an open interval (a, b) with $r \in (a, b)$ such that whenever $x \in (a, b)$ and $x \neq r$, we have $f(x) \in (L - \epsilon, L + \epsilon)$. Let $\delta = \min\{r - a, b - r\}$. Since $\delta \leq r - a$, we have $-\delta \geq -(r - a) = -r + a$. Therefore, $r - \delta \geq r + (-r + a) = a$. Furthermore, since $\delta \leq b - r$, we have $r + \delta \leq r + (b - r) = b$. So, $(r - \delta, r + \delta) \subseteq (a, b)$. If $x \in (r - \delta, r + \delta)$ and $x \neq r$, then since $(r - \delta, r + \delta) \subseteq (a, b)$, $x \in (a, b)$. Therefore, $f(x) \in (L - \epsilon, L + \epsilon)$.

$(3 \to 1)$ Suppose 3 holds and $H = \mathbb{R} \times (c, d)$ is a horizontal strip that contains L. Since $c < L < d$, we have $L - c > 0$ and $d - L > 0$. Therefore, $\epsilon = \min\{L - c, d - L\} > 0$. So, there is $\delta > 0$ such that whenever $x \in (r - \delta, r + \delta)$ and $x \neq r$, then $f(x) \in (L - \epsilon, L + \epsilon)$. Let $V = (r - \delta, r + \delta) \times \mathbb{R}$. Then V contains r. We now show that $H \cap V = (r - \delta, r + \delta) \times (c, d)$ traps f around r. Let $x \in (r - \delta, r + \delta)$ with $x \neq r$. Then $f(x) \in (L - \epsilon, L + \epsilon)$. So, $f(x) > L - \epsilon \geq L - (L - c) = c$ and $f(x) < L + \epsilon \leq L + (d - L) = d$. Therefore, $f(x) \in (c, d)$, and so, $H \cap V$ traps f around r. $\qquad \square$

Notes: (1) ϵ and δ are Greek letters pronounced "epsilon" and "delta," respectively. Mathematicians tend to use these two symbols to represent arbitrarily small numbers.

(2) If $a \in \mathbb{R}$ and $\epsilon > 0$. Then the ϵ-neighborhood of a is the interval $N_\epsilon(a) = (a - \epsilon, a + \epsilon)$ and the deleted ϵ-neighborhood of a is the "punctured" interval $N_\epsilon^\odot(a) = (a - \epsilon, a) \cup (a, a + \epsilon)$. We can visualize the deleted ϵ-neighborhood $N_\epsilon^\odot(a)$ as follows:

For a specific example, let's look at $N_2^{\circ}(1) = (1 - 2, 1) \cup (1, 1 + 2) = (-1, 1) \cup (1, 3)$.

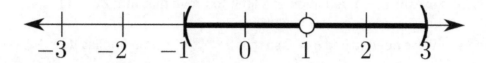

(3) The third part of Theorem 13.1 can be written in terms of neighborhoods as follows:

"For every positive real number ϵ, there is a positive real number δ such that whenever $x \in N_\delta^{\circ}(r)$, $f(x) \in N_\epsilon(L)$."

(4) $x \in (a - \epsilon, a + \epsilon)$ is equivalent to $a - \epsilon < x < a + \epsilon$. If we subtract a from each part of this inequality, we get $-\epsilon < x - a < \epsilon$. This last expression is equivalent to $|x - a| < \epsilon$. So, we have the following sequence of equivalences:

$$x \in N_\epsilon(a) \Leftrightarrow x \in (a - \epsilon, a + \epsilon) \Leftrightarrow a - \epsilon < x < a + \epsilon \Leftrightarrow |x - a| < \epsilon.$$

(5) $x \neq a$ is equivalent to $x - a \neq 0$. Since the absolute value of a real number can never be negative, $x - a \neq 0$ is equivalent to $|x - a| > 0$. This can also be written $0 < |x - a|$. So, we have the following sequence of equivalences:

$$x \in N_\epsilon^{\circ}(a) \Leftrightarrow x \in (a - \epsilon, a) \cup (a, a + \epsilon) \Leftrightarrow 0 < |x - a| < \epsilon.$$

(6) The third part of Theorem 13.1 can be written using absolute values as follows:

"For every positive real number ϵ, there is a positive real number δ such that whenever $0 < |x - r| < \delta$, $|f(x) - L| < \epsilon$."

(7) We can abbreviate the expression from Note 6 using quantifiers as follows:

$$\forall \epsilon > 0 \, \exists \delta > 0 \, (0 < |x - r| < \delta \rightarrow |f(x) - L| < \epsilon)$$

We will refer to this expression as the $\epsilon - \delta$ **definition of a limit**.

For each equivalent formulation of a limit, we have a corresponding formulation for the definition of continuity.

Theorem 13.2: Let $A \subseteq \mathbb{R}$, let $f : A \rightarrow \mathbb{R}$, and let $r \in A$. The following are equivalent:

1. f is continuous at r.

2. For every open interval (c, d) with $f(r) \in (c, d)$, there is an open interval (a, b) with $r \in (a, b)$ such that whenever $x \in (a, b)$, $f(x) \in (c, d)$.

3. For every positive real number ϵ, there is a positive real number δ such that whenever $x \in (r - \delta, r + \delta)$, $f(x) \in (f(r) - \epsilon, f(r) + \epsilon)$.

4. $\forall \epsilon > 0 \, \exists \delta > 0 \, (|x - r| < \delta \rightarrow |f(x) - f(r)| < \epsilon)$.

The proof of Theorem 13.2 is left to the reader. It is very similar to the proof of Theorem 13.1.

Basic Examples

Example 13.8: Let's use the $\epsilon - \delta$ definition of a limit to prove that $\lim\limits_{x \to 1}(2x + 1) = 3$.

Analysis: Given $\epsilon > 0$, we need to find $\delta > 0$ so that $0 < |x - 1| < \delta$ implies $|(2x + 1) - 3| < \epsilon$. First note that $|(2x + 1) - 3| = |2x - 2| = |2(x - 1)| = |2||x - 1| = 2|x - 1|$. So, $|(2x + 1) - 3| < \epsilon$ is equivalent to $|x - 1| < \frac{\epsilon}{2}$. Therefore, $\delta = \frac{\epsilon}{2}$ should work.

Proof: Let $\epsilon > 0$ and let $\delta = \frac{\epsilon}{2}$. Suppose that $0 < |x - 1| < \delta$. Then we have

$$|(2x + 1) - 3| = |2x - 2| = |2(x - 1)| = |2||x - 1| = 2|x - 1| < 2\delta = 2 \cdot \frac{\epsilon}{2} = \epsilon.$$

Since $\epsilon > 0$ was arbitrary, we have $\forall \epsilon > 0 \,\exists \delta > 0 \,(0 < |x - 1| < \delta \to |(2x + 1) - 3| < \epsilon)$.

Therefore, $\lim\limits_{x \to 1}(2x + 1) = 3$. $\qquad\qquad\square$

Notes: (1) Even though we're using the "$\epsilon - \delta$ definition" instead of the "strip definition," we can still visualize the situation in terms of the strip game. When we say "Let $\epsilon > 0$," we can think of this as Player 1 "attacking" with the horizontal strip $H = \mathbb{R} \times (3 - \epsilon, 3 + \epsilon)$. In the proof above, Player 2 is then "defending" with the vertical strip $V = \left(1 - \frac{\epsilon}{2}, 1 + \frac{\epsilon}{2}\right) \times \mathbb{R}$. This defense is successful because when $1 - \frac{\epsilon}{2} < x < 1 + \frac{\epsilon}{2}$, we have $2 - \epsilon < 2x < 2 + \epsilon$, and so, $3 - \epsilon < 2x + 1 < 3 + \epsilon$, or equivalently, $2x + 1 \in (3 - \epsilon, 3 + \epsilon)$. In other words, for $x \in \left(1 - \frac{\epsilon}{2}, 1 + \frac{\epsilon}{2}\right)$, $H \cap V$ traps f.

(2) Instead of playing the strip game, we can play the $\epsilon - \delta$ game instead. The idea is the same. Suppose we are trying to figure out if $\lim\limits_{x \to r} f(x) = L$. Player 1 "attacks" by choosing a positive number ϵ. This is equivalent to Player 1 choosing the horizontal strip $H = \mathbb{R} \times (L - \epsilon, L + \epsilon)$. Player 2 then tries to "defend" by finding a positive number δ. This is equivalent to Player 2 choosing the vertical strip $V = (r - \delta, r + \delta) \times \mathbb{R}$. The defense is successful if whenever $x \in (r - \delta, r + \delta)$, $x \neq r$, we have $f(x) \in (L - \epsilon, L + \epsilon)$. This is equivalent to $H \cap V$ trapping f around r.

The figure to the right shows what happens during one round of the $\epsilon - \delta$ game corresponding to checking if $\lim\limits_{x \to 1}(2x + 1) = 3$. In the figure, Player 1 chooses $\epsilon = 0.5$, so that $L - \epsilon = 3 - 0.5 = 2.5$ and $L + \epsilon = 3 + 0.5 = 3.5$. Notice how we drew the corresponding horizontal strip $H = \mathbb{R} \times (2.5, 3.5)$. According to our proof, Player 1 chooses $\delta = \frac{\epsilon}{2} = \frac{0.5}{2} = 0.25$. So $r - \delta = 1 - 0.25 = 0.75$ and $r + \delta = 1 + 0.25 = 1.25$. Notice how we drew the corresponding vertical strip $V = (0.75, 1.25) \times \mathbb{R}$. Also notice how the rectangle $H \cap V$ traps f.

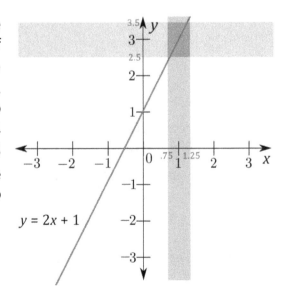

178

(3) Observe that the value for δ that Player 2 chose here is the largest value of δ that would result in a successful defense. If we widen the vertical strip at all on either side, then f would escape from the resulting rectangle. However, any smaller value of δ will still work. If we shrink the vertical strip, then f is still trapped. After all, we have less that we need to trap.

(4) In the next round, Player 1 will want to choose a smaller value for ϵ. If Player 1 chooses a larger value for ϵ, then the same δ that was already played will work to defend against that larger ϵ. But for this problem, it doesn't matter how small a value for ϵ Player 1 chooses—Player 1 simply cannot win. All Player 2 needs to do is defend with $\delta = \frac{\epsilon}{2}$ (or any smaller positive number).

(5) Essentially the same argument can be used to show that the function f defined by $f(x) = 2x + 1$ is continuous at $x = 1$. Simply replace the expression $0 < |x - 1| < \delta$ by the expression $|x - 1| < \delta$ everywhere it appears in the proof. The point is that $f(1) = 2 \cdot 1 + 1 = 3$. Since this value is equal to $\lim_{x \to 1}(2x + 1)$, we don't need to exclude $x = 1$ from consideration when trying to trap f.

Example 13.9: Let's use the $\epsilon - \delta$ definition of a limit to prove that $\lim_{x \to 3}(x^2 - 2x + 1) = 4$.

Analysis: This is quite a bit more difficult than Example 13.8.

Given $\epsilon > 0$, we need to find $\delta > 0$ so that $0 < |x - 3| < \delta$ implies $|(x^2 - 2x + 1) - 4| < \epsilon$. First note that $|(x^2 - 2x + 1) - 4| = |x^2 - 2x - 3| = |(x - 3)(x + 1)| = |x - 3||x + 1|$. Therefore, $|(x^2 - 2x + 1) - 4| < \epsilon$ is equivalent to $|x - 3||x + 1| < \epsilon$.

There is a small complication here. The $|x - 3|$ is not an issue because we're going to be choosing δ so that this expression is small enough. But to make the argument work we need to make $|x + 1|$ small too. Remember from Note 3 after Example 13.8 that if we find a value for δ that works, then any smaller positive number will work too. This allows us to start by assuming that δ is smaller than any positive number we choose. So, let's just assume that $\delta \leq 1$ and see what effect that has on $|x + 1|$.

Well, if $\delta \leq 1$ and $0 < |x - 3| < \delta$, then $|x - 3| < 1$. Therefore, $-1 < x - 3 < 1$. We now add 4 to each part of this inequality to get $3 < x + 1 < 5$. Since $-5 < 3$, this implies that $-5 < x + 1 < 5$, which is equivalent to $|x + 1| < 5$.

So, if we assume that $\delta \leq 1$, then $|(x^2 - 2x + 1) - 4| = |x - 3||x + 1| < \delta \cdot 5 = 5\delta$. Therefore, if we want to make sure that $|(x^2 - 2x + 1) - 4| < \epsilon$, then is suffices to choose δ so that $5\delta \leq \epsilon$, as long as we also have $\delta \leq 1$. So, we will let $\delta = \min\left\{1, \frac{\epsilon}{5}\right\}$.

Proof: Let $\epsilon > 0$ and let $\delta = \min\left\{1, \frac{\epsilon}{5}\right\}$. Suppose that $0 < |x - 3| < \delta$. Then since $\delta \leq 1$, we have $|x - 3| < 1$, and so, $|x + 1| < 5$ (see the algebra in the analysis above). Also, since $\delta \leq \frac{\epsilon}{5}$, we have $|x - 3| < \frac{\epsilon}{5}$. It follows that $|(x^2 - 2x + 1) - 4| = |x^2 - 2x - 3| = |x - 3||x + 1| < \frac{\epsilon}{5} \cdot 5 = \epsilon$.

Since $\epsilon > 0$ was arbitrary, we have $\forall \epsilon > 0 \, \exists \delta > 0 \, (0 < |x - 3| < \delta \to |(x^2 - 2x + 1) - 4| < \epsilon)$. Therefore, $\lim_{x \to 1}(x^2 - 2x + 1) = 4$. $\qquad\square$

Example 13.10: Let $m, b \in \mathbb{R}$ with $m \neq 0$. Let's use the $\epsilon - \delta$ definition of continuity to prove that the function $f: \mathbb{R} \to \mathbb{R}$ defined by $f(x) = mx + b$ is continuous everywhere.

A function of the form $f(x) = mx + b$, where $m, b \in \mathbb{R}$ and $m \neq 0$ is called a **linear function**. So, we will now show that every linear function is continuous everywhere.

Analysis: Given $a \in \mathbb{R}$ and $\epsilon > 0$, we will find $\delta > 0$ so that $|x - a| < \delta$ implies $|f(x) - f(a)| < \epsilon$. First note that $|f(x) - f(a)| = |(mx + b) - (ma + b)| = |mx - ma| = |m||x - a|$. Therefore, $|f(x) - f(a)| < \epsilon$ is equivalent to $|x - a| < \frac{\epsilon}{|m|}$. So, $\delta = \frac{\epsilon}{|m|}$ should work.

Proof: Let $a \in \mathbb{R}$, let $\epsilon > 0$, and let $\delta = \frac{\epsilon}{|m|}$. Suppose that $|x - a| < \delta$. Then we have

$$|f(x) - f(a)| = |(mx + b) - (ma + b)| = |mx - ma| = |m||x - a| < |m|\delta = |m| \cdot \frac{\epsilon}{|m|} = \epsilon.$$

Since $\epsilon > 0$ was arbitrary, we have $\forall \epsilon > 0 \exists \delta > 0 \, (|x - a| < \delta \to |f(x) - f(a)| < \epsilon)$. Therefore, f is continuous at $x = a$. Since $a \in \mathbb{R}$ was arbitrary, f is continuous everywhere. $\square$

Notes: (1) We proved $\forall a \in \mathbb{R} \, \forall \epsilon > 0 \, \exists \delta > 0 \, \forall x \in \mathbb{R}(|x - a| < \delta \to |f(x) - f(a)| < \epsilon)$. In words, we proved that for every real number a, given a positive real number ϵ, we can find a positive real number δ such that whenever the distance between x and a is less than δ, the distance between $f(x)$ and $f(a)$ is less than ϵ. And of course, a simpler way to say this is "for every real number a, f is continuous at a," or $\forall a \in \mathbb{R} \, (f$ is continuous at $a)$."

(2) If we move the expression $\forall a \in \mathbb{R}$ next to $\forall x \in \mathbb{R}$, we get a concept that is stronger than continuity. We say that a function $f: A \to \mathbb{R}$ is uniformly continuous on A if

$$\forall \epsilon > 0 \, \exists \delta > 0 \, \forall a, x \in A \, (|x - a| < \delta \to |f(x) - f(a)| < \epsilon).$$

(3) As a quick example of uniform continuity, every linear function is uniformly continuous on $\mathbb{R}$. We can see this by modifying the proof above just slightly:

New proof: Let $\epsilon > 0$ and let $\delta = \frac{\epsilon}{|m|}$. Let $a, x \in \mathbb{R}$ and suppose that $|x - a| < \delta$. Then we have

$$|f(x) - f(a)| = |(mx + b) - (ma + b)| = |mx - ma| = |m||x - a| < |m|\delta = |m| \cdot \frac{\epsilon}{|m|} = \epsilon.$$

Since $\epsilon > 0$ was arbitrary, we have $\forall \epsilon > 0 \, \exists \delta > 0 \, \forall a, x \in \mathbb{R} \, (|x - a| < \delta \to |f(x) - f(a)| < \epsilon)$. Therefore, f is uniformly continuous on $\mathbb{R}$.

(4) The difference between continuity and uniform continuity on a set A can be described as follows: In both cases, an ϵ is given and then a δ is chosen. For continuity, for each value of x, we can choose a different δ. For uniform continuity, once we choose a δ for some value of x, we need to be able to use the **same** δ for every other value of x in A.

In terms of strips, once a horizontal strip is given, we need to be more careful how we choose a vertical strip. As we check different x-values, we can move the vertical strip left and right. However, we are not allowed to decrease the width of the vertical strip.

Try to come up with a function that is continuous on a set A, but not uniformly continuous on A. This will be explored a little more in the problem set below.

Limit and Continuity Theorems

Theorem 13.3: Let $A, B \subseteq \mathbb{R}$, let $f: A \to \mathbb{R}$, $g: B \to \mathbb{R}$, let $r, k \in \mathbb{R}$, and suppose that $\lim_{x \to r}[f(x)]$ and $\lim_{x \to r}[g(x)]$ are both finite real numbers. Then $\lim_{x \to r}[f(x) + g(x)] = \lim_{x \to r}[f(x)] + \lim_{x \to r}[g(x)]$.

Analysis: If $\lim_{x \to r}[f(x)] = L$, then given $\epsilon > 0$, there is $\delta > 0$ such that $0 < |x - r| < \delta$ implies $|f(x) - L| < \epsilon$. If $\lim_{x \to r}[g(x)] = K$, then given $\epsilon > 0$, there is $\delta > 0$ such that $0 < |x - r| < \delta$ implies $|g(x) - K| < \epsilon$. We should acknowledge something here. If we are given a single positive real value for ϵ, there is no reason that we would necessarily choose the same δ for both f and g. However, using the fact that once we find a δ that works, any smaller δ will also work, it is easy to see that we **could** choose a single value for δ that would work for both f and g. This should be acknowledged in some way in the proof. There are several ways to work this into the argument. The way we will handle this is to use δ_1 for f and δ_2 for g, and then let δ be the smaller of δ_1 and δ_2.

Next, recall from Theorem 7.3 from Lesson 7 that the Triangle Inequality says that for all $x, y \in \mathbb{R}$, $|x + y| \le |x| + |y|$. (The theorem is stated to be true for all complex numbers, but since $\mathbb{R} \subseteq \mathbb{C}$, it is equally true for all real numbers.) After assuming $0 < |x - r| < \delta$, we will use the Triangle Inequality to write

$$|f(x) + g(x) - (L + K)| = |(f(x) - L) + (g(x) - K)| \le |f(x) - L| + |g(x) - K| < \epsilon + \epsilon = 2\epsilon.$$

It seems that we wound up with 2ϵ on the right-hand side instead of ϵ. Now, if ϵ is an arbitrarily small positive real number, then so is 2ϵ, and vice versa. So, getting 2ϵ on the right-hand side instead of ϵ really isn't too big of a deal. However, to be rigorous, we should prove that it is okay. There are at least two ways we can handle this. One possibility is to prove a theorem that says 2ϵ works just as well as ϵ. A second possibility (and the way I usually teach it in basic analysis courses) is to edit the original ϵ's, so it all works out to ϵ in the end. The idea is simple. If ϵ is a positive real number, then so is $\frac{\epsilon}{2}$. So, after we are given ϵ, we can pretend that Player 1 (in the $\epsilon - \delta$ game) is "attacking" with $\frac{\epsilon}{2}$ instead. Let's see how this all plays out in the proof.

Proof: Suppose that $\lim_{x \to r}[f(x)] = L$ and $\lim_{x \to r}[g(x)] = K$, and let $\epsilon > 0$. Since $\lim_{x \to r}[f(x)] = L$, there is $\delta_1 > 0$ such that $0 < |x - r| < \delta_1$ implies $|f(x) - L| < \frac{\epsilon}{2}$. Since $\lim_{x \to r}[g(x)] = K$, there is $\delta_2 > 0$ such that $0 < |x - r| < \delta_2$ implies $|g(x) - L| < \frac{\epsilon}{2}$. Let $\delta = \min\{\delta_1, \delta_2\}$ and suppose that $0 < |x - r| < \delta$. Then since $\delta \le \delta_1$, $|f(x) - L| < \frac{\epsilon}{2}$. Since $\delta \le \delta_2$, $|g(x) - K| < \frac{\epsilon}{2}$. By the Triangle Inequality, we have

$$|f(x) + g(x) - (L + K)| = |(f(x) - L) + (g(x) - K)| \le |f(x) - L| + |g(x) - K| < \frac{\epsilon}{2} + \frac{\epsilon}{2} = \epsilon.$$

So, $\lim_{x \to r}[f(x) + g(x)] = L + K = \lim_{x \to r}[f(x)] + \lim_{x \to r}[g(x)]$. $\square$

Theorem 13.4: Let $A, B \subseteq \mathbb{R}$, let $f: A \to \mathbb{R}$, $g: B \to \mathbb{R}$, let $r \in \mathbb{R}$, and suppose that $\lim_{x \to r}[f(x)]$ and $\lim_{x \to r}[g(x)]$ are both finite real numbers. Then $\lim_{x \to r}[f(x)g(x)] = \lim_{x \to r}[f(x)] \cdot \lim_{x \to r}[g(x)]$.

Analysis: As in Theorem 13.3, we let $\lim_{x \to r}[f(x)] = L$ and $\lim_{x \to r}[g(x)] = K$. If $\epsilon > 0$ is given, we will find a single $\delta > 0$ such that $0 < |x - r| < \delta$ implies $|f(x) - L| < \epsilon$ and $|g(x) - K| < \epsilon$ (like we did for Theorem 13.3). Now, we want to show that whenever $0 < |x - r| < \delta$, $|f(x)g(x) - LK| < \epsilon$. This is quite a bit more challenging than anything we had to do in Theorem 13.3.

To show that $|f(x)g(x) - LK| < \epsilon$ we will apply the Standard Advanced Calculus Trick (SACT – see Note 7 following Example 4.5 from Lesson 4). We would like for $|f(x) - L|$ and $|g(x) - K|$ to appear as factors in our expression. To make this happen, we subtract $Lg(x)$ from $f(x)g(x)$ to get $f(x)g(x) - Lg(x) = (f(x) - L)g(x)$. To "undo the damage," we then add back $Lg(x)$. The application of SACT together with the Triangle Inequality looks like this:

$$|f(x)g(x) - LK| = |(f(x)g(x) - Lg(x)) + (Lg(x) - LK)|$$
$$\leq |f(x)g(x) - Lg(x)| + |Lg(x) - LK| = |f(x) - L||g(x)| + |L||g(x) - K|$$
$$< \epsilon|g(x)| + |L|\epsilon = \epsilon(|g(x)| + |L|).$$

Uh oh! How can we possibly get rid of $|g(x)| + |L|$? We have seen how to handle a constant multiple of ϵ in the proof of Theorem 13.3. But this time we are multiplying ϵ by a function of x. We will resolve this issue by making sure we choose δ small enough so that $g(x)$ is sufficiently **bounded**.

We do this by taking a specific value for ϵ, and then using the fact that $\lim_{x \to r}[g(x)] = K$ to come up with a $\delta > 0$ and a bound M for g on the deleted δ-neighborhood of r. For simplicity, let's choose $\epsilon = 1$. Then since $\lim_{x \to r}[g(x)] = K$, we can find $\delta > 0$ such that $0 < |x - r| < \delta$ implies $|g(x) - K| < 1$. Now, $|g(x) - K| < 1 \Leftrightarrow -1 < g(x) - K < 1 \Leftrightarrow K - 1 < g(x) < K + 1$. For example, if $K = 5$, we would have $4 < g(x) < 6$. Since this implies $-6 < g(x) < 6$, or equivalently, $|g(x)| < 6$, we could choose $M = 6$. If, on the other hand, $K = -3$, we would have $-4 < g(x) < -2$. Since this implies $-4 < g(x) < 4$, or equivalently, $|g(x)| < 4$, we could choose $M = 4$. In general, we will let $M = \max\{|K - 1|, |K + 1|\}$.

We will now be able to get $|f(x)g(x) - (LK)| < \epsilon(|g(x)| + |L|) < \epsilon(M + |L|)$. Great! Now it looks just like the situation we had in Theorem 13.3. The number $M + |L|$ looks messier, but it is just a number, and so we can finish cleaning up the argument by replacing Player 1's ϵ-attacks by $\frac{\epsilon}{M + |L|}$.

Proof: Suppose that $\lim_{x \to r}[f(x)] = L$ and $\lim_{x \to r}[g(x)] = K$, and let $\epsilon > 0$. Since $\lim_{x \to r}[g(x)] = K$, there is $\delta_1 > 0$ such that $0 < |x - r| < \delta_1$ implies $|g(x) - K| < 1$. Now, $|g(x) - K| < 1$ is equivalent to $-1 < g(x) - K < 1$, or by adding K, $K - 1 < g(x) < K + 1$. Let $M = \max\{|K - 1|, |K + 1|\}$. Then, $0 < |x - r| < \delta_1$ implies $-M < g(x) < M$, or equivalently, $|g(x)| < M$. Note also that $M > 0$. Therefore, $M + |L| > 0$.

Now, since $\lim_{x \to r}[f(x)] = L$, there is $\delta_2 > 0$ such that $0 < |x - r| < \delta_2$ implies $|f(x) - L| < \frac{\epsilon}{M + |L|}$. Since $\lim_{x \to r}[g(x)] = K$, there is $\delta_3 > 0$ such that $0 < |x - r| < \delta_3$ implies $|g(x) - L| < \frac{\epsilon}{M + |L|}$. Let $\delta = \min\{\delta_1, \delta_2, \delta_3\}$ and suppose that $0 < |x - r| < \delta$. Then since $\delta \leq \delta_1$, $|g(x)| < M$. Since $\delta \leq \delta_2$, $|f(x) - L| < \frac{\epsilon}{M + |L|}$. Since $\delta \leq \delta_3$, $|g(x) - K| < \frac{\epsilon}{M + |L|}$. By the Triangle Inequality (and SACT), we have

$$|f(x)g(x) - LK| = |(f(x)g(x) - Lg(x)) + (Lg(x) - LK)|$$
$$\leq |f(x)g(x) - Lg(x)| + |Lg(x) - LK| = |f(x) - L||g(x)| + |L||g(x) - K|$$
$$< \frac{\epsilon}{M+|L|} \cdot M + |L|\frac{\epsilon}{M+|L|} = \frac{\epsilon}{M+|L|}(M + |L|) = \epsilon.$$

So, $\lim\limits_{x \to r}[f(x)g(x)] = LK = \lim\limits_{x \to r}[f(x)] \cdot \lim\limits_{x \to r}[g(x)]$.   □

Limits Involving Infinity

Recall that a **horizontal strip** in $\mathbb{R} \times \mathbb{R}$ is a set of the form $\mathbb{R} \times (c,d) = \{(x,y) \mid c < y < d\}$ and a **vertical strip** is a set of the form $(a,b) \times \mathbb{R} = \{(x,y) \mid a < x < b\}$. If we allow a and/or c to take on the value $-\infty$ (in which case we say that the strip **contains** $-\infty$) and we allow b and/or d to take on the value $+\infty$ (in which case we say that the strip **contains** $+\infty$), we can extend our definition of limit to handle various situations involving infinity.

Example 13.11: Let's take a look at the horizontal strip $\mathbb{R} \times (1, +\infty)$ and the vertical strip $(-\infty, -2) \times \mathbb{R}$ in the xy-plane. These can be visualized as follows:

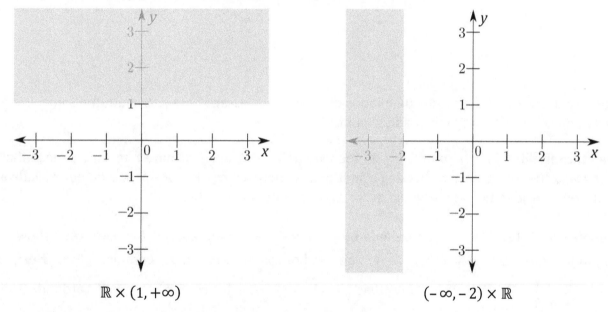

$$\mathbb{R} \times (1, +\infty) \qquad\qquad (-\infty, -2) \times \mathbb{R}$$

The horizontal strip $\mathbb{R} \times (1, +\infty)$ contains $+\infty$ and the vertical strip $(-\infty, -2) \times \mathbb{R}$ contains $-\infty$.

Note: Strips that contain $+\infty$ or $-\infty$ are usually called **half planes**. Here, we will continue to use the expression "strip" because it allows us to handle all types of limits (finite and infinite) without having to discuss every case individually.

By allowing strips to contain $+\infty$ or $-\infty$, intersections of horizontal and vertical strips can now be **unbounded**. The resulting open rectangles $(a,b) \times (c,d)$ can have a and/or c taking on the value $-\infty$ and b and/or d taking on the value $+\infty$.

Example 13.12: Consider the horizontal strip $H = \mathbb{R} \times (1, +\infty)$ and the vertical strip $V = (-2, -1) \times \mathbb{R}$. The intersection of these strips is the open rectangle $R = (-2, -1) \times (1, +\infty)$. The rectangle R traps $(-1.5, 3)$, whereas $(-1.5, 0)$ escapes from R. This can be seen in the figure below on the left. Also, consider the horizontal strip $H = \mathbb{R} \times (1, +\infty)$ and the vertical strip $V = (-\infty, -2) \times \mathbb{R}$. The intersection of these strips is the open rectangle $S = (-\infty, -2) \times (1, +\infty)$. The rectangle S traps $(-3, 2)$, whereas $(-3, -1)$ escapes from S. This can be seen in the figure below on the right.

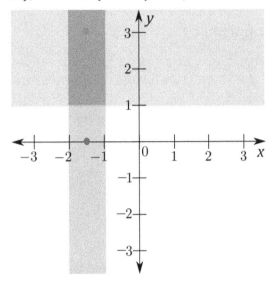 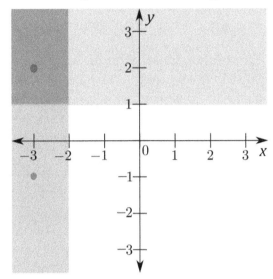

When we allow $+\infty$ and $-\infty$, the definitions of "trap" and "escape" are just about the same. We just need to make the following minor adjustment.

Small technicality: If $r = +\infty$ or $r = -\infty$, then we define **R traps f around r** to simply mean that **R traps f**. In other words, when checking a limit that is approaching $+\infty$ or $-\infty$, we do not exclude any point from consideration as we would do if r were a finite real number.

Example 13.13: Let $f : \mathbb{R} \to \mathbb{R}$ be defined by $f(x) = \frac{1}{x^2}$, let $r = 0$, and let $L = +\infty$. Let's show that $\lim_{x \to 0} f(x) = +\infty$. Let $H = \mathbb{R} \times (c, +\infty)$ be a horizontal strip that contains $+\infty$. Next, let $V = \left(-\frac{1}{\sqrt{c}}, \frac{1}{\sqrt{c}} \right) \times \mathbb{R}$. We will show that $H \cap V = \left(-\frac{1}{\sqrt{c}}, \frac{1}{\sqrt{c}} \right) \times (c, +\infty)$ traps f around 0. Let $x \in \left(-\frac{1}{\sqrt{c}}, \frac{1}{\sqrt{c}} \right) \setminus \{0\}$, so that $-\frac{1}{\sqrt{c}} < x < \frac{1}{\sqrt{c}}$ and $x \neq 0$. Then $-\frac{1}{\sqrt{c}} < x < 0$ or $0 < x < \frac{1}{\sqrt{c}}$. In either case, $x^2 < \frac{1}{c}$, and therefore, $c < \frac{1}{x^2} = f(x)$. Since $x \in \left(-\frac{1}{\sqrt{c}}, \frac{1}{\sqrt{c}} \right) \setminus \{0\}$ and $f(x) \in (c, +\infty)$, it follows that $\left(x, f(x) \right) \in \left(-\frac{1}{\sqrt{c}}, \frac{1}{\sqrt{c}} \right) \times (c, +\infty) = H \cap V$. Therefore, $H \cap V$ traps f around 0. So, $\lim_{x \to 0} f(x) = +\infty$.

Example 13.14: Let $f : \mathbb{R} \to \mathbb{R}$ be defined by $f(x) = -x + 3$, let $r = +\infty$, and let $L = -\infty$. Let's show that $\lim_{x \to +\infty} f(x) = -\infty$. Let $H = \mathbb{R} \times (-\infty, d)$ be a horizontal strip that contains $-\infty$. Next, let $V = (3 - d, +\infty) \times \mathbb{R}$. We will show that $H \cap V = (3 - d, +\infty) \times (-\infty, d)$ traps f around $+\infty$ (or more simply, that $(3 - d, +\infty) \times (-\infty, d)$ traps f). Let $x \in (3 - d, +\infty)$, so that $x > 3 - d$. Then we have $-x < d - 3$, and so, $f(x) = -x + 3 < d$. Since $x \in (3 - d, +\infty)$ and $f(x) \in (-\infty, d)$, it follows that $\left(x, f(x) \right) \in (3 - d, +\infty) \times (-\infty, d) = H \cap V$. Therefore, $H \cap V$ traps f. So, $\lim_{x \to +\infty} f(x) = -\infty$.

We can find equivalent definitions for limits involving infinity on a case-by-case basis. We will do one example here and you will look at others in Problem 15 in the problem set below.

Theorem 13.5: $\lim\limits_{x \to r} f(x) = +\infty$ if and only if $\forall M > 0 \, \exists \delta > 0 \, (0 < |x - r| < \delta \to f(x) > M)$.

Proof: Suppose that $\lim\limits_{x \to r} f(x) = +\infty$ and let $M > 0$. Let $H = \mathbb{R} \times (M, +\infty)$. Since $\lim\limits_{x \to r} f(x) = +\infty$, there is a vertical strip $V = (a, b) \times \mathbb{R}$ that contains r such that the rectangle $(a, b) \times (M, +\infty)$ traps f around r. Let $\delta = \min\{r - a, b - r\}$, and let $0 < |x - r| < \delta$. Then $x \neq r$ and $-\delta < x - r < \delta$. So, $r - \delta < x < r + \delta$. Since $\delta \leq r - a$, we have $a \leq r - \delta$. Since $\delta \leq b - r$, we have $b \geq r + \delta$. Therefore, $a < x < b$, and so, $x \in (a, b)$. Since $x \neq r$, $x \in (a, b)$, and $(a, b) \times (M, +\infty)$ traps f around r, we have $f(x) \in (M, +\infty)$. Thus, $f(x) > M$.

Conversely, suppose that $\forall M > 0 \, \exists \delta > 0 \, (0 < |x - r| < \delta \to f(x) > M)$. Let $H = \mathbb{R} \times (c, +\infty)$ be a horizontal strip containing $+\infty$ and let $M = \max\{c, 1\}$. Then there is $\delta > 0$ such that $0 < |x - r| < \delta$ implies $f(x) > M$. Let $H = (r - \delta, r + \delta) \times \mathbb{R}$ and let $R = H \cap V = (r - \delta, r + \delta) \times (c, +\infty)$. We show that R traps f around r. Indeed, if $x \in (r - \delta, r + \delta)$ and $x \neq r$, then $0 < |x - r| < \delta$ and so, $f(x) > M$. So, $(x, f(x)) \in (r - \delta, r + \delta) \times (M, +\infty) \subseteq (r - \delta, r + \delta) \times (c, +\infty)$ (because $c \leq M$). So, R traps f around r. $\qquad \square$

One-sided Limits

Let $A \subseteq \mathbb{R}$, let $f: A \to \mathbb{R}$, and let $r \in \mathbb{R}$ and $L \in \mathbb{R} \cup \{-\infty, +\infty\}$. We say that the **limit of f as x approaches r from the right is L**, written $\lim\limits_{x \to r^+} f(x) = L$, if for every horizontal strip H that contains L there is a vertical strip V of the form $(r, b) \times \mathbb{R}$ such that the rectangle $H \cap V$ traps f.

Example 13.15: Let $f: \mathbb{R} \setminus \{1\} \to \mathbb{R}$ be defined by $f(x) = \frac{1}{x - 1}$, let $r = 1$, and let $L = +\infty$. Let's show that $\lim\limits_{x \to 1^+} f(x) = +\infty$. Let $H = \mathbb{R} \times (c, +\infty)$ be a horizontal strip that contains $+\infty$ and let $M = \max\{1, c\}$. Let $V = \left(1, \frac{1}{M} + 1\right) \times \mathbb{R}$. We will show that $H \cap V = \left(1, \frac{1}{M} + 1\right) \times (c, +\infty)$ traps f. Let $x \in \left(1, \frac{1}{M} + 1\right)$, so that $1 < x < \frac{1}{M} + 1$. Then we have $0 < x - 1 < \frac{1}{M}$, and so, $\frac{1}{x - 1} > M \geq c$. So, $f(x) > c$. Since $x \in \left(1, \frac{1}{M} + 1\right)$ and $f(x) \in (c, +\infty)$, $(x, f(x)) \in \left(1, \frac{1}{M} + 1\right) \times (c, +\infty) = H \cap V$. Therefore, $H \cap V$ traps f. So, $\lim\limits_{x \to 1^+} f(x) = +\infty$.

Theorem 13.6: $\lim\limits_{x \to r^+} f(x) = L$ (L real) if and only if $\forall \epsilon > 0 \, \exists \delta > 0 \, (0 < x - r < \delta \to |f(x) - L| < \epsilon)$.

Proof: Suppose that $\lim\limits_{x \to r^+} f(x) = L$ and let $\epsilon > 0$. Let $H = \mathbb{R} \times (L - \epsilon, L + \epsilon)$. Since $\lim\limits_{x \to r^+} f(x) = L$, there is a vertical strip $V = (r, b) \times \mathbb{R}$ such that the rectangle $H \cap V = (r, b) \times (L - \epsilon, L + \epsilon)$ traps f. Let $\delta = b - r$, and let $0 < x - r < \delta$. Then $r < x < b$ and so, $x \in (r, b)$. Since $(r, b) \times (L - \epsilon, L + \epsilon)$ traps f, we have $f(x) \in (L - \epsilon, L + \epsilon)$. Thus, $L - \epsilon < f(x) < L + \epsilon$, or equivalently, $|f(x) - L| < \epsilon$.

Conversely, suppose that $\forall \epsilon > 0 \, \exists \delta > 0 \, (0 < x - r < \delta \to |f(x) - L| < \epsilon)$. Let $H = \mathbb{R} \times (c, d)$ be a horizontal strip containing L and let $\epsilon = \min\{L - c, d - L\}$. Then there is $\delta > 0$ such that $0 < x - r < \delta$ implies $|f(x) - L| < \epsilon$. Let $V = (r, r + \delta) \times \mathbb{R}$ and $R = H \cap V = (r, r + \delta) \times (c, d)$. We show that R traps f. If $x \in (r, r + \delta)$, then $r < x < r + \delta$, or equivalently, $0 < x - r < \delta$. So, $|f(x) - L| < \epsilon$. Therefore, $-\epsilon < f(x) - L < \epsilon$, or equivalently, $L - \epsilon < f(x) < L + \epsilon$. Thus, $(x, f(x)) \in (r, r + \delta) \times (L - \epsilon, L + \epsilon) \subseteq (r, r + \delta) \times (c, d)$ (Check this!). So, R traps f. $\qquad \square$

Problem Set 13

Full solutions to these problems are available for free download here:

www.SATPrepGet800.com/PMFBXSG

LEVEL 1

1. Let $f: \mathbb{R} \to \mathbb{R}$ be defined by $f(x) = 5x - 1$.

   (i)   Prove that $\lim_{x \to 3} f(x) = 14$.

   (ii) Prove that f is continuous on $\mathbb{R}$.

2. Let $r, c \in \mathbb{R}$ and let $f: \mathbb{R} \to \mathbb{R}$ be defined by $f(x) = c$. Prove that $\lim_{x \to r}[f(x)] = c$.

3. Let $A \subseteq \mathbb{R}$, let $f: A \to \mathbb{R}$, let $r, k \in \mathbb{R}$, and suppose that $\lim_{x \to r}[f(x)]$ is a finite real number. Prove that $\lim_{x \to r}[kf(x)] = k \lim_{x \to r}[f(x)]$.

LEVEL 2

4. Let $A \subseteq \mathbb{R}$, let $f: A \to \mathbb{R}$, and let $r \in \mathbb{R}$. Prove that f is continuous at r if and only if $\lim_{x \to r}[f(x)] = f(r)$.

5. Prove that every polynomial function $p: \mathbb{R} \to \mathbb{R}$ is continuous on $\mathbb{R}$.

LEVEL 3

6. Let $g: \mathbb{R} \to \mathbb{R}$ be defined by $g(x) = 2x^2 - 3x + 7$.

   (i)   Prove that $\lim_{x \to 1} g(x) = 6$.

   (ii) Prove that g is continuous on $\mathbb{R}$.

7. Suppose that $f, g: \mathbb{R} \to \mathbb{R}$, $a \in \mathbb{R}$, f is continuous at a, and g is continuous at $f(a)$. Prove that $g \circ f$ is continuous at a.

LEVEL 4

8. Let $h: \mathbb{R} \to \mathbb{R}$ be defined by $h(x) = \frac{x^3 - 4}{x^2 + 1}$. Prove that $\lim_{x \to 2} h(x) = \frac{4}{5}$.

9. Let $k: (0, \infty) \to \mathbb{R}$ be defined by $k(x) = \sqrt{x}$.

   (i)   Prove that $\lim_{x \to 25} k(x) = 5$.

   (ii)   Prove that f is continuous on $(0, \infty)$.

   (iii) Is f uniformly continuous on $(0, \infty)$?

10. Let $f: \mathbb{R} \to \mathbb{R}$ be defined by $f(x) = x^2$. Prove that f is continuous on $\mathbb{R}$, but not uniformly continuous on $\mathbb{R}$.

11. Prove that if $\lim\limits_{x \to r}[f(x)] > 0$, then there is a deleted neighborhood N of r such that $f(x) > 0$ for all $x \in N$.

12. Let $A \subseteq \mathbb{R}$, let $f: A \to \mathbb{R}$, let $r \in \mathbb{R}$, and suppose that $\lim\limits_{x \to r}[f(x)]$ is a finite real number. Prove that there is $M \in \mathbb{R}$ and an open interval (a, b) containing r such that $|f(x)| \le M$ for all $x \in (a, b) \setminus \{r\}$.

13. Let $A \subseteq \mathbb{R}$, let $f, g, h: A \to \mathbb{R}$, let $r \in \mathbb{R}$, let $f(x) \le g(x) \le h(x)$ for all $x \in A \setminus \{r\}$, and suppose that $\lim\limits_{x \to r}[f(x)] = \lim\limits_{x \to r}[h(x)] = L$. Prove that $\lim\limits_{x \to r}[g(x)] = L$.

LEVEL 5

14. Let $A \subseteq \mathbb{R}$, let $f, g: A \to \mathbb{R}$ such that $g(x) \ne 0$ for all $x \in A$, let $r \in \mathbb{R}$, and suppose that $\lim\limits_{x \to r}[f(x)]$ and $\lim\limits_{x \to r}[g(x)]$ are both finite real numbers such that $\lim\limits_{x \to r}[g(x)] \ne 0$. Prove that $\lim\limits_{x \to r}\left[\dfrac{f(x)}{g(x)}\right] = \dfrac{\lim\limits_{x \to r} f(x)}{\lim\limits_{x \to r} g(x)}$.

15. Give a reasonable equivalent definition for each of the following limits (like what was done in Theorem 13.5). r and L are finite real numbers.

   (i) $\quad \lim\limits_{x \to r} f(x) = -\infty$

   (ii) $\quad \lim\limits_{x \to +\infty} f(x) = L$

   (iii) $\quad \lim\limits_{x \to -\infty} f(x) = L$

   (iv) $\quad \lim\limits_{x \to +\infty} f(x) = +\infty$

   (v) $\quad \lim\limits_{x \to +\infty} f(x) = -\infty$

   (vi) $\quad \lim\limits_{x \to -\infty} f(x) = +\infty$

   (vii) $\quad \lim\limits_{x \to -\infty} f(x) = -\infty$

16. Let $f(x) = -x^2 + x + 1$. Use the $M - K$ definition of an infinite limit (that you came up with in Problem 15) to prove $\lim\limits_{x \to +\infty} f(x) = -\infty$.

17. Give a reasonable definition for each of the following limits (like what was done in Theorem 13.6). r and L are finite real numbers.

    (i) $\lim\limits_{x \to r^-} f(x) = L$

    (ii) $\lim\limits_{x \to r^+} f(x) = +\infty$

    (iii) $\lim\limits_{x \to r^+} f(x) = -\infty$

    (iv) $\lim\limits_{x \to r^-} f(x) = +\infty$

    (v) $\lim\limits_{x \to r^-} f(x) = -\infty$

18. Use the $M - \delta$ definition of a one-sided limit (that you came up with in Problem 17) to prove that $\lim\limits_{x \to 3^-} \dfrac{1}{x-3} = -\infty$.

19. Let $f(x) = \dfrac{x+1}{(x-1)^2}$. Prove that

    (i) $\lim\limits_{x \to +\infty} f(x) = 0$.

    (ii) $\lim\limits_{x \to 1^+} f(x) = +\infty$.

20. Let $f: \mathbb{R} \to \mathbb{R}$ be defined by $f(x) = \begin{cases} 0 & \text{if } x \text{ is rational.} \\ 1 & \text{if } x \text{ is irrational.} \end{cases}$ Prove that for all $r \in \mathbb{R}$, $\lim\limits_{x \to r}[f(x)]$ does not exist.

Topological Spaces

A topological space consists of a set S together with a collection of "open" subsets of S. Before we give the formal definition of "open," let's quickly review a standard example that most of us are somewhat familiar with.

Consider the set $\mathbb{R}$ of real numbers and call a subset X of $\mathbb{R}$ open if for every real number $x \in X$, there is an open interval (a, b) with $x \in (a, b)$ and $(a, b) \subseteq X$. We were first introduced to this definition of an open set in Lesson 6. In that same lesson, we showed that $\emptyset$ and $\mathbb{R}$ are both open sets (Theorem 6.4), we proved that an arbitrary union of open sets is open (Theorem 6.7), and we proved that a finite intersection of open sets is open (Theorem 6.9 and part (iii) of Problem 6 from that lesson). As it turns out, with this definition of open, every open set can be expressed as a union of open intervals (Theorem 6.8).

In this lesson we will move to a more general setting and explore arbitrary sets together with various collections of "open" subsets of these sets. Let's begin by giving the formal definition of a topological space.

Let S be a set and let $\mathcal{T}$ be a collection of subsets of S. $\mathcal{T}$ is said to be a **topology** on S if the following three properties are satisfied:

1. $\emptyset \in \mathcal{T}$ and $S \in \mathcal{T}$.

2. If $X \subseteq \mathcal{T}$, then $\bigcup X \in \mathcal{T}$ ($\mathcal{T}$ is closed under taking arbitrary unions).

3. If $Y \subseteq \mathcal{T}$ and Y is finite, then $\bigcap Y \in \mathcal{T}$ ($\mathcal{T}$ is closed under taking finite intersections).

A **topological space** is a pair $(S, \mathcal{T})$, where S is a set and $\mathcal{T}$ is a topology on S. We will call the elements of $\mathcal{T}$ **open sets**. Complements of elements of $\mathcal{T}$ will be called **closed sets** (A is closed if and only if $S \setminus A$ is open).

We may sometimes refer to the topological space S. When we do, there is a topology $\mathcal{T}$ on S that we are simply not mentioning explicitly.

Example 14.1:

1. Let $S = \{a\}$ be a set consisting of just the one element a. There is just one topology on S. It is the topology $\mathcal{T} = \{\emptyset, \{a\}\}$.

   Note that the power set of S is $\mathcal{P}(S) = \{\emptyset, \{a\}\}$ and $\mathcal{P}(\mathcal{P}(S)) = \{\emptyset, \{\emptyset\}, \{\{a\}\}, \{\emptyset, \{a\}\}\}$. Notice that the topology $\mathcal{T} = \{\emptyset, \{a\}\}$ is an element of $\mathcal{P}(\mathcal{P}(S))$. However, the other three elements of $\mathcal{P}(\mathcal{P}(S))$ are **not** topologies on $S = \{a\}$.

   In general, for any set S, a topology on S is a subset of $\mathcal{P}(S)$, or equivalently, an element of $\mathcal{P}(\mathcal{P}(S))$. If $S \neq \emptyset$, then not every element of $\mathcal{P}(\mathcal{P}(S))$ will be a topology on S.

For example, if $S = \{a\}$, Then $\emptyset, \{\emptyset\}$, and $\{\{a\}\}$ are all elements of $\mathcal{P}\big(\mathcal{P}(S)\big)$ that are **not** topologies on S. $\emptyset$ and $\{\emptyset\}$ fail to be topologies on $\{a\}$ because they do not contain $\{a\}$, while $\{\{a\}\}$ fails to be a topology on $\{a\}$ because it does not contain $\emptyset$.

2. Let $S = \{a, b\}$ be a set consisting of the two distinct elements a and b. There are four topologies on S: $\mathcal{T}_1 = \{\emptyset, \{a, b\}\}$, $\mathcal{T}_2 = \{\emptyset, \{a\}, \{a, b\}\}$, $\mathcal{T}_3 = \{\emptyset, \{b\}, \{a, b\}\}$, and $\mathcal{T}_4 = \{\emptyset, \{a\}, \{b\}, \{a, b\}\}$. We can visualize these topologies as follows.

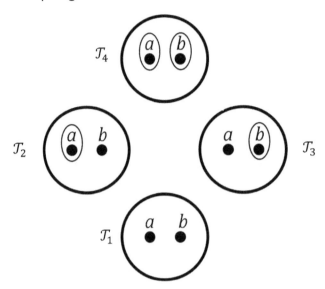

Notice that all four topologies in the figure have the elements a and b inside a large circle because $S = \{a, b\}$ is in all four topologies. Also, it is understood that $\emptyset$ is in all the topologies.

$\mathcal{T}_1$ is called the **trivial topology** (or **indiscrete topology**) on S because it contains only $\emptyset$ and S. $\mathcal{T}_4$ is called the **discrete topology** on S, as it contains every subset of S. The discrete topology is just $\mathcal{P}(S)$ (the power set of S).

The topologies $\mathcal{T}_2$, $\mathcal{T}_3$, and $\mathcal{T}_4$ are **finer** than the topology $\mathcal{T}_1$ because $\mathcal{T}_1 \subseteq \mathcal{T}_2$, $\mathcal{T}_1 \subseteq \mathcal{T}_3$ and $\mathcal{T}_1 \subseteq \mathcal{T}_4$. We can also say that $\mathcal{T}_1$ is **coarser** than $\mathcal{T}_2$, $\mathcal{T}_3$, and $\mathcal{T}_4$. Similarly, $\mathcal{T}_4$ is finer than $\mathcal{T}_2$ and $\mathcal{T}_3$, or equivalently, $\mathcal{T}_2$ and $\mathcal{T}_3$ are coarser than $\mathcal{T}_4$. The topologies $\mathcal{T}_2$ and $\mathcal{T}_3$ are **incomparable**. Neither one is finer than the other. To help understand the terminology "finer" and "coarser," we can picture the open sets as a pile of rocks. If we were to smash that pile of rocks (the open sets) with a hammer, the rocks will break into smaller pieces (creating more open sets), and the pile of rocks (the topology) will have been made "finer."

Note that for any set S, the discrete topology is always the finest topology and the trivial topology is always the coarsest.

3. Let $S = \{a, b, c\}$ be a set consisting of the three distinct elements a, b, and c. There are 29 topologies on S. Let's look at a few of them.

We have the trivial topology $\mathcal{T}_1 = \{\emptyset, \{a, b, c\}\}$.

If we throw in just a singleton set (a set consisting of just one element), we get the three topologies $\mathcal{T}_2 = \{\emptyset, \{a\}, \{a, b, c\}\}$, $\mathcal{T}_3 = \{\emptyset, \{b\}, \{a, b, c\}\}$, $\mathcal{T}_4 = \{\emptyset, \{c\}, \{a, b, c\}\}$.

Note that we can't throw in just two singleton sets. For example, $\{\emptyset, \{a\}, \{b\}, \{a, b, c\}\}$ is **not** a topology on S. Do you see the problem? It's not closed under taking unions: $\{a\}$ and $\{b\}$ are there, but $\{a, b\} = \{a\} \cup \{b\}$ is not! However, $\mathcal{T}_5 = \{\emptyset, \{a\}, \{b\}, \{a, b\}, \{a, b, c\}\}$ **is** a topology on S.

Here are a few **chains** of topologies on S written in order from the coarsest to the finest topology (chains are linearly ordered subsets of $\{\mathcal{T} \mid \mathcal{T}$ is a topology on $S\}$).

$$\{\emptyset, \{a, b, c\}\} \subseteq \{\emptyset, \{a\}, \{a, b, c\}\} \subseteq \{\emptyset, \{a\}, \{a, b\}, \{a, b, c\}\} \subseteq \{\emptyset, \{a\}, \{b\}, \{a, b\}, \{a, b, c\}\}$$
$$\subseteq \{\emptyset, \{a\}, \{b\}, \{a, b\}, \{a, c\}, \{a, b, c\}\} \subseteq \{\emptyset, \{a\}, \{b\}, \{c\}, \{a, b\}, \{b, c\}, \{a, c\}, \{a, b, c\}\}$$

$$\{\emptyset, \{a, b, c\}\} \subseteq \{\emptyset, \{a\}, \{a, b, c\}\} \subseteq \{\emptyset, \{a\}, \{b, c\}, \{a, b, c\}\} \subseteq \{\emptyset, \{a\}, \{b\}, \{a, b\}, \{b, c\}, \{a, b, c\}\}$$
$$\subseteq \{\emptyset, \{a\}, \{b\}, \{c\}, \{a, b\}, \{b, c\}, \{a, c\}, \{a, b, c\}\}$$

$$\{\emptyset, \{a, b, c\}\} \subseteq \{\emptyset, \{b, c\}, \{a, b, c\}\} \subseteq \{\emptyset, \{c\}, \{b, c\}, \{a, b, c\}\} \subseteq \{\emptyset, \{b\}, \{c\}, \{b, c\}, \{a, b, c\}\}$$
$$\subseteq \{\emptyset, \{b\}, \{c\}, \{a, b\}, \{b, c\}, \{a, b, c\}\} \subseteq \{\emptyset, \{a\}, \{b\}, \{c\}, \{a, b\}, \{b, c\}, \{a, c\}, \{a, b, c\}\}$$

Below is a picture of all 29 topologies on $\{a, b, c\}$ (to avoid clutter we left out the names of the elements). Again, a large circle surrounds a, b, and c in all cases because $S = \{a, b, c\}$ is in all 29 topologies. Also, it is understood that the empty set is in all these topologies.

I organized these topologies by the number of sets in each topology. The lowest row consists of just the trivial topology. The next row up consists of the topologies with just one additional set (three sets in total because $\emptyset$ and S are in every topology), and so on.

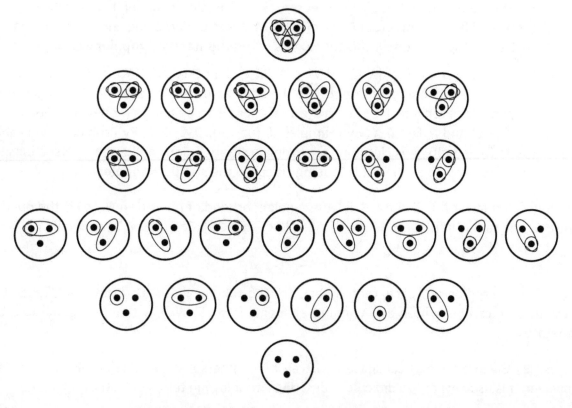

Below we see a visual representation of the three chains described above. As each path moves from the bottom to the top of the picture, we move from coarser to finer topologies.

191

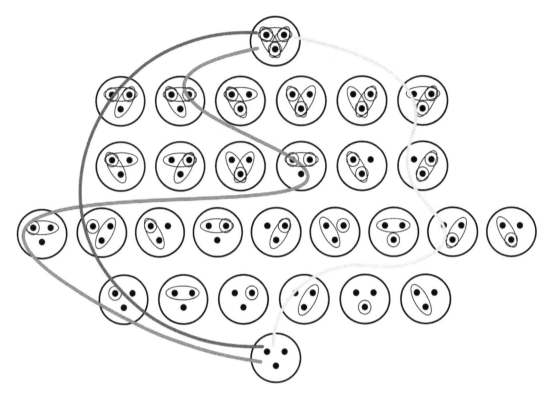

4. Let $S = \mathbb{R}$ and let $\mathcal{T} = \{X \subseteq \mathbb{R} \mid \forall x \in X \; \exists a, b \in \mathbb{R}(x \in (a, b) \wedge (a, b) \subseteq X\}$. In other words, we are defining a subset of $\mathbb{R}$ to be open as we did in Lesson 6. That is, a subset X of $\mathbb{R}$ is open if for every real number $x \in X$, there is an open interval (a, b) with $x \in (a, b)$ and $(a, b) \subseteq X$. By Theorem 6.4, $\emptyset, \mathbb{R} \in \mathcal{T}$. By Theorem 6.7, $\mathcal{T}$ is closed under taking arbitrary unions. By Problem 6 from Problem Set 6 (part (iii)), $\mathcal{T}$ is closed under taking finite intersections. It follows that $\mathcal{T}$ is a topology on $\mathbb{R}$. This topology is called the **standard topology on $\mathbb{R}$**.

5. Let $S = \mathbb{C}$ and let $\mathcal{T} = \{X \subseteq \mathbb{C} \mid \forall z \in X \; \exists a \in \mathbb{C} \; \exists r \in \mathbb{R}^+(z \in N_r(a) \wedge N_r(a) \subseteq X\}$. In other words, we are defining a subset of $\mathbb{C}$ to be open as we did in Lesson 7. That is, a subset X of $\mathbb{C}$ is open if for every complex number $z \in X$, there is an open disk (or neighborhood) $N_r(a)$ with $z \in N_r(a)$ and $N_r(a) \subseteq X$. By Example 7.8 (part 4), $\emptyset, \mathbb{C} \in \mathcal{T}$. By Problem 8 in Problem Set 7 (parts (i) and (ii)), $\mathcal{T}$ is closed under taking arbitrary unions and finite intersections. It follows that $\mathcal{T}$ is a topology on $\mathbb{C}$. This topology is called the **standard topology on $\mathbb{C}$**.

Note: Recall that for $a \in \mathbb{C}$ and $r \in \mathbb{R}^+$ the r-neighborhood of a, written $N_r(a)$ is the open disk with center a and radius r. That is, $N_r(a) = \{z \in \mathbb{C} \mid |z - a| < r\}$. See Lesson 7 for details.

Bases

If $(S, \mathcal{T})$ is a topological space, then a **basis** for the topology $\mathcal{T}$ is a subset $\mathcal{B} \subseteq \mathcal{T}$ such that every element of $\mathcal{T}$ can be written as a union of elements from $\mathcal{B}$. We say that $\mathcal{T}$ is **generated** by $\mathcal{B}$ or $\mathcal{B}$ **generates** $\mathcal{T}$.

Notes: (1) Given a topological space $\mathcal{T}$, it can be cumbersome to describe all the open sets in $\mathcal{T}$. However, it is usually not too difficult to describe a topology in terms of its basis elements.

(2) If $(S, \mathcal{T})$ is a topological space and $\mathcal{B}$ is a basis for $\mathcal{T}$, then $\mathcal{T} = \{\bigcup X \mid X \subseteq \mathcal{B}\}$.

(3) More generally, if $\mathcal{X}$ is any collection of subsets of S, then we can say that $\mathcal{X}$ generates $\{\cup X \mid X \subseteq \mathcal{X}\}$. However, this set will not always be a topology on S.

Example 14.2:

1. Let $S = \{a, b, c\}$ and $\mathcal{T} = \{\emptyset, \{a\}, \{b\}, \{a, b\}, \{b, c\}, \{a, b, c\}\}$. The set $\mathcal{B} = \{\{a\}, \{b\}, \{b, c\}\}$ is a basis for $\mathcal{T}$. Indeed, we have $\{a\} = \cup\{\{a\}\}$, $\{b\} = \cup\{\{b\}\}$, $\{a, b\} = \cup\{\{a\}, \{b\}\} = \{a\} \cup \{b\}$, $\{b, c\} = \cup\{\{b, c\}\}$, $\{a, b, c\} = \cup\{\{a\}, \{b, c\}\} = \{a\} \cup \{b, c\}$, and $\emptyset = \cup\emptyset$.

   (Note that $\cup\emptyset = \{y \mid$ there is $Y \in \emptyset$ with $y \in Y\} = \emptyset$. It follows that $\emptyset$ does **not** need to be included in a basis.)

   We can visualize the basis $\mathcal{B}$ and the topology $\mathcal{T}$ that is generated by $\mathcal{B}$ as follows.

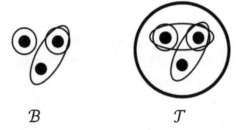

$$\mathcal{B} \qquad\qquad \mathcal{T}$$

   We know $\emptyset \in \mathcal{T}$ (even though $\emptyset$ is not indicated in the picture of $\mathcal{T}$) because $\mathcal{T}$ is a topology. On the other hand, it is unclear from the picture of $\mathcal{B}$ whether $\emptyset \in \mathcal{B}$. However, it doesn't really matter. Since $\emptyset$ is equal to an empty union, $\emptyset$ will always be generated from $\mathcal{B}$ anyway.

   There can be more than one basis for the same topology. Here are a few more bases for the topology $\mathcal{T}$ just discussed (are there any others?):

   $$\mathcal{B}_1 = \{\{a\}, \{b\}, \{a, b\}, \{b, c\}\} \qquad \mathcal{B}_2 = \{\{a\}, \{b\}, \{a, b\}, \{b, c\}, \{a, b, c\}\}$$
   $$\mathcal{B}_3 = \{\emptyset, \{a\}, \{b\}, \{b, c\}\} \qquad\qquad \mathcal{B}_4 = \mathcal{T} = \{\emptyset, \{a\}, \{b\}, \{a, b\}, \{b, c\}, \{a, b, c\}\}$$

2. Let $S = \{a, b, c\}$ and let $\mathcal{X} = \{\{a\}, \{b\}\}$. In this case, $\mathcal{X}$ generates $\{\emptyset, \{a\}, \{b\}, \{a, b\}\}$. This set is **not** a topology on S because $S = \{a, b, c\}$ is not in the set. The reason that $\mathcal{X}$ failed to generate a topology on S is that it didn't completely "cover" S. Specifically, c is not in any set in $\mathcal{X}$.

   In general, if an element x from a set S does not appear in any of the sets in a set $\mathcal{X}$, then no matter how large a union we take from $\mathcal{X}$, we will never be able to generate a set from $\mathcal{X}$ with x in it, and therefore, $\mathcal{X}$ will not generate a topology on S (although it **might** generate a topology on a subset of S).

3. Let $S = \{a, b, c\}$ and $\mathcal{X} = \{\{a, b\}, \{b, c\}\}$. In this case, $\mathcal{X}$ generates $\{\emptyset, \{a, b\}, \{b, c\}, \{a, b, c\}\}$. This set is also **not** a topology because $\{a, b\} \cap \{b, c\} = \{b\}$ is not in the set. In other words, the set is not closed under finite intersections.

   In general, if there are two sets A and B in $\mathcal{X}$ such that the intersection $A \cap B$ does **not** include some set in $\mathcal{X}$, then the set generated by $\mathcal{X}$ will not be closed under finite intersections, and therefore, $\mathcal{X}$ will not generate a topology on S. Note that $A \cap B$ itself does not necessarily need to be in $\mathcal{X}$. However, there does need to be a set C with $C \subseteq A \cap B$ and $C \in \mathcal{X}$.

Parts 2 and 3 from Example 14.2 show us that not every collection X of subsets of a set S is the basis for a topology on S. Let's see if we can find conditions on a collection X of subsets of S that will guarantee that X is a basis for a topology on S.

We say that X **covers** S if every element of S belongs to at least one member of X. Symbolically, we have

$$\forall x \in S \, \exists A \in X (x \in A).$$

We say that X has the **intersection containment property** on S if every element of S that is in the intersection of two sets in X is also in some set in X that is contained in that intersection.

$$\forall x \in S \, \forall A, B \in X\big(x \in A \cap B \to \exists C \in X \, (x \in C \wedge C \subseteq A \cap B)\big).$$

Example 14.3:

1. Once again, let $S = \{a, b, c\}$. $X_1 = \{\{b\}, \{b, c\}\}$ does **not** cover S because $a \in S$ does not belong to any member of X_1. X_1 does have the intersection containment property—the only element of $\{b\} \cap \{b, c\} = \{b\}$ is b, and $b \in \{b\} \in X_1$ and $\{b\}$ is contained in $\{b\} \cap \{b, c\}$. Notice that the set that X_1 generates is $\{\emptyset, \{b\}, \{b, c\}\}$. This set is not a topology on S because $S = \{a, b, c\}$ is not in this set. However, it is a topology on $\{b, c\}$.

   $X_2 = \{\{a, b\}, \{b, c\}\}$ covers S, but does **not** have the intersection containment property. Indeed, $\{a, b\} \cap \{b, c\} = \{b\}$ and $b \in \{b\}$, but $\{b\} \notin X_2$. Notice that the set that X_2 generates is $\{\emptyset, \{a, b\}, \{b, c\}, \{a, b, c\}\}$. This set is not a topology on S because $\{a, b\} \cap \{b, c\} = \{b\}$ is not in the set.

   $B = \{\{b\}, \{a, b\}, \{b, c\}\}$ covers S and has the intersection containment property. The set that B generates is the topology $\mathcal{T} = \{\emptyset, \{b\}, \{a, b\}, \{b, c\}, \{a, b, c\}\}$.

   We can visualize the sets X_1, X_2, B, and $\mathcal{T}$ as follows.

   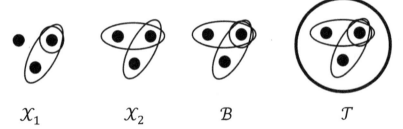

   | X_1 | X_2 | B | $\mathcal{T}$ |

2. Let $S = \mathbb{R}$ and let $B = \{(a, b) \mid a, b \in \mathbb{R} \wedge a < b\}$ be the set of open intervals with endpoints in $\mathbb{R}$. B covers $\mathbb{R}$ because if $x \in \mathbb{R}$, then $x \in (x - 1, x + 1) \in B$. B also has the intersection containment property. Indeed, if $x \in \mathbb{R}$ and $(a, b), (c, d) \in B$ with $x \in (a, b) \cap (c, d)$, then $x \in (a, b) \cap (c, d) = (e, f)$, where $e = \max\{a, c\}$ and $f = \min\{b, d\}$ (see part (ii) of Problem 6 from Problem Set 6) and $(e, f) \in B$. In fact, B is a basis on $\mathbb{R}$ that generates the standard topology of $\mathbb{R}$.

To see that $\mathcal{B}$ generates the standard topology on $\mathbb{R}$, let $\mathcal{T}$ be the standard topology on $\mathbb{R}$ and let $\mathcal{T}'$ be the topology generated by $\mathcal{B}$. First, let $X \in \mathcal{T}$. By Theorem 6.8, X can be expressed as a union of bounded open intervals. So, $X \in \mathcal{T}'$. Since $X \in \mathcal{T}$ was arbitrary, $\mathcal{T} \subseteq \mathcal{T}'$. Now, let $X \in \mathcal{T}'$. Then X is a union of bounded open intervals, say $X = \bigcup Y$. Let $x \in X$. Since $X = \bigcup Y$, $x \in \bigcup Y$. So, $x \in (a, b)$ for some $(a, b) \in Y$. Since $(a, b) \in Y$, $(a, b) \subseteq \bigcup Y = X$. Therefore, $X \in \mathcal{T}$. Since $X \in \mathcal{T}'$ was arbitrary, $\mathcal{T}' \subseteq \mathcal{T}$. Since $\mathcal{T} \subseteq \mathcal{T}'$ and $\mathcal{T}' \subseteq \mathcal{T}$, $\mathcal{T}' = \mathcal{T}$.

3. Let $S = \mathbb{R}$ and let $\mathcal{X} = \{(-\infty, b) \mid b \in \mathbb{R}\} \cup \{(a, \infty) \mid a \in \mathbb{R}\}$. $\mathcal{X}$ covers $\mathbb{R}$ because if $x \in \mathbb{R}$, then $x \in (x - 1, \infty) \in \mathcal{X}$. However, $\mathcal{X}$ does **not** have the intersection containment property. For example, $0 \in (-\infty, 1) \cap (-1, \infty) = (-1, 1)$, but there is no set in $\mathcal{X}$ contained in $(-1, 1)$. The set generated by $\mathcal{X}$ is $\mathcal{X} \cup \{(-\infty, b) \cup (a, \infty) \mid a, b \in \mathbb{R} \land b < a\} \cup \{\emptyset, \mathbb{R}\}$. This set is **not** closed under finite intersections, and therefore, it is **not** a topology on $\mathbb{R}$.

Based on the previous examples, the next theorem should come as no surprise.

Theorem 14.1: Let S be a nonempty set and let $\mathcal{B}$ be a collection of subsets of S. $\mathcal{B}$ is a basis for a topology on S if and only if $\mathcal{B}$ covers S and $\mathcal{B}$ has the intersection containment property on S.

Note: The set generated by $\mathcal{B}$ is $\{\bigcup X \mid X \subseteq \mathcal{B}\}$. This set can also be written in the alternative form $\{A \subseteq S \mid \forall x \in A \, \exists B \in \mathcal{B}(x \in B \land B \subseteq A)\}$. You will be asked to verify that these two sets are equal in Problem 6 below. We will use this alternative form of the set generated by $\mathcal{B}$ in the proof of Theorem 14.1.

Proof of Theorem 14.1: Suppose that $\mathcal{B}$ covers S and $\mathcal{B}$ has the intersection containment property on S. The set generated by $\mathcal{B}$ is $\mathcal{T} = \{A \subseteq S \mid \forall x \in A \, \exists B \in \mathcal{B}(x \in B \land B \subseteq A)\}$. Let's check that $\mathcal{T}$ is a topology on S.

Since $A = \emptyset$ vacuously satisfies the condition $\forall x \in A \, \exists B \in \mathcal{B}(x \in B \land B \subseteq A)$, we have $\emptyset \in \mathcal{T}$.

To see that $S \in \mathcal{T}$, let $x \in S$. Since $\mathcal{B}$ covers S, there is $B \in \mathcal{B}$ such that $x \in B$ and $B \subseteq S$. So, $S \in \mathcal{T}$.

Let $X \subseteq \mathcal{T}$ and let $x \in \bigcup X$. Then there is $A \in X$ with $x \in A$. Since $X \subseteq \mathcal{T}$, $A \in \mathcal{T}$. So, there is $B \in \mathcal{B}$ such that $x \in B$ and $B \subseteq A$. Since $B \subseteq A$ and $A \subseteq \bigcup X$, $B \subseteq \bigcup X$. It follows that the condition $\forall x \in \bigcup X \, \exists B \in \mathcal{B}(x \in B \land B \subseteq \bigcup X)$ is satisfied. So, $\bigcup X \in \mathcal{T}$.

We now prove by induction on $n \in \mathbb{N}$ that for $n \geq 2$, the intersection of n sets in $\mathcal{T}$ is also in $\mathcal{T}$.

Base Case ($n = 2$): Let $A_1, A_2 \in \mathcal{T}$ and let $x \in A_1 \cap A_2$. Then there are $B_1, B_2 \in \mathcal{B}$ with $x \in B_1$, $x \in B_2$, $B_1 \subseteq A_1$ and $B_2 \subseteq A_2$. Since $x \in B_1$ and $x \in B_2$, $x \in B_1 \cap B_2$. Since $\mathcal{B}$ has the intersection containment property, there is $C \in \mathcal{B}$ such that $x \in C$ and $C \subseteq B_1 \cap B_2$. Since $B_1 \subseteq A_1$ and $B_2 \subseteq A_2$, $C \subseteq A_1 \cap A_2$. Therefore, $A_1 \cap A_2 \in \mathcal{T}$.

Inductive Step: Suppose that the intersection of k sets in $\mathcal{T}$ is always in $\mathcal{T}$. Let $A_1, A_2, \ldots, A_k, A_{k+1} \in \mathcal{T}$ and let $x \in A_1 \cap A_2 \cap \cdots \cap A_k \cap A_{k+1}$. By the inductive hypothesis, $A_1 \cap A_2 \cap \cdots \cap A_k \in \mathcal{T}$. If we let $C = A_1 \cap A_2 \cap \cdots \cap A_k$ and $D = A_{k+1}$, then we have $C, D \in \mathcal{T}$. By the base case, $C \cap D \in \mathcal{T}$. It follows that $A_1 \cap A_2 \cap \cdots \cap A_k \cap A_{k+1} = (A_1 \cap A_2 \cap \cdots \cap A_k) \cap A_{k+1} = C \cap D \in \mathcal{T}$.

Since $\emptyset, S \in \mathcal{T}$, $\mathcal{T}$ is closed under arbitrary unions, and $\mathcal{T}$ is closed under finite intersections, it follows that $\mathcal{T}$ is a topology. By the note following the statement of Theorem 14.1, $\mathcal{B}$ generates $\mathcal{T}$.

Conversely, suppose that $\mathcal{B}$ is a basis for a topology $\mathcal{T}$ on S. Since $\mathcal{T}$ is a topology on S, $S \in \mathcal{T}$. Since $\mathcal{B}$ is a basis for $\mathcal{T}$, $S = \bigcup \mathcal{X}$ for some $\mathcal{X} \subseteq \mathcal{B}$. Let $x \in S$. Then $x \in \bigcup \mathcal{X}$. So, there is $A \in \mathcal{X}$ with $x \in A$. Since $\mathcal{X} \subseteq \mathcal{B}$, $A \in \mathcal{B}$. Since $x \in S$ was arbitrary, $\mathcal{B}$ covers S.

Let $x \in A_1 \cap A_2$, where $A_1, A_2 \in \mathcal{B}$. Then $A_1, A_2 \in \mathcal{T}$, and since $\mathcal{T}$ is a topology on S, $A_1 \cap A_2 \in \mathcal{T}$. Since $\mathcal{B}$ is a basis for $\mathcal{T}$, $A_1 \cap A_2 = \bigcup \mathcal{X}$ for some $\mathcal{X} \subseteq \mathcal{B}$. It follows that $x \in \bigcup \mathcal{X}$. So, there is $C \in \mathcal{X}$ with $x \in C$. Since $\mathcal{X} \subseteq \mathcal{B}$, $C \in \mathcal{B}$. Also, $C \subseteq \bigcup \mathcal{X} = A_1 \cap A_2$. Since $A_1, A_2 \in \mathcal{B}$ and $x \in S$ were arbitrary, $\mathcal{B}$ has the intersection containment property. $\qquad \square$

Example 14.4:

1. If S is any set, then $\mathcal{B} = \{S\}$ is a basis for the trivial topology on S. Note that $\{S\}$ covers S and $\{S\}$ has the intersection containment property on S (there is just one instance to check: $S \cap S = S$ and $S \in \{S\}$).

2. If S is any set, then $\mathcal{B} = \{\{x\} \mid x \in S\}$ is a basis for the discrete topology on S. $\mathcal{B}$ covers S because if $x \in S$, then $\{x\} \in \mathcal{B}$ and $x \in \{x\}$. $\mathcal{B}$ vacuously has the intersection containment property because $\mathcal{B}$ is pairwise disjoint.

3. Let $S = \mathbb{R}$ and let $\mathcal{B} = \{(a, b) \mid a, b \in \mathbb{R} \wedge a < b\}$. We saw in Example 14.3 (part 2) that $\mathcal{B}$ covers $\mathbb{R}$ and that $\mathcal{B}$ has the finite containment property on $\mathbb{R}$. It follows that $\mathcal{B}$ is a basis for a topology on $\mathbb{R}$. In fact, we already saw in the same Example that $\mathcal{B}$ generates the standard topology on $\mathbb{R}$.

    The basis $\mathcal{B}$ just described is uncountable because $\mathbb{R}$ is uncountable and the function $f : \mathbb{R} \to \mathcal{B}$ defined by $f(r) = (r, r + 1)$ is injective. Does $\mathbb{R}$ with the standard topology have a countable basis? In fact, it does! Let $\mathcal{B}' = \{(a, b) \mid a, b \in \mathbb{Q} \wedge a < b\}$. In Problem 9 below you will be asked to show that $\mathcal{B}'$ is countable and that $\mathcal{B}'$ is a basis for $\mathbb{R}$ with the standard topology.

4. We saw in part 3 of Example 14.3 that $\mathcal{X} = \{(-\infty, b) \mid b \in \mathbb{R}\} \cup \{(a, \infty) \mid a \in \mathbb{R}\}$ does **not** have the intersection containment property. It follows from Theorem 14.1 that $\mathcal{X}$ is **not** a basis for a topology on $\mathbb{R}$.

    However, $\mathcal{B}^* = \{(a, \infty) \mid a \in \mathbb{R}\}$ covers $\mathbb{R}$ and has the intersection containment property. Therefore, $\mathcal{B}^*$ is a basis for a topology $\mathcal{T}^*$ on $\mathbb{R}$. Since every set of the form (a, ∞) is open in the standard topology, $\mathcal{T}^*$ is coarser than the standard topology on $\mathbb{R}$. Since no bounded open interval is in $\mathcal{T}^*$, we see that $\mathcal{T}^*$ is **strictly** coarser than the standard topology on $\mathbb{R}$.

Note: Although the set $\mathcal{X} = \{(-\infty, b) \mid b \in \mathbb{R}\} \cup \{(a, \infty) \mid a \in \mathbb{R}\}$ is not a basis for a topology on $\mathbb{R}$, if we let $\mathcal{B}$ be the collection of all finite intersections of sets in $\mathcal{X}$, then $\mathcal{B}$ **does** form a basis for $\mathbb{R}$ (because $\mathcal{X}$ covers $\mathbb{R}$). In this case, we call $\mathcal{X}$ a **subbasis** for the topology generated by $\mathcal{B}$. Since every bounded open interval is in $\mathcal{B}$, it is not hard to see that $\mathcal{B}$ generates the standard topology on $\mathbb{R}$. We can also say that the standard topology on $\mathbb{R}$ is generated by the subbasis $\mathcal{X}$.

Types of Topological Spaces

A topological space $(S, \mathcal{T})$ is a **T_0-space** (or **Kolmogorov space**) if for all $x, y \in S$ with $x \neq y$, there is $U \in \mathcal{T}$ such that either $x \in U$ and $y \notin U$ or $x \notin U$ and $y \in U$.

In other words, in a T_0-space, given any two elements, there is an open set that contains one of the elements and excludes the other. In the picture on the right we see two typical elements a and b in a T_0-space. We have drawn an open set containing a and excluding b. There does not need to be an open set containing b and excluding a (although there can be).

Example 14.5:

1. Let $S = \{a, b\}$ where $a \neq b$. S together with the trivial topology $\{\emptyset, \{a, b\}\}$ is **not** a T_0-space. In fact, the trivial topology on any set with more than one element is not a T_0-space.

    $\{a, b\}$ together with the discrete topology $\{\emptyset, \{a\}, \{b\}, \{a, b\}\}$ **is** a T_0-space because the open set $\{a\}$ satisfies $a \in \{a\}$ and $b \notin \{a\}$. In fact, the discrete topology on any set is a T_0-space.

    The other two topologies on $\{a, b\}$ are also T_0-spaces. For example, $\{\emptyset, \{a\}, \{a, b\}\}$ is a T_0-space because $\{a\}$ is open, $a \in \{a\}$ and $b \notin \{a\}$.

2. Let $S = \mathbb{R}$ and let $\mathcal{T}$ be the topology generated by the basis $\{(a, \infty) \mid a \in \mathbb{R}\}$. Then $(S, \mathcal{T})$ is a T_0-space. If $a, b \in \mathbb{R}$ with $a < b$, then $U = (a, \infty)$ is an open set with $b \in U$ and $a \notin U$.

3. If $(S, \mathcal{T})$ is a T_0-space and $\mathcal{T}'$ is finer than $\mathcal{T}$, then $(S, \mathcal{T}')$ is also a T_0-space. Indeed, if $U \in \mathcal{T}$ with $x \in U$ and $y \notin U$, then since $\mathcal{T}'$ is finer than $\mathcal{T}$, we have $U \in \mathcal{T}'$.

    For example, since the standard topology on $\mathbb{R}$ is finer than the topology generated by $\{(a, \infty) \mid a \in \mathbb{R}\}$, $\mathbb{R}$ together with the standard topology on $\mathbb{R}$ is a T_0-space.

A topological space $(S, \mathcal{T})$ is a **T_1-space** (or **accessible space** or **Tikhonov space**) if for all $x, y \in S$ with $x \neq y$, there are $U, V \in \mathcal{T}$ such that $x \in U$ and $y \notin U$ and $x \notin V$ and $y \in V$.

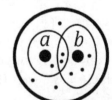

In the picture on the right we see two typical elements a and b in a T_1-space. We have drawn an open set containing a and excluding b and an open set containing b and excluding a. These two open sets **do not** need to be disjoint. The smaller dots in the picture are representing some elements of the space other than a and b.

Example 14.6:

1. $S = \{a, b\}$ together with the discrete topology $\{\emptyset, \{a\}, \{b\}, \{a, b\}\}$ **is** a T_1-space because the open sets $\{a\}$ and $\{b\}$ satisfy $a \in \{a\}$, $b \notin \{a\}$, $b \in \{b\}$, and $a \notin \{b\}$. In fact, the discrete topology on any set is a T_1-space.

    It should be clear from the definitions that every T_1-space is a T_0-space. It follows that the trivial topology on any set with more than one element is **not** a T_1-space.

The other two topologies on $\{a, b\}$ are **not** T_1-spaces. For example, $\{\emptyset, \{a\}, \{a, b\}\}$ is not a T_1-space because the only open set containing b also contains a.

In fact, the only topology on any finite set that is T_1 is the discrete topology. To see this, let $\mathcal{T}$ be a topology on a finite set X that is T_1 and let $x \in X$. For each $y \in X$ with $y \neq x$, there is an open set U_y such that $x \in U_y$ and $y \notin U_y$. It follows that $U = \cap\{U_y \mid y \in X \wedge y \neq x\}$ is open and it is easy to see that $U = \{x\}$. So, $\mathcal{T}$ is generated by the one point sets, and therefore, $\mathcal{T}$ is the discrete topology on X.

2. Let $S = \mathbb{R}$ and let $\mathcal{T}$ be the topology generated by the basis $\{(a, \infty) \mid a \in \mathbb{R}\}$. Then $(S, \mathcal{T})$ is **not** a T_1-space. To see this, let $x, y \in \mathbb{R}$ with $x < y$. Let U be an open set containing x, say $U = (a, \infty)$. Since $x < y$ and $a < x$, we have $a < y$, and so, $y \in U$. Therefore, there is no open set U with $x \in U$ and $y \notin U$.

   It's worth noting that the topology generated by $\{(a, \infty) \mid a \in \mathbb{R}\}$ is $\{(a, \infty) \mid a \in \mathbb{R}\} \cup \{\emptyset, \mathbb{R}\}$.

3. Let $S = \mathbb{R}$ and let $\mathcal{T}$ be the topology generated by the basis $\mathcal{B} = \{X \subseteq \mathbb{R} \mid \mathbb{R} \setminus X \text{ is finite}\}$. $\mathcal{T}$ is called the **cofinite topology** on $\mathbb{R}$. I leave it to the reader to verify that $\mathcal{B}$ generates a topology on $\mathbb{R}$ that is strictly coarser than the standard topology (Problem 3 below). It's easy to see that $(S, \mathcal{T})$ is a T_1-space. Indeed, if $a, b \in \mathbb{R}$ with $a \neq b$, then let $U = \mathbb{R} \setminus \{b\}$ and $V = \mathbb{R} \setminus \{a\}$.

4. If $(S, \mathcal{T})$ is a T_1-space and $\mathcal{T}'$ is finer than $\mathcal{T}$, then $(S, \mathcal{T}')$ is also a T_1-space. Indeed, if $U, V \in \mathcal{T}$ with $x \in U$ and $y \notin U$ and $x \notin V$ and $y \in V$, then since $\mathcal{T}'$ is finer than $\mathcal{T}$, we have $U, V \in \mathcal{T}'$.

   For example, since the standard topology on $\mathbb{R}$ is finer than the cofinite topology on $\mathbb{R}$, it follows that $\mathbb{R}$ together with the standard topology on $\mathbb{R}$ is a T_1-space.

Theorem 14.2: A topological space $(S, \mathcal{T})$ is a T_1-space if and only if for all $x \in S$, $\{x\}$ is a closed set.

Proof: Let $(S, \mathcal{T})$ be a topological space. First, assume that $(S, \mathcal{T})$ is a T_1-space and let $x \in S$. For each $y \in S$ with $y \neq x$, there is an open set U_y with $y \in U_y$ and $x \notin U_y$. Then $U = \cup\{U_y \mid y \in S \wedge y \neq x\}$ is open (because U is a union of open sets). Let's check that $\{x\} = S \setminus U$. Since $x \notin U_y$ for all $y \neq x$, $x \notin U$. So, $x \in S \setminus U$. It follows that $\{x\} \subseteq S \setminus U$. If $z \in S \setminus U$, then $z \notin U$. So, for all $y \neq x$, $z \notin U_y$. Thus, for all $y \neq x$, $z \neq y$. Therefore, $z = x$, and so, $z \in \{x\}$. So, $S \setminus U \subseteq \{x\}$. Since $\{x\} \subseteq S \setminus U$ and $S \setminus U \subseteq \{x\}$, we have $\{x\} = S \setminus U$. Since U is open, $\{x\} = S \setminus U$ is closed.

Conversely, suppose that for all $x \in S$, $\{x\}$ is a closed set. Let $x, y \in S$ with $x \neq y$, let $U = S \setminus \{y\}$, and let $V = S \setminus \{x\}$. Then U and V are open sets such that $x \in U$ and $y \notin U$ and $x \notin V$ and $y \in V$. So, $(S, \mathcal{T})$ is a T_1-space. $\qquad \square$

A topological space $(S, \mathcal{T})$ is a T_2-**space** (or **Hausdorff space**) if for all $x, y \in S$ with $x \neq y$, there are $U, V \in \mathcal{T}$ with $x \in U$, $y \in V$, and $U \cap V = \emptyset$.

In the picture on the right we see two typical elements a and b in a T_2-space. We have drawn disjoint open sets, one including a and the other including b. The smaller dots in the picture represent some elements of the space other than a and b.

Example 14.7:

1. The discrete topology on any set is a T_2-space. Indeed, if a and b are distinct points from a T_2-space, then $\{a\}$ and $\{b\}$ are disjoint open sets.

   It should be clear from the definitions that every T_2-space is a T_1-space. It follows that except for the discrete topology, every other topology on a finite set is **not** a T_2-space.

2. The topological space $(\mathbb{R}, \mathcal{T})$, where $\mathcal{T}$ is the cofinite topology on $\mathbb{R}$ (see part 3 of Example 14.6) is **not** a T_2-space. Indeed, if U and V are open sets containing $a, b \in \mathbb{R}$, respectively, then $\mathbb{R} \setminus (U \cap V) = (\mathbb{R} \setminus U) \cup (\mathbb{R} \setminus V)$ (this is **De Morgan's law**), which is finite. So, $U \cap V$ is infinite, and therefore, nonempty.

3. The standard topologies on $\mathbb{R}$ and $\mathbb{C}$ are both T_2. The same argument can be used for both (although the geometry looks very different).

   Let $S = \mathbb{R}$ or $\mathbb{C}$ and let $x, y \in S$. Let $\epsilon = \frac{1}{2}d(x,y) = \frac{1}{2}|x-y|$. Then $U = N_\epsilon(x)$ and $V = N_\epsilon(y)$ are disjoint open sets with $x \in U$ and $y \in V$.

   In the picture below, we have drawn two typical real numbers x and y on the real line and then separated them with the disjoint neighborhoods $U = N_\epsilon(x)$ and $V = N_\epsilon(y)$.

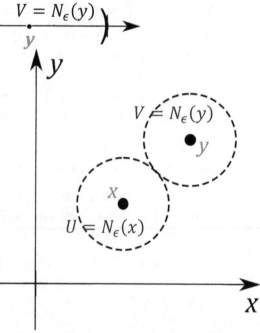

   In the picture to the right, we have drawn two typical complex numbers x and y in the complex plane and then separated them with the disjoint neighborhoods $U = N_\epsilon(x)$ and $V = N_\epsilon(y)$.

   Note once again that neighborhoods on the real line are open intervals, whereas neighborhoods in the complex plane are open disks.

4. If $(S, \mathcal{T})$ is a T_2-space and $\mathcal{T}'$ is finer than $\mathcal{T}$, then $(S, \mathcal{T}')$ is also a T_2-space. Indeed, if $U, V \in \mathcal{T}$ with $x \in U$, $y \in V$, and $U \cap V = \emptyset$, then since $\mathcal{T}'$ is finer than $\mathcal{T}$, we have $U, V \in \mathcal{T}'$. Let's look at an example of this.

Let $K = \left\{ \frac{1}{n} \mid n \in \mathbb{Z}^+ \right\}$, $\mathcal{B} = \{(a,b) \mid a, b \in \mathbb{R} \wedge a < b\} \cup \{(a,b) \setminus K \mid a, b \in \mathbb{R} \wedge a < b\}$. In Problem 4 below, the reader will be asked to verify that $\mathcal{B}$ is a basis for a topology $\mathcal{T}_K$ on $\mathbb{R}$. Since $\mathcal{T}_K$ contains every basis element of the standard topology on $\mathbb{R}$, we see that $\mathcal{T}_K$ is finer than the standard topology. It follows that $(\mathbb{R}, \mathcal{T}_K)$ is a T_2-space.

A topological space $(S, \mathcal{T})$ is a T_3-**space** (or **Regular space**) if $(S, \mathcal{T})$ is a T_1-space and for every $x \in S$ and closed set A with $A \subseteq S \setminus \{x\}$, there are $U, V \in \mathcal{T}$ with $x \in U$, $A \subseteq V$, and $U \cap V = \emptyset$.

In the picture on the right we see a typical element a and a closed set K in a T_3-space. We have drawn disjoint open sets, one including a and the other containing K. The smaller dots in the picture represent some elements of the space other than a that are not included in K.

Example 14.8:

1. The discrete topology on any set S is a T_3-space. Indeed, if $x \in S$ and A is any subset of $S \setminus \{x\}$ (all subsets of S are closed), simply let $U = \{x\}$ and $V = A$ (all subsets of S are also open).

    Some authors call a set **clopen** if it is both open and closed. If S is given the discrete topology, then all subsets of S are clopen.

2. Every T_3-space is a T_2-space. This follows easily from the fact that a T_3-space is a T_1-space and Theorem 14.2. It follows that except for the discrete topology, every other topology on a finite set is **not** a T_3-space.

3. The standard topologies on $\mathbb{R}$ and $\mathbb{C}$ are both T_3. This follows from Problem 14 below.

4. Consider the T_2-space $(\mathbb{R}, \mathcal{T}_K)$ from part 4 of Example 14.7. Recall that $K = \left\{ \frac{1}{n} \mid n \in \mathbb{Z}^+ \right\}$ and $(\mathbb{R}, \mathcal{T}_K)$ has basis $\mathcal{B} = \{(a, b) \mid a, b \in \mathbb{R} \wedge a < b\} \cup \{(a, b) \setminus K \mid a, b \in \mathbb{R} \wedge a < b\}$. Let $x = 0$ and $A = K$. $\mathbb{R} \setminus K = (-\infty, 0) \cup [(-1, 1) \setminus K] \cup (1, \infty)$, which is a union of three open sets, thus open. Therefore, K is a closed set in this topology. Let U be an open set containing 0 and let V be an open set containing K. For some $\epsilon > 0$, $(0, \epsilon) \setminus K \subseteq U$. By the Archimedean Property of $\mathbb{R}$, there is $n \in \mathbb{N}$ with $n > \frac{1}{\epsilon}$, or equivalently, $\frac{1}{n} < \epsilon$. There is $0 < \delta \le \epsilon - \frac{1}{n}$ such that $\left(\frac{1}{n} - \delta, \frac{1}{n} + \delta \right) \subseteq V$. Let r be an irrational number in $\left(\frac{1}{n}, \frac{1}{n} + \delta \right)$. $r \in U \cap V$ and therefore, $U \cap V \neq \emptyset$. Since we cannot separate 0 and K with open sets, $(\mathbb{R}, \mathcal{T}_K)$ is **not** a T_3-space.

    Unlike T_0, T_1, and T_2-spaces, T_3-spaces are not closed under upward refinement. In other words, if $(S, \mathcal{T})$ is a T_3-space and $\mathcal{T}'$ is finer than $\mathcal{T}$, then $(S, \mathcal{T}')$ is **not necessarily** a T_3-space. The topological space $(\mathbb{R}, \mathcal{T}_K)$ proves this.

    Also, since $(\mathbb{R}, \mathcal{T})$ is T_3, where $\mathcal{T}$ is the standard topology on $\mathbb{R}$, but $(\mathbb{R}, \mathcal{T}_K)$ is not, the two topological spaces cannot be the same. It follows that $\mathcal{T}_K$ is strictly finer than the standard topology on $\mathbb{R}$.

A topological space $(S, \mathcal{T})$ is a T_4-**space** (or **Normal space**) if $(S, \mathcal{T})$ is a T_1-space and for every pair A, B of disjoint closed subsets of S, there are $U, V \in \mathcal{T}$ with $A \subseteq U$, $B \subseteq V$, and $U \cap V = \emptyset$.

In the picture on the right we see two closed sets K and L in a T_4-space. We have drawn disjoint open sets, one containing K and the other containing L. The smaller dots in the picture represent some elements of the space not included in K or L.

Example 14.9:

1. The discrete topology on any set S is a T_4-space. Indeed, if A and B are disjoint closed subsets of S, then A and B are also disjoint open subsets of S (because all subsets of S are both open and closed).

    Every T_4-space is a T_3-space. This follows easily from the fact that a T_4-space is a T_1-space and Theorem 14.2. It follows that except for the discrete topology, every other topology on a finite set is **not** a T_4-space.

2. The standard topologies on $\mathbb{R}$ and $\mathbb{C}$ are both T_4. This follows immediately from Problem 14 below.

3. In Problem 15 below, you will see a T_3-space that is **not** a T_4-space.

The definitions of T_0, T_1, T_2, T_3, and T_4 are called **separation axioms** because they all involve "separating" points and/or closed sets from each other by open sets.

We will now look at two more types of topological spaces that appear frequently in mathematics.

A **metric space** is a pair (S, d), where S is a set and d is a function $d: S \times S \to \mathbb{R}$ with the following properties:

1. For all $x, y \in S$, $d(x, y) = 0$ if and only if $x = y$.

2. For all $x, y \in S$, $d(x, y) = d(y, x)$.

3. For all $x, y, z \in S$, $d(x, z) \leq d(x, y) + d(y, z)$.

The function d is called a **metric** or **distance function**. It is a consequence of the definition that for all $x \in S$, $d(x, x) \geq 0$. You will be asked to prove this in Problem 2 below.

If (S, d) is a metric space, $a \in S$, and $r \in \mathbb{R}^+$, then the **open ball** centered at a with radius r, written $B_r(a)$ (or $B_r(a; d)$ if we need to distinguish this metric from other metrics), is the set of all elements of S whose distance to a is less than r. That is,

$$B_r(a) = \{x \in S \mid d(a, x) < r\}.$$

The collection $\mathcal{B} = \{B_r(a) \mid a \in S \land r \in \mathbb{R}^+\}$ covers S. Indeed, if $a \in S$, then $d(a, a) = 0 < 1$, and so, $a \in B_1(a)$.

Also, the collection $\mathcal{B} = \{B_r(a) \mid a \in S \land r \in \mathbb{R}^+\}$ has the intersection containment property. To see this, let $x \in B_r(a) \cap B_s(b)$ and $k = \min\{r - d(a, x), s - d(b, x)\}$. We have $x \in B_k(x)$ because $d(x, x) = 0 < k$. Now, let $y \in B_k(x)$. Then $d(x, y) < k$. So, we have

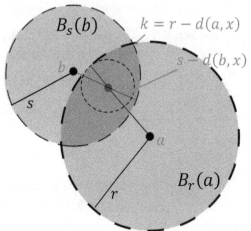

$$d(a, y) \leq d(a, x) + d(x, y) < d(a, x) + k$$
$$\leq d(a, x) + r - d(a, x) = r.$$

So, $y \in B_r(a)$. A similar argument shows that $y \in B_s(b)$. So, $y \in B_r(a) \cap B_s(b)$. It follows that $B_k(x) \subseteq B_r(a) \cap B_s(b)$.

This verifies that $\mathcal{B}$ has the finite containment property.

Since the collection of open balls covers S and has the finite containment property, it follows that this collection is a basis for a topology on S.

Note: Open balls can be visualized as open intervals on the real line $\mathbb{R}$, open disks in the Complex Plane $\mathbb{C}$ (or $\mathbb{R}^2$), or open balls in three-dimensional space $\mathbb{R}^3$.

When proving theorems about metric spaces, it's usually most useful to visualize open balls as open disks in $\mathbb{C}$. This does **not** mean that all metric spaces look like $\mathbb{C}$. The visualization should be used as evidence that a theorem might be true. Of course, a detailed proof still needs to be written.

This is exactly what we did when we drew the picture above. That picture represents the open balls $B_r(a)$ and $B_s(b)$ as intersecting open disks. Inside this intersection, we can see the open ball $B_k(x)$. The reader may also want to draw another picture to help visualize the triangle inequality. A picture similar to this is drawn to the right of Note 1 following the proof of Theorem 7.4 in Lesson 7.

A topological space $(S, \mathcal{T})$ is **metrizable** if there is a metric $d: S \times S \to \mathbb{R}$ such that $\mathcal{T}$ is generated from the open balls in (S, d). We also say that the metric d **induces** the topology $\mathcal{T}$.

Example 14.10:

1. $(\mathbb{C}, d)$ is a metric space, where $d: \mathbb{C} \times \mathbb{C} \to \mathbb{R}$ is defined by $d(z, w) = |z - w|$. Let's check that the 3 properties of a metric space are satisfied. Property 3 is the Triangle Inequality (Theorem 7.3 and Problem 4 in Problem Set 7). Let's verify the other two properties. Let $z = a + bi$ and $w = c + di$. Then $d(z, w) = |z - w| = \sqrt{(a - c)^2 + (b - d)^2}$. So, $d(z, w) = 0$ if and only if $\sqrt{(a - c)^2 + (b - d)^2} = 0$ if and only if $(a - c)^2 + (b - d)^2 = 0$ if and only if $a - c = 0$ and $b - d = 0$ if and only if $a = c$ and $b = d$ if and only if $z = w$. So, property 1 holds. We have

$$d(z, w) = |z - w| = |-(w - z)| = |-1(w - z)| = |-1||w - z| = 1|w - z| = d(w, z).$$

   Therefore, property 2 holds.

   If $z \in \mathbb{C}$ and $r \in \mathbb{R}^+$, then the open ball $B_r(z)$ is the set $B_r(z) = \{w \in \mathbb{C} \mid |z - w| < r\}$. This is just an open disk in the complex plane, as we defined in Lesson 7.

   Since the collection of open disks in the complex plane generates the standard topology on $\mathbb{C}$, we see that $\mathbb{C}$ with the standard topology is a metrizable space.

2. Similarly, $(\mathbb{R}, d)$ is a metric space, where $d: \mathbb{R} \times \mathbb{R} \to \mathbb{R}$ is defined by $d(x, y) = |x - y|$. The proof is similar to the proof above for $(\mathbb{C}, d)$.

   In this case, the open ball $B_r(a)$ is the open interval $(a - r, a + r)$. To see this, observe that we have

$$B_r(a) = \{x \in \mathbb{R} \mid |x - a| < r\} = \{x \in \mathbb{R} \mid -r < x - a < r\}$$
$$= \{x \in \mathbb{R} \mid a - r < x < a + r\} = (a - r, a + r).$$

   Since the collection of bounded open intervals of real numbers generates the standard topology on $\mathbb{R}$, we see that $\mathbb{R}$ with the standard topology is a metrizable space.

3. Define the functions d_1 and d_2 from $\mathbb{C} \times \mathbb{C}$ to $\mathbb{R}$ by $d_1(z,w) = |\operatorname{Re} z - \operatorname{Re} w| + |\operatorname{Im} z - \operatorname{Im} w|$ and $d_2(z,w) = \max\{|\operatorname{Re} z - \operatorname{Re} w|, |\operatorname{Im} z - \operatorname{Im} w|\}$. In Problem 7 below, you will be asked to verify that $(\mathbb{C}, d_1)$ and $(\mathbb{C}, d_2)$ are metric spaces that induce the standard topology on $\mathbb{C}$.

So, we see that a metrizable space can be induced by many different metrics.

The open balls $B_r(a; d_1)$ and $B_r(a; d_2)$ are both interiors of squares. For example, the unit open ball in the metric d_1 is $B_1(0; d_1) = \{w \in \mathbb{C} \mid d_1(0,w) < 1\} = \{w \in \mathbb{C} \mid |\operatorname{Re} w| + |\operatorname{Im} w| < 1\}$, which is the interior of a square with vertices $1, i, -1$, and $-i$. Similarly, the unit open ball in the metric d_2 is $B_1(0; d_2) = \{w \in \mathbb{C} \mid d_2(0,w) < 1\} = \{w \in \mathbb{C} \mid \max\{|\operatorname{Re} w|, |\operatorname{Im} w|\} < 1\}$, which is the interior of a square with vertices $1 + i, -1 + i, -1 - i$, and $1 - i$.

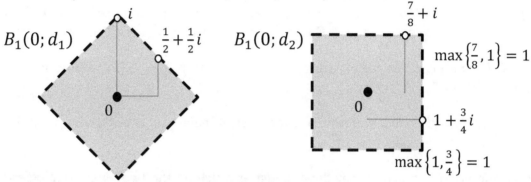

4. We can turn any nonempty set S into a metric space by defining $d: S \times S \to \mathbb{R}$ by

$$d(x,y) = \begin{cases} 0 & \text{if } x = y \\ 1 & \text{if } x \neq y \end{cases}$$

Properties 1 and 2 are obvious. For Property 3, let $x, y, z \in S$. If $x = z$, then $d(x,z) = 0$, and so, $d(x,z) = 0 \leq d(x,y) + d(y,z)$. If $x \neq z$, then $d(x,z) = 1$. Also, y cannot be equal to both x and z (otherwise $y = x \wedge y = z \to x = z$). So, $d(x,y) = 1$ or $d(y,z) = 1$ (or both). Therefore, $d(x,y) + d(y,z) \geq 1 = d(x,z)$.

If $r > 1$, then $B_r(x) = S$ and if $0 < r \leq 1$, then $B_r(x) = \{x\}$. It follows that every singleton set $\{x\}$ is open and therefore, (S, d) induces the discrete topology on S.

Let $(S, \mathcal{T})$ be a topological space. A collection $\mathcal{C}$ of subsets of S is a **covering** of S (or we can say that $\mathcal{C}$ **covers** S) if $\bigcup \mathcal{C} = S$. If $\mathcal{C}$ consists of only open sets, then we will say that $\mathcal{C}$ is an **open covering** of S.

A topological space $(S, \mathcal{T})$ is **compact** if every open covering of S contains a finite subcollection that covers S.

Example 14.11:

1. If S is a finite set, then for any topology $\mathcal{T}$ on S, $(S, \mathcal{T})$ is compact. After all, any open covering of S is already finite.

2. If S is an infinite set and $\mathcal{T}$ is the discrete topology on S, then $(S, \mathcal{T})$ is **not** compact. Indeed, $\{\{x\} \mid x \in S\}$ is an open covering of S with no finite subcollection covering S.

3. $(\mathbb{R}, \mathcal{T})$, where $\mathcal{T}$ is the standard topology on $\mathbb{R}$, is **not** compact. Indeed, $\{(n, n+2) \mid n \in \mathbb{Z}\}$ is an open covering of $\mathbb{R}$ with no finite subcollection covering $\mathbb{R}$.

4. The topological space $(\mathbb{R}, \mathcal{T})$, where $\mathcal{T}$ is the cofinite topology on $\mathbb{R}$ (see part 3 of Example 14.6) is compact. To see this, let $\mathcal{C}$ be an open covering of $\mathbb{R}$, and let A_0 be any set in $\mathcal{C}$. Then $\mathbb{R} \setminus A_0$ is finite, say $\mathbb{R} \setminus A_0 = \{a_1, a_2, \dots, a_n\}$. For each $i = 1, 2, \dots, n$, let $A_i \in \mathcal{C}$ with $a_i \in A_i$. Then the collection $\{A_0, A_1, A_2, \dots, A_n\}$ is a finite subcollection from $\mathcal{C}$ that covers $\mathbb{R}$.

There is actually nothing special about $\mathbb{R}$ in this example. If S is any set, we can define the cofinite topology on S to be the topology $\mathcal{T}$ generated from the basis $\{X \subseteq S \mid S \setminus X \text{ is finite}\}$. If we replace $\mathbb{R}$ by S in the argument above, we see that the topological space $(S, \mathcal{T})$ is compact.

Continuous Functions and Homeomorphisms

If $f: X \to Y$ and $A \subseteq X$, then the **image of A under f** is the set $f[A] = \{f(x) \mid x \in A\}$. Similarly, if $B \subseteq Y$, then the **inverse image of B under f** is the set $f^{-1}[B] = \{x \in X \mid f(x) \in B\}$.

Let $(X, \mathcal{T})$ and $(Y, \mathcal{U})$ be topological spaces. A function $f: X \to Y$ is **continuous** if for each $V \in \mathcal{U}$, we have $f^{-1}[V] \in \mathcal{T}$.

Notes: (1) In words, a function from one topological space to another is continuous if the inverse image of each open set is open.

(2) Continuity of a function may depend just as much on the two given topologies as it does on the function f.

(3) As an example of Note 2, if X is given the discrete topology, then any function $f: X \to Y$ is continuous. After all, **every** subset of X is open in X, and therefore every subset of X of the form $f^{-1}[V]$, where V is an open set in Y, is open in X.

(4) As another example, if $X = \{a, b\}$ is given the trivial topology, and $Y = X = \{a, b\}$ is given the discrete topology, then the identity function $i_X: X \to Y$ is **not** continuous. To see this, just note that $\{a\}$ is open in Y (because **every** subset of Y is open), but $i_X^{-1}(\{a\}) = \{a\}$ is **not** open in X (because $\{a\} \neq \emptyset$ and $\{a\} \neq X$).

(5) Constant functions are **always** continuous. Indeed, let $b \in Y$ and suppose that $f: X \to Y$ is defined by $f(x) = b$ for all $x \in X$. Let $B \subseteq Y$. If $b \in B$, then $f^{-1}[B] = X$ and if $b \notin B$, then $f^{-1}[B] = \emptyset$. Since X and $\emptyset$ are open in any topology on X, f is continuous.

(6) If $\mathcal{B}$ is a basis for $\mathcal{U}$, then to determine if f is continuous, we need only check that for each $V \in \mathcal{B}$, we have $f^{-1}[V] \in \mathcal{T}$. To see this, assume that for each $V \in \mathcal{B}$, we have $f^{-1}[V] \in \mathcal{T}$, and let $O \in \mathcal{U}$. Since $\mathcal{B}$ is a basis for $\mathcal{U}$, $O = \bigcup X$, for some subset X of $\mathcal{B}$. So, $f^{-1}[O] = f^{-1}[\bigcup X] = \bigcup\{f^{-1}[V] \mid V \in X\}$ (by part (ii) of Problem 1 below). Since $\mathcal{T}$ is a topology, it is closed under taking arbitrary unions, and therefore, $\bigcup\{f^{-1}[V] \mid V \in X\} \in \mathcal{T}$.

Similarly, if $\mathcal{S}$ is a subbasis for $\mathcal{U}$, then to determine if f is continuous, we need only check that for each $V \in \mathcal{S}$, we have $f^{-1}[V] \in \mathcal{T}$. To see this, let's assume that for each $V \in \mathcal{S}$, we have $f^{-1}[V] \in \mathcal{T}$ and let $\mathcal{B}$ be the collection of all finite intersections of sets in $\mathcal{S}$. Then $\mathcal{B}$ is a basis for $\mathcal{U}$. Let $A \in \mathcal{B}$. Then $A = \bigcap X$ for some finite subset X of $\mathcal{S}$. So, $f^{-1}[A] = f^{-1}[\bigcap X] = \bigcap\{f^{-1}[V] \mid V \in X\}$ (Check this!). Since $\mathcal{T}$ is a topology, it is closed under taking finite intersections, and so, $\bigcap\{f^{-1}[V] \mid V \in X\} \in \mathcal{T}$.

Example 14.12:

1. Let $(A, \mathcal{T})$ and $(B, \mathcal{U})$ be the topological spaces with sets $A = \{a, b\}$ and $B = \{1, 2, 3\}$ and topologies $\mathcal{T} = \{\emptyset, \{a\}, \{a, b\}\}$ and $\mathcal{U} = \{\emptyset, \{1, 2\}, \{1, 2, 3\}\}$. The function $f: A \to B$ defined by $f(a) = 1$ and $f(b) = 3$ is continuous because $f^{-1}[\{1, 2\}] = \{a\}$, which is open in $(A, \mathcal{T})$. On the other hand, the function $g: A \to B$ defined by $g(a) = 3$ and $g(b) = 1$ is **not** continuous because $g^{-1}[\{1, 2\}] = \{b\}$, which is **not** open in $(A, \mathcal{T})$. We can visualize these two functions as follows:

 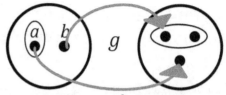

continuous   **not continuous**

2. Consider $(\mathbb{R}, \mathcal{T})$ and $(\mathbb{R}, \mathcal{U})$, where $\mathcal{T}$ is the standard topology on $\mathbb{R}$ and $\mathcal{U}$ is the topology generated by the basis $\{(a, \infty) \mid a \in \mathbb{R}\}$. To avoid confusion, let's use the notation $\mathbb{R}_{\mathcal{T}}$ and $\mathbb{R}_{\mathcal{U}}$ to indicate that we are considering $\mathbb{R}$ with the topologies $\mathcal{T}$ and $\mathcal{U}$, respectively. The identity function $i_1: \mathbb{R}_{\mathcal{T}} \to \mathbb{R}_{\mathcal{U}}$ is continuous because $i_1^{-1}[(a, \infty)] = (a, \infty)$ is open in $(\mathbb{R}, \mathcal{T})$ for every $a \in \mathbb{R}$. However, the identity function $i_2: \mathbb{R}_{\mathcal{U}} \to \mathbb{R}_{\mathcal{T}}$ is **not** continuous because $(0, 1)$ is open in $(\mathbb{R}, \mathcal{T})$, but $i_2^{-1}[(0, 1)] = (0, 1)$ is **not** open in $(\mathbb{R}, \mathcal{U})$.

3. Consider $(\mathbb{R}, \mathcal{T})$ and $(S, \mathcal{U})$, where $\mathcal{T}$ is the standard topology on $\mathbb{R}$, $S = \{a, b, c\}$, and $\mathcal{U}$ is the topology $\{\emptyset, \{a\}, \{a, b\}, \{a, b, c\}\}$. The function $f: \mathbb{R} \to S$ defined by $f(x) = \begin{cases} b & \text{if } x < 0 \\ c & \text{if } x \geq 0 \end{cases}$ is continuous because $f^{-1}[\{a\}] = \emptyset$ and $f^{-1}[\{a, b\}] = (-\infty, 0)$ are both open in $(\mathbb{R}, \mathcal{T})$.

   If we replace the topology $\mathcal{U}$ by the topology $\mathcal{V} = \{\emptyset, \{c\}, \{a, b, c\}\}$, then the same function f is **not** continuous because $f^{-1}[\{c\}] = [0, \infty)$, which is **not** open in $(\mathbb{R}, \mathcal{T})$.

Let $(X, \mathcal{T})$ and $(Y, \mathcal{U})$ be topological spaces. A function $f: X \to Y$ is **continuous** at $x \in X$ if for each $V \in \mathcal{U}$ with $f(x) \in V$, there is $U \in \mathcal{T}$ with $x \in U$ such that $f[U] \subseteq V$.

Example 14.13:

1. Consider the functions f and g from part 1 of Example 14.12. They are pictured below.

 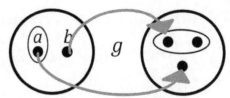

continuous   **not continuous**

Let's check that f is continuous at a. There are two open sets containing $f(a) = 1$. The first one is $\{1, 2\}$. The set $\{a\}$ is open and $f[\{a\}] = \{1\} \subseteq \{1, 2\}$. The second open set containing 1 is $\{1, 2, 3\}$. We can use the open set $\{a\}$ again because $f[\{a\}] = \{1\} \subseteq \{1, 2, 3\}$. Alternatively, we can use the open set $\{a, b\}$ because $f[\{a, b\}] = \{1, 3\} \subseteq \{1, 2, 3\}$.

Let's also check that f is continuous at b. The only open set containing $f(b) = 3$ is $\{1, 2, 3\}$. We have $b \in \{a, b\}$ and $f[\{a, b\}] = \{1, 3\} \subseteq \{1, 2, 3\}$.

The function g is continuous at a because the only open set containing $g(a) = 3$ is $\{1, 2, 3\}$ and we have $a \in \{a\}$ and $g[\{a\}] = \{3\} \subseteq \{1, 2, 3\}$.

The function g is **not** continuous at b. The open set $\{1, 2\}$ contains $g(b) = 1$. However, the only open set containing b is $\{a, b\}$ and $g[\{a, b\}] = \{1, 3\} \nsubseteq \{1, 2\}$.

2. Define $f : \mathbb{R} \to \mathbb{R}$ by $f(x) = \begin{cases} x & \text{if } x < 0 \\ x + 1 & \text{if } x \geq 0 \end{cases}$. Then f is **not** continuous at 0. To see this, note that $f(0) = 1 \in (0, 2)$ and if $0 \in (a, b)$, then $f[(a, b)] = (a, 0) \cup [1, b + 1) \nsubseteq (0, 2)$ because $\frac{a}{2} \in (a, 0)$, so that $\frac{a}{2} < 0$, and therefore, $\frac{a}{2} \notin (0, 2)$.

If $a > 0$, then f is continuous at a. To see this, let (c, d) be an open interval containing $f(a) = a + 1$. Then $c < a + 1 < d$, and so, $c - 1 < a < d - 1$. Let $k = \max\{0, c - 1\}$. Then we have $k < a < d - 1$. So, $a \in (k, d - 1)$. Since $k > 0$, $f[(k, d - 1)] = (k + 1, d)$. We now show that $(k + 1, d) \subseteq (c, d)$. Let $y \in (k + 1, d)$. Then $k + 1 < y < d$. Since $k \geq c - 1$, $k + 1 \geq c$. Thus, $c < y < d$, and therefore, $y \in (c, d)$. It follows that $f[(k, d - 1)] \subseteq (c, d)$.

Also, if $a < 0$, then f is continuous at a. To see this, let (c, d) be an open interval containing $f(a) = a$. Then $c < a < d$. Let $k = \min\{0, d\}$. Then we have $c < a < k$. So, $a \in (c, k)$. Finally, note that $f[(c, k)] = (c, k) \subseteq (c, d)$.

We will see in Theorem 14.4 below that if $f : \mathbb{R} \to \mathbb{R}$, where $\mathbb{R}$ is given the standard topology, then the topological definition of continuity here agrees with all the equivalent definitions of continuity from Lesson 13.

Theorem 14.3: Let $(X, \mathcal{T})$ and $(Y, \mathcal{U})$ be topological spaces and let $f : X \to Y$. Then f is continuous if and only if f is continuous at each $x \in X$.

Proof: Let $(X, \mathcal{T})$ and $(Y, \mathcal{U})$ be topological spaces and let $f : X \to Y$. First, suppose that f is continuous. Let $x \in X$ and let $V \in \mathcal{U}$ with $f(x) \in V$. Since f is continuous, $f^{-1}[V] \in \mathcal{T}$. If we let $U = f^{-1}[V]$, then by part (i) of Problem 1 below, we have $f[U] = f[f^{-1}[V]] \subseteq V$.

Conversely, suppose that f is continuous at each $x \in X$. Let $V \in \mathcal{U}$. If $f^{-1}[V] = \emptyset$, then $f^{-1}[V] \in \mathcal{T}$ because every topology contains the empty set. If $f^{-1}[V] \neq \emptyset$, let $x \in f^{-1}[V]$. Then $f(x) \in V$. So, there is $U_x \in \mathcal{T}$ with $x \in U_x$ such that $f[U_x] \subseteq V$. Let $U = \cup\{U_x \mid x \in f^{-1}[V]\}$. Since U is a union of open sets, $U \in \mathcal{T}$. We will show that $U = f^{-1}[V]$. Let $z \in U$. Then there is $x \in X$ with $z \in U_x$. So, we have $f(z) \in f[U_x]$. Since $f[U_x] \subseteq V$, $f(z) \in V$. Thus, $z \in f^{-1}[V]$. Since $z \in U$ was arbitrary, we have shown that $U \subseteq f^{-1}[V]$. Now, let $z \in f^{-1}[V]$. Then $f(z) \in V$. So, $z \in U_z$. Since $U_z \subseteq U$, we have $z \in U$. Since $z \in f^{-1}[V]$ was arbitrary, we have shown that $f^{-1}[V] \subseteq U$. Since $U \subseteq f^{-1}[V]$ and $f^{-1}[V] \subseteq U$, we have $U = f^{-1}[V]$. $\square$

We now give an $\epsilon - \delta$ definition of continuity for metrizable topological spaces.

Theorem 14.4: Let $(X, \mathcal{T})$ and $(Y, \mathcal{U})$ be metrizable topological spaces where $\mathcal{T}$ and $\mathcal{U}$ are induced by the metrics d and ρ, respectively. $f : X \to Y$ is continuous at $x \in X$ if and only if for all $\epsilon > 0$ there is $\delta > 0$ such that $d(x, y) < \delta$ implies $\rho(f(x), f(y)) < \epsilon$.

206

Proof: Let $(X, \mathcal{T})$ and $(Y, \mathcal{U})$ be topological spaces with corresponding metrics d and ρ and let $x \in X$.

First, suppose that $f: X \to Y$ is continuous at $x \in X$ and let $\epsilon > 0$. $f(x) \in B_\epsilon(f(x))$ and $B_\epsilon(f(x))$ is open in $\mathcal{U}$. Since f is continuous at x, there is $U \in \mathcal{T}$ with $x \in U$ such that $f[U] \subseteq B_\epsilon(f(x))$. Since the open balls form a basis for $\mathcal{U}$, we can find $\delta > 0$ such that $B_\delta(x) \subseteq U$ (Why?). It follows that $f[B_\delta(x)] \subseteq f[U]$ and so, $f[B_\delta(x)] \subseteq B_\epsilon(f(x))$. Now, if $d(x, y) < \delta$, then $y \in B_\delta(x)$. So, $f(y) \in f[B_\delta(x)]$. Since $f[B_\delta(x)] \subseteq B_\epsilon(f(x))$, we have $f(y) \in B_\epsilon(f(x))$. So, $\rho(f(x), f(y)) < \epsilon$.

Conversely, suppose that for all $\epsilon > 0$ there is $\delta > 0$ such that $d(x, y) < \delta$ implies $\rho(f(x), f(y)) < \epsilon$. Let $V \in \mathcal{U}$ with $f(x) \in V$. Since the open balls form a basis for V, there is $\epsilon > 0$ such that $f(x) \in B_\epsilon(f(x))$ and $B_\epsilon(f(x)) \subseteq V$ (Why?). Choose $\delta > 0$ such that $d(x, y) < \delta$ implies $\rho(x, y) < \epsilon$. Let $U = B_\delta(x)$. Then $U \in \mathcal{T}$ and $x \in U$. We show that $f[U] \subseteq V$. Let $y \in f[U]$. Then there is $z \in U$ with $y = f(z)$. Since $z \in U = B_\delta(x), d(x, z) < \delta$. Therefore, $\rho(f(x), f(z)) < \epsilon$. So, $f(z) \in B_\epsilon(f(x))$. Since $B_\epsilon(f(x)) \subseteq V$, $f(z) \in V$. Since $y = f(z)$, we have $y \in V$, as desired. $\square$

Note: If we consider a function $f: \mathbb{R} \to \mathbb{R}$ with the metric $d(x, y) = |x - y|$, Theorem 14.4 shows that all our definitions of continuity given in Lesson 13 are equivalent to the topological definitions given here.

Let $(X, \mathcal{T})$ and $(Y, \mathcal{U})$ be topological spaces. A function $f: X \to Y$ is a **homeomorphism** if f is a bijection such that $O \in \mathcal{T}$ if and only if $f[O] \in \mathcal{U}$.

Notes: (1) If $f: X \to Y$ is a bijection, then every subset $V \subseteq Y$ can be written as $f[O]$ for exactly one subset $O \subseteq X$. If f is also continuous, then given $O \subseteq X$ with $f[O] \in \mathcal{U}$, we have $O = f^{-1}[f[O]] \in \mathcal{T}$. Conversely, suppose that f is a bijection such that for every subset O of X, $f[O] \in \mathcal{U}$ implies $O \in \mathcal{T}$. Then, given $V \in \mathcal{U}$, since there is $O \subseteq X$ with $V = f[O]$, by our assumption, we have $f^{-1}[V] = f^{-1}[f[O]] = O \in \mathcal{T}$, showing that f is continuous. It follows that f is a continuous bijection if and only if f is a bijection such that $\forall O \subseteq X(f[O] \in \mathcal{U} \to O \in \mathcal{T})$.

(2) Similarly, $f: X \to Y$ is a bijective function with continuous inverse $f^{-1}: Y \to X$ if and only if f is a bijection such that $\forall O \subseteq X(O \in \mathcal{T} \to f[O] \in \mathcal{U})$.

(3) Notes 1 and 2 tell us that $f: X \to Y$ is a homeomorphism if and only if f is a continuous bijective function with a continuous inverse.

(4) Since a homeomorphism is bijective, it provides a one to one correspondence between the elements of X and the elements of Y. However, a homeomorphism does much more than this. It also provides a one to one correspondence between the sets in $\mathcal{T}$ and the sets in $\mathcal{U}$.

(5) A homeomorphism between two topological spaces is analogous to an isomorphism between two algebraic structures (see Lesson 11). From the topologists point of view, if there is a homeomorphism from one space to another, the two topological spaces are indistinguishable.

We say that two topological spaces $(X, \mathcal{T})$ and $(Y, \mathcal{U})$ are **homeomorphic** or **topologically equivalent** if there is a homeomorphism $f: X \to Y$.

Example 14.14:

1. Let $S = \{a, b\}$, $\mathcal{T} = \{\emptyset, \{a\}, \{a, b\}\}$, and $\mathcal{U} = \{\emptyset, \{b\}, \{a, b\}\}$. The map $f: S \to S$ defined by $f(a) = b$ and $f(b) = a$ is a homeomorphism from $(S, \mathcal{T})$ to $(S, \mathcal{U})$. Notice that the inverse image of the open set $\{b\} \in \mathcal{U}$ is the open set $\{a\} \in \mathcal{T}$. This shows that f is continuous. Conversely, the image of the open set $\{a\} \in \mathcal{T}$ is the open set $\{b\} \in \mathcal{U}$. This shows that f^{-1} is continuous. Since f is also a bijection, we have shown that f is a homeomorphism. On the other hand, the identity function $g: S \to S$ defined by $g(a) = a$ and $g(b) = b$ is **not** a homeomorphism because it is not continuous. For example, the inverse image of the open set $\{b\} \in \mathcal{U}$ is the set $\{b\}$ which is **not** in the topology $\mathcal{T}$. We can visualize these two functions as follows:

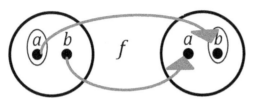 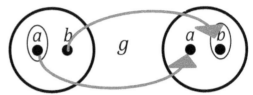

homeomorphism   **not a homeomorphism**

Notice that f and g are both bijections from S to S, but only the function f also gives a one to one correspondence between the open sets of the topology $(S, \mathcal{T})$ and the open sets of the topology $(S, \mathcal{U})$.

The homeomorphism f shows that $(S, \mathcal{T})$ and $(S, \mathcal{U})$ are topologically equivalent. So, up to topological equivalence, there are only three topologies on a set with two elements: the trivial topology, the discrete topology, and the topology with exactly three open sets.

2. Let $S = \{a, b, c\}$, $\mathcal{T} = \{\emptyset, \{b\}, \{a, b\}, \{a, b, c\}\}$, and $\mathcal{U} = \{\emptyset, \{a, b\}, \{a, b, c\}\}$. Then the identity function $f: S \to S$ is a continuous bijection from $(S, \mathcal{T})$ to $(S, \mathcal{U})$. Indeed, the inverse image of the open set $\{a, b\} \in \mathcal{U}$ is the open set $\{a, b\} \in \mathcal{T}$. However, f is **not** a homeomorphism because f^{-1} is not continuous. The set $\{b\}$ is open in $\mathcal{T}$, but its image $f[\{b\}] = \{b\}$ is **not** open in $\mathcal{U}$.

3. We saw in part 3 of Example 14.1 that there are 29 topologies on a set with three elements. However, up to topological equivalence, there are only 9. Below is a visual representation of the 9 distinct topologies on the set $S = \{a, b, c\}$, up to topological equivalence.

The dedicated reader should verify that each of the other 20 topologies are topologically equivalent to one of these and that no two topologies displayed here are topologically equivalent.

208

4. Consider $\mathbb{R}$ together with the standard topology. Define $f: \mathbb{R} \to \mathbb{R}$ by $f(x) = 2x + 3$. Let's check that f is a homeomorphism. If $x \neq y$, then $2x \neq 2y$, and so, $2x + 3 \neq 2y + 3$. Therefore, $\forall x, y \in \mathbb{R}\left(x \neq y \to f(x) \neq f(y)\right)$. That is, f is injective. Next, if $y \in \mathbb{R}$, let $x = \frac{y-3}{2}$. Then $f(x) = f\left(\frac{y-3}{2}\right) = 2\left(\frac{y-3}{2}\right) + 3 = (y - 3) + 3 = y$. So, $\forall y \in \mathbb{R} \, \exists x \in \mathbb{R}(f(x) = y)$. That is, f is surjective. Now, let (a, b) be a bounded open interval. $f^{-1}[(a, b)] = \left(\frac{a-3}{2}, \frac{b-3}{2}\right)$, which is open. So, f is continuous. Also, $f[(a, b)] = (2a + 3, 2b + 3)$, which is open. So, f^{-1} is continuous. Since f is a continuous bijection with a continuous inverse, f is a homeomorphism.

5. Consider $(\mathbb{R}, \mathcal{T})$ and $(\mathbb{R}, \mathcal{U})$, where $\mathcal{T}$ is the standard topology on $\mathbb{R}$ and $\mathcal{U}$ is the topology generated by the basis $\{(a, \infty) \mid a \in \mathbb{R}\}$. We saw in part 2 of Example 14.12 that the identity function $i: \mathbb{R}_{\mathcal{T}} \to \mathbb{R}_{\mathcal{U}}$ is continuous because $i^{-1}[(a, \infty)] = (a, \infty)$ is open in $(\mathbb{R}, \mathcal{T})$ for every $a \in \mathbb{R}$. However, this function is **not** a homeomorphism because i^{-1} is not continuous. For example, $(0, 1)$ is open in $(\mathbb{R}, \mathcal{T})$, but $i[(0, 1)] = (0, 1)$ is **not** open in $(\mathbb{R}, \mathcal{U})$.

A **topological property** or **topological invariant** is a property that is preserved under homeomorphisms. More specifically, we say that property P is a topological property if whenever the topological space $(S, \mathcal{T})$ has property P and $(X, \mathcal{U})$ is topologically equivalent to $(S, \mathcal{T})$, then $(X, \mathcal{U})$ also has property P.

In Problem 5 below, you will be asked to show that compactness is a topological property. As another example, let's show that the property of being a T_2-space is a topological property.

Theorem 14.5: Let $(S, \mathcal{T})$ be a T_2-space and let $(X, \mathcal{U})$ be topologically equivalent to $(S, \mathcal{T})$. Then $(X, \mathcal{U})$ is a T_2-space.

Proof: Let $(S, \mathcal{T})$ be a T_2-space and let $f: S \to X$ be a homeomorphism. Let $x, y \in X$ with $x \neq y$. Since f is bijective, there are $z, w \in S$ with $z \neq w$ such that $f(z) = x$ and $f(w) = y$. Since $(S, \mathcal{T})$ is a T_2-space, there are open sets $U, V \in \mathcal{T}$ with $z \in U$, $w \in V$, and $U \cap V = \emptyset$. Since f is a homeomorphism, $f[U], f[V] \in \mathcal{U}$. We also have $x = f(z) \in f[U]$ and $y = f(w) \in f[V]$. We show that $f[U] \cap f[V] = \emptyset$. If not, there is $c \in f[U] \cap f[V]$. So, there are $a \in U$ and $b \in V$ with $f(a) = c$ and $f(b) = c$. So, $f(a) = f(b)$. Since f is injective, $a = b$. But then $a \in U \cap V$, contradicting that $U \cap V = \emptyset$. It follows that $f[U] \cap f[V] = \emptyset$. Therefore, $(X, \mathcal{U})$ is a T_2-space. $\square$

The dedicated reader might want to show that each of the other separation axioms (T_0 through T_4) are topological properties and that metrizability is a topological property.

Full solutions to these problems are available for free download here:

www.SATPrepGet800.com/PMFBXSG

LEVEL 1

1. Let $f: A \to B$ and let X be a nonempty collection of subsets of B. Prove the following:

   (i) For any $V \in X$, $f[f^{-1}[V]] \subseteq V$.

   (ii) $f^{-1}[\cup X] = \cup\{f^{-1}[V] \mid V \in X\}$.

2. Let (X, d) be a metric space. Prove that for all $x \in S$, $d(x, x) \geq 0$.

LEVEL 2

3. Prove that $\mathcal{B} = \{X \subseteq \mathbb{R} \mid \mathbb{R} \setminus X \text{ is finite}\}$ generates a topology $\mathcal{T}$ on $\mathbb{R}$ that is strictly coarser than the standard topology. $\mathcal{T}$ is called the **cofinite topology** on $\mathbb{R}$.

4. Let $K = \{\frac{1}{n} \mid n \in \mathbb{Z}^+\}$, $\mathcal{B} = \{(a, b) \mid a, b \in \mathbb{R} \wedge a < b\} \cup \{(a, b) \setminus K \mid a, b \in \mathbb{R} \wedge a < b\}$. Prove that $\mathcal{B}$ is a basis for a topology $\mathcal{T}_K$ on $\mathbb{R}$ that is strictly finer than the standard topology on $\mathbb{R}$.

LEVEL 3

5. Let $(K, \mathcal{T})$ and $(L, \mathcal{U})$ be topological spaces with $(K, \mathcal{T})$ compact and let $f: K \to L$ be a homeomorphism. Prove that $(L, \mathcal{U})$ is compact.

6. Let S be a nonempty set and let $\mathcal{B}$ be a collection of subsets of S. Prove that the set generated by $\mathcal{B}$, $\{\cup X \mid X \subseteq \mathcal{B}\}$, is equal to $\{A \subseteq S \mid \forall x \in A \, \exists B \in \mathcal{B}(x \in B \wedge B \subseteq A)\}$.

7. Define the functions d_1 and d_2 from $\mathbb{C} \times \mathbb{C}$ to $\mathbb{R}$ by $d_1(z, w) = |\text{Re } z - \text{Re } w| + |\text{Im } z - \text{Im } w|$ and $d_2(z, w) = \max\{|\text{Re } z - \text{Re } w|, |\text{Im } z - \text{Im } w|\}$. Prove that $(\mathbb{C}, d_1)$ and $(\mathbb{C}, d_2)$ are metric spaces such that d_1 and d_2 induce the standard topology on $\mathbb{C}$.

8. Let $(S, \mathcal{T})$ be a topological space and let $A \subseteq S$. Prove that $\mathcal{T}_A = \{A \cap X \mid X \in \mathcal{T}\}$ is a topology on A. Then prove that if $\mathcal{B}$ is a basis for $\mathcal{T}$, then $\mathcal{B}_A = \{A \cap B \mid B \in \mathcal{B}\}$ is a basis for $\mathcal{T}_A$. $\mathcal{T}_A$ is called the **subspace topology** on A.

LEVEL 4

9. Let $\mathcal{B}' = \{(a, b) \mid a, b \in \mathbb{Q} \wedge a < b\}$. Prove that $\mathcal{B}'$ is countable and that $\mathcal{B}'$ is a basis for a topology on $\mathbb{R}$. Then show that the topology generated by $\mathcal{B}'$ is the standard topology on $\mathbb{R}$.

10. Let $(S, \mathcal{T})$ be a T_2-space and $A \subseteq S$. Prove that $(A, \mathcal{T}_A)$ is a T_2-space (see Problem 8 for the definition of $\mathcal{T}_A$). Determine if the analogous statement is true for T_3-spaces.

11. Let $(S_1, \mathcal{T}_1)$ and $(S_2, \mathcal{T}_2)$ be topological spaces. Let $\mathcal{B} = \{U \times V \mid U \in \mathcal{T}_1 \wedge V \in \mathcal{T}_2\}$. Prove that $\mathcal{B}$ is a basis for a topology $\mathcal{T}$ on $S_1 \times S_2$, but in general, $\mathcal{B}$ itself is not a topology on $S_1 \times S_2$. Then prove that if $\mathcal{B}_1$ is a basis for $\mathcal{T}_1$ and $\mathcal{B}_2$ is a basis for $\mathcal{T}_2$, then $\mathcal{C} = \{U \times V \mid U \in \mathcal{B}_1 \wedge V \in \mathcal{B}_2\}$ is a basis for $\mathcal{T}$. The topology $\mathcal{T}$ is called the **product topology** on $S_1 \times S_2$.

LEVEL 5

12. Let $(S_1, \mathcal{T}_1)$ and $(S_2, \mathcal{T}_2)$ be T_2-spaces. Prove that $S_1 \times S_2$ with the product topology (as defined in Problem 11) is also a T_2-space. Determine if the analogous statement is true for T_3-spaces.

13. Let T_L be the set generated by the half open intervals of the form $[a, b)$ with $a, b \in \mathbb{R}$. Show that T_L is a topology on $\mathbb{R}$ that is strictly finer than the standard topology on $\mathbb{R}$ and incomparable with the topology $\mathcal{T}_K$.

14. Prove that every metrizable space is T_4.

15. Consider the topological space $(\mathbb{R}, \mathcal{T}_L)$. Prove that $\mathbb{R}^2$ with the corresponding product topology (as defined in Problem 11) is a T_3-space, but not a T_4-space.

16. Let $(S_1, \mathcal{T}_1)$ and $(S_2, \mathcal{T}_2)$ be metrizable spaces. Prove that $S_1 \times S_2$ with the product topology is metrizable. Use this to show that $(\mathbb{R}, \mathcal{T}_L)$ is not metrizable.

Lesson 15 – Complex Analysis
Complex Valued Functions

The Unit Circle

Recall from Lesson 7 that a **circle** in the Complex Plane is the set of all points that are at a fixed distance (called the **radius** of the circle) from a fixed point (called the **center** of the circle).

The **circumference** of a circle is the distance around the circle.

If C and C' are the circumferences of two circles with radii r and r', respectively, then it turns out that $\frac{C}{2r} = \frac{C'}{2r'}$. In other words, the value of the ratio $\frac{\text{Circumference}}{2(\text{radius})}$ is independent of the circle that we use to form this ratio. We leave the proof of this fact for the interested reader to investigate themselves. We call the common value of this ratio π (pronounced "pi"). So, we have $\frac{C}{2r} = \pi$, or equivalently, $C = 2\pi r$.

Example 15.1: The **unit circle** is the circle with radius 1 and center $(0,0)$. The equation of this circle is $|z| = 1$. If we write z in the standard form $z = x + yi$, we see that $|z| = \sqrt{x^2 + y^2}$, and so, the equation of the unit circle can also be written $x^2 + y^2 = 1$. To the right is a picture of the unit circle in the Complex Plane.

The circumference of the unit circle is $2\pi \cdot 1 = 2\pi$.

An **angle in standard position** consists of two **rays**, both of which have their initial point at the origin, and one of which is the positive x-axis. We call the positive x-axis the **initial ray** and we call the second ray the **terminal ray**. The **radian measure** of the angle is the part of the circumference of the unit circle beginning at the point $(1, 0)$ on the positive x-axis and *eventually* ending at the point on the unit circle intercepted by the second ray. If the motion is in the counterclockwise direction, the radian measure is positive and if the motion is in the clockwise direction, the radian measure is negative.

Example 15.2: Let's draw a few angles where the terminal ray lies along the line $y = x$.

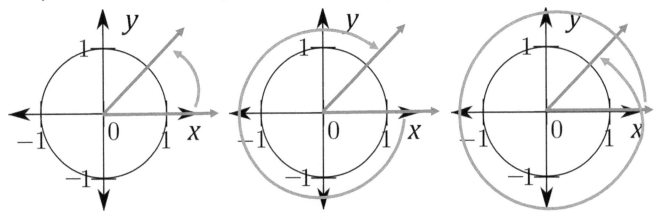

Observe that in the leftmost picture, the arc intercepted by the angle has a length that is one-eighth of the circumference of the circle. Since the circumference of the unit circle is 2π and the motion is in the counterclockwise direction, the angle has a radian measure of $\frac{2\pi}{8} = \frac{\pi}{4}$.

Similarly, in the center picture, the arc intercepted by the angle has a length that is seven-eighths of the circumference of the circle. This time the motion is in the clockwise direction, and so, the radian measure of the angle is $-\frac{7}{8} \cdot 2\pi = -\frac{7\pi}{4}$.

In the rightmost picture, the angle consists of a complete rotation, tracing out the entire circumference of the circle, followed by tracing out an additional length that is one-eighth the circumference of the circle. Since the motion is in the counterclockwise direction, the radian measure of the angle is $2\pi + \frac{2\pi}{8} = \frac{8\pi}{4} + \frac{\pi}{4} = \frac{9\pi}{4}$.

Let's find the point of intersection of the unit circle with the terminal ray of the angle $\frac{\pi}{4}$ that lies along the line with equation $y = x$ (as shown in the leftmost figure from Example 15.2 above). If we call this point (a, b), then we have $b = a$ (because (a, b) is on the line $y = x$) and $a^2 + b^2 = 1$ (because (a, b) is on the unit circle). Replacing b by a in the second equation gives us $a^2 + a^2 = 1$, or equivalently, $2a^2 = 1$. So, $a^2 = \frac{1}{2}$. The two solutions to this equation are $a = \pm\sqrt{\frac{1}{2}} = \pm\frac{\sqrt{1}}{\sqrt{2}} = \pm\frac{1}{\sqrt{2}}$. From the picture, it should be clear that we are looking for the positive solution, so that $a = \frac{1}{\sqrt{2}}$. Since $b = a$, we also have $b = \frac{1}{\sqrt{2}}$. Therefore, the point of intersection is $\left(\frac{1}{\sqrt{2}}, \frac{1}{\sqrt{2}}\right)$.

Notes: (1) The number $\frac{1}{\sqrt{2}}$ can also be written in the form $\frac{\sqrt{2}}{2}$. To see that these two numbers are equal, observe that we have

$$\frac{1}{\sqrt{2}} = \frac{1}{\sqrt{2}} \cdot 1 = \frac{1}{\sqrt{2}} \cdot \frac{\sqrt{2}}{\sqrt{2}} = \frac{1 \cdot \sqrt{2}}{\sqrt{2} \cdot \sqrt{2}} = \frac{\sqrt{2}}{2}.$$

(2) In the figure below on the left, we see a visual representation of the circle, the given angle, and the desired point of intersection.

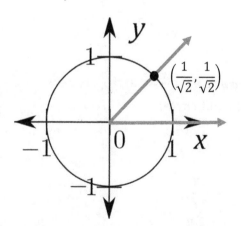
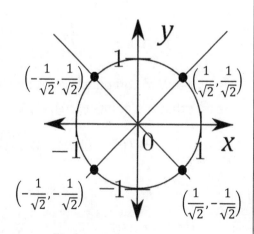

(3) In the figure above on the right, we have divided the Complex Plane into eight regions using the lines with equations $y = x$ and $y = -x$ (together with the x- and y-axes). We then used the symmetry of the circle to label the four points of intersection of the unit circle with each of these two lines.

If θ (pronounced "theta") is the radian measure of an angle in standard position such that the terminal ray intersects the unit circle at the point (x, y), then we will say that $W(\theta) = (x, y)$. This expression defines a function $W: \mathbb{R} \to \mathbb{R} \times \mathbb{R}$ called the **wrapping function**. Observe that the inputs of the wrapping function are real numbers, which we think of as the radian measure of angles in standard position. The outputs of the wrapping function are pairs of real numbers, which we think of as points in the Complex Plane. Also, observe that the range of the wrapping function is the unit circle.

We now define the cosine and sine of the angle θ by $\cos\theta = x$ and $\sin\theta = y$, where $W(\theta) = (x, y)$. For convenience, we also define the tangent of the angle by $\tan\theta = \frac{\sin\theta}{\cos\theta} = \frac{y}{x}$.

Notes: (1) The wrapping function is **not** one to one. For example, $W\left(\frac{\pi}{2}\right) = (0, 1)$ and $W\left(\frac{5\pi}{2}\right) = (0, 1)$. However, $\frac{\pi}{2} \neq \frac{5\pi}{2}$. There are actually infinitely many real numbers that map to $(0, 1)$ under the wrapping function. Specifically, $W\left(\frac{\pi}{2} + 2k\pi\right) = (0, 1)$ for every $k \in \mathbb{Z}$.

In general, each point on the unit circle is the image of infinitely many real numbers. Indeed, if $W(\theta) = (a, b)$, then $W(\theta + 2k\pi) = (a, b)$ for all $k \in \mathbb{Z}$.

(2) The wrapping function gives us a convenient way to associate an angle θ in standard position with the corresponding point (x, y) on the unit circle. It is mostly used only as a notational convenience. We will usually be more interested in the expressions $\cos\theta = x$ and $\sin\theta = y$.

Example 15.3: Using the rightmost figure above, we can make the following computations:

$$W\left(\frac{\pi}{4}\right) = \left(\frac{1}{\sqrt{2}}, \frac{1}{\sqrt{2}}\right) \quad W\left(\frac{3\pi}{4}\right) = \left(-\frac{1}{\sqrt{2}}, \frac{1}{\sqrt{2}}\right) \quad W\left(\frac{5\pi}{4}\right) = \left(-\frac{1}{\sqrt{2}}, -\frac{1}{\sqrt{2}}\right) \quad W\left(\frac{7\pi}{4}\right) = \left(\frac{1}{\sqrt{2}}, -\frac{1}{\sqrt{2}}\right)$$

$$\cos\frac{\pi}{4} = \frac{1}{\sqrt{2}} \qquad \sin\frac{\pi}{4} = \frac{1}{\sqrt{2}} \qquad \cos\frac{3\pi}{4} = -\frac{1}{\sqrt{2}} \qquad \sin\frac{3\pi}{4} = \frac{1}{\sqrt{2}}$$

$$\cos\frac{5\pi}{4} = -\frac{1}{\sqrt{2}} \qquad \sin\frac{5\pi}{4} = -\frac{1}{\sqrt{2}} \qquad \cos\frac{7\pi}{4} = \frac{1}{\sqrt{2}} \qquad \sin\frac{7\pi}{4} = -\frac{1}{\sqrt{2}}$$

It's also easy to compute the cosine and sine of the four **quadrantal angles** $0, \frac{\pi}{2}, \pi$, and $\frac{3\pi}{2}$. Here we use the fact that the points $(1, 0)$, $(0, 1)$, $(-1, 0)$, and $(0, -1)$ lie on the unit circle.

$$W(0) = (1, 0) \quad W\left(\frac{\pi}{2}\right) = (0, 1) \quad W(\pi) = (-1, 0) \quad W\left(\frac{3\pi}{2}\right) = (0, -1)$$

$$\cos 0 = 1 \qquad \sin 0 = 0 \qquad \cos\frac{\pi}{2} = 0 \qquad \sin\frac{\pi}{2} = 1$$

$$\cos\pi = -1 \qquad \sin\pi = 0 \qquad \cos\frac{3\pi}{2} = 0 \qquad \sin\frac{3\pi}{2} = -1$$

214

Also, if we add any integer multiple of 2π to an angle, the cosine and sine of the new angle have the same values as the old angle. For example, $\cos\frac{9\pi}{4} = \cos\left(\frac{\pi}{4} + \frac{8\pi}{4}\right) = \cos\left(\frac{\pi}{4} + 2\pi\right) = \cos\frac{\pi}{4} = \frac{1}{\sqrt{2}}$. This is a direct consequence of the fact that $W(\theta + 2k\pi) = W(\theta)$ for all $k \in \mathbb{Z}$.

We can also compute the tangent of each angle by dividing the sine of the angle by the cosine of the angle. For example, we have

$$\tan\frac{\pi}{4} = \frac{\sin\frac{\pi}{4}}{\cos\frac{\pi}{4}} = \frac{\frac{1}{\sqrt{2}}}{\frac{1}{\sqrt{2}}} = 1.$$

Similarly, we have

$$\tan\frac{3\pi}{4} = -1 \qquad \tan\frac{5\pi}{4} = 1 \qquad \tan\frac{7\pi}{4} = -1 \qquad \tan 0 = 0 \qquad \tan\pi = 0$$

When $\theta = \frac{\pi}{2}$ or $\frac{3\pi}{2}$, $\tan\theta$ is **undefined**.

Notes: (1) If $z = x + yi$ is any complex number, then the point (x, y) lies on a circle of radius r centered at the origin, where $r = |z| = \sqrt{x^2 + y^2}$. If θ is the radian measure of an angle in standard position such that the terminal ray intersects this circle at the point (x, y), then it can be proved that the cosine and sine of the angle are equal to $\cos\theta = \frac{x}{r}$ and $\sin\theta = \frac{y}{r}$.

(2) It is standard to use the abbreviations $\cos^2\theta$ and $\sin^2\theta$ for $(\cos\theta)^2$ and $(\sin\theta)^2$, respectively.

From the definition of cosine and sine, we have the following formula called the **Pythagorean Identity**:
$$\cos^2\theta + \sin^2\theta = 1$$

(3) Also, from the definition of cosine and sine, we have the following two formulas called the **Negative Identities**:
$$\cos(-\theta) = \cos\theta \qquad\qquad \sin(-\theta) = -\sin\theta.$$

Theorem 15.1: Let θ and ϕ be the radian measures of angles A and B, respectively. Then we have
$$\cos(\theta + \phi) = \cos\theta\cos\phi - \sin\theta\sin\phi$$
$$\sin(\theta + \phi) = \sin\theta\cos\phi + \cos\theta\sin\phi.$$

Notes: (1) The two formulas appearing in Theorem 15.1 are called the **Sum Identities**. You will be asked to prove Theorem 15.1 in Problem 14 below (parts (i) and (v)).

(2) Theorem 15.1 will be used to prove De Moivre's Theorem (Theorem 15.2) below. De Moivre's Theorem provides a fast method for performing exponentiation of complex numbers.

(3) θ and ϕ are Greek letters pronounced "theta" and "phi," respectively. These letters are often used to represent angle measures. We may sometimes also use the capital versions of these letters, Θ and Φ, especially when insisting that the radian measures of the given angles are between $-\pi$ and π.

Exponential Form of a Complex Number

The **standard form** (or **rectangular form**) of a complex number z is $z = x + yi$, where x and y are real numbers. Recall from Lesson 7 that we can visualize the complex number $z = x + yi$ as the point (x, y) in the Complex Plane.

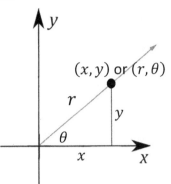

If for $z \neq 0$, we let $r = |z| = |x + yi| = \sqrt{x^2 + y^2}$ and we let θ be the radian measure of an angle in standard position such that the terminal ray passes through the point (x, y), then we see that r and θ determine this point. So, we can also write this point as (r, θ).

In Note 1 following Example 15.3, we saw that $\cos \theta = \frac{x}{r}$ and $\sin \theta = \frac{y}{r}$. By multiplying each side of the last two equations by r, we get $x = r \cos \theta$ and $y = r \sin \theta$. These equations allow us to rewrite the complex number $z = x + yi$ in the **polar form** $z = r \cos \theta + ri \sin \theta = r(\cos \theta + i \sin \theta)$.

If we also make the definition $e^{i\theta} = \cos \theta + i \sin \theta$, we can write the complex number $z = x + yi$ in the **exponential form** $z = re^{i\theta}$.

Recall from Lesson 7 that $r = |z|$ is called the **absolute value** or **modulus** of the complex number. We will call the angle θ an **argument** of the complex number and we may sometimes write $\theta = \arg z$.

Note that although $r = |z|$ and $\theta = \arg z$ uniquely determine a point (r, θ), there are infinitely many other values for $\arg z$ that represent the same point. Indeed, $(r, \theta + 2k\pi)$ represents the same point for each $k \in \mathbb{Z}$. However, there is a unique such value Θ for $\arg z$ such that $-\pi < \Theta \leq \pi$. We call this value Θ the **principal argument** of z, and we write $\Theta = \text{Arg } z$.

Notes: (1) The definition $e^{i\theta} = \cos \theta + i \sin \theta$ is known as **Euler's formula**.

(2) When written in exponential form, two complex numbers $z = re^{i\theta}$ and $w = se^{i\phi}$ are equal if and only if $r = s$ and $\phi = \theta + 2k\pi$ for some $k \in \mathbb{Z}$.

Example 15.4: Let's convert the complex number $z = 1 + i$ to exponential form. To do this, we need to find r and θ. We have $r = |z| = \sqrt{1^2 + 1^2} = \sqrt{1 + 1} = \sqrt{2}$. Next, we have $\tan \theta = \frac{1}{1} = 1$. It follows that $\theta = \frac{\pi}{4}$. So, in exponential form, we have $\boldsymbol{z = \sqrt{2}e^{\frac{\pi}{4}i}}$.

Note: $\frac{\pi}{4}$ is the principal argument of $z = 1 + i$ because $-\pi < \frac{\pi}{4} \leq \pi$. When we write a complex number in exponential form, we will usually use the principle argument.

If $z \in \mathbb{C}$, we define z^2 to be the complex number $z \cdot z$. Similarly, $z^3 = z \cdot z \cdot z = z^2 \cdot z$. More generally, for $z \in \mathbb{C}$ and $n \in \mathbb{Z}$ we define z^n as follows:

- For $n = 0$, $z^n = z^0 = 1$.

- For $n \in \mathbb{Z}^+$, $z^{n+1} = z^n \cdot z$.

- For $n \in \mathbb{Z}^-$, $z^n = (z^{-n})^{-1} = \frac{1}{z^{-n}}$.

216

Due to the following theorem, it's often easier to compute z^n when z is written in exponential form.

Theorem 15.2 (De Moivre's Theorem): For all $n \in \mathbb{Z}$, $\left(e^{i\theta}\right)^n = e^{i(n\theta)}$.

Proof: For $n = 0$, we have $\left(e^{i\theta}\right)^0 = (\cos\theta + i\sin\theta)^0 = 1 = e^0 = e^{i(0\theta)}$.

We prove De Moivre's Theorem for $n \in \mathbb{Z}^+$ by induction on n.

Base Case $(k = 1)$: $\left(e^{i\theta}\right)^1 = e^{i\theta} = e^{i(1\theta)}$.

Inductive Step: Assume that $k \geq 1$ and $\left(e^{i\theta}\right)^k = e^{i(k\theta)}$. We then have

$$\left(e^{i\theta}\right)^{k+1} = (\cos\theta + i\sin\theta)^{k+1} = (\cos\theta + i\sin\theta)^k(\cos\theta + i\sin\theta) = \left(e^{i\theta}\right)^k(\cos\theta + i\sin\theta)$$

$$= e^{i(k\theta)}(\cos\theta + i\sin\theta) = (\cos k\theta + i\sin k\theta)(\cos\theta + i\sin\theta)$$

$$= [(\cos k\theta)(\cos\theta) - (\sin k\theta)(\sin\theta)] + [(\sin k\theta)(\cos\theta) + (\cos k\theta)(\sin\theta)]i.$$

$$= \cos\big((k+1)\theta\big) + \sin\big((k+1)\theta\big)i \text{ (by Theorem 15.1)} = e^{i((k+1)\theta)}.$$

By the Principle of Mathematical Induction, $\left(e^{i\theta}\right)^n = e^{i(n\theta)}$ for all $n \in \mathbb{Z}^+$.

If $n < 0$, then

$$\left(e^{i\theta}\right)^n = \frac{1}{(e^{i\theta})^{-n}} = \frac{1}{e^{i(-n\theta)}} = \frac{1}{\cos(-n\theta) + i\sin(-n\theta)}$$

$$= \frac{1}{\cos(n\theta) - i\sin(n\theta)} \text{ (by the Negative Identities)}$$

$$= \frac{1}{\cos(n\theta) - i\sin(n\theta)} \cdot \frac{\cos(n\theta) + i\sin(n\theta)}{\cos(n\theta) + i\sin(n\theta)} = \frac{\cos(n\theta) + i\sin(n\theta)}{\cos^2(n\theta) + \sin^2(n\theta)}$$

$$= \cos(n\theta) + i\sin(n\theta) \text{ (by the Pythagorean Identity)} = e^{i(n\theta)}. \qquad \square$$

Note: De Moivre's Theorem generalizes to all $n \in \mathbb{C}$ with a small "twist." In general, the expression $\left(e^{i\theta}\right)^n$ may have multiple values, whereas $e^{i(n\theta)}$ takes on just one value. However, for all $n \in \mathbb{C}$, $\left(e^{i\theta}\right)^n = e^{i(n\theta)}$ in the sense that $e^{i(n\theta)}$ is equal to one of the possible values of $\left(e^{i\theta}\right)^n$.

As a very simple example, let $\theta = 0$ and $n = \frac{1}{2}$. Then $e^{i(n\theta)} = e^0 = 1$ and $\left(e^{i\theta}\right)^n = 1^{\frac{1}{2}}$, which has two values: 1 and -1 (because $1^2 = 1$ and $(-1)^2 = 1$). Observe that $e^{i(n\theta)}$ is equal to one of the two possible values of $\left(e^{i\theta}\right)^n$.

We will not prove this more general result here.

Example 15.5: Let's compute $(2 - 2i)^6$. If we let $z = 2 - 2i$, we have $\tan\theta = \frac{-2}{2} = -1$, so that $\theta = \frac{7\pi}{4}$ (Why?). Also, $r = |z| = \sqrt{2^2 + (-2)^2} = \sqrt{2^2(1+1)} = \sqrt{2^2 \cdot 2} = \sqrt{2^2} \cdot \sqrt{2} = 2\sqrt{2}$. So, in exponential form, $z = 2\sqrt{2}e^{\frac{7\pi}{4}i}$, and therefore,

$$z^6 = \left(2\sqrt{2}e^{\frac{7\pi}{4}i}\right)^6 = 2^6\sqrt{2}^6\left(e^{\frac{7\pi}{4}i}\right)^6 = 64 \cdot 8e^{6\left(\frac{7\pi}{4}\right)i} = 512e^{\frac{21\pi}{2}i} = 512e^{\left(\frac{\pi}{2}+10\pi\right)i}$$

$$= 512e^{\frac{\pi}{2}i} = 512\left(\cos\frac{\pi}{2} + i\sin\frac{\pi}{2}\right) = 512(0 + i \cdot 1) = \mathbf{512i}.$$

Recall that a **square root** of a complex number z is a complex number w such that $z = w^2$ (see Lesson 7). More generally, if $z \in \mathbb{C}$ and $n \in \mathbb{Z}^+$, we say that $w \in \mathbb{C}$ is an **nth root** of z if $z = w^n$.

Suppose that $z = re^{i\theta}$ and $w = se^{i\phi}$ are exponential forms of $z, w \in \mathbb{C}$ and that w is an nth root of z. Let's derive a formula for w in terms of r and θ.

We have $w^n = s^n(e^{i\phi})^n = s^n e^{i(n\phi)}$. Since $z = w^n$, $re^{i\theta} = s^n e^{i(n\phi)}$. So, $s^n = r$ and $n\phi = \theta + 2k\pi$, where $k \in \mathbb{Z}$. Therefore, $s = \sqrt[n]{r}$ and $\phi = \frac{\theta+2k\pi}{n} = \frac{\theta}{n} + \frac{2k\pi}{n}$ for $k \in \mathbb{Z}$. Thus, $w = \sqrt[n]{r}e^{i\left(\frac{\theta}{n}+\frac{2k\pi}{n}\right)}$, $k \in \mathbb{Z}$.

If $k \geq n$, then $\frac{\theta}{n} + \frac{2k\pi}{n} = \frac{\theta}{n} + \frac{2(n+k-n)\pi}{n} = \frac{\theta}{n} + \frac{2n\pi+2(k-n)\pi}{n} = \frac{\theta}{n} + \frac{2n\pi}{n} + \frac{2(k-n)\pi}{n} = \frac{\theta}{n} + \frac{2(k-n)\pi}{n} + 2\pi$, and therefore, $e^{i\left(\frac{\theta}{n}+\frac{2k\pi}{n}\right)} = e^{i\left(\frac{\theta}{n}+\frac{2(k-n)\pi}{n}\right)}$.

It follows that there are exactly n distinct n^{th} roots of z given by $w = \sqrt[n]{r}e^{i\left(\frac{\theta}{n}+\frac{2k\pi}{n}\right)}$, $k = 0, 1, \ldots, n-1$. The **principal n^{th} root** of z, written $\sqrt[n]{z}$, is $\sqrt[n]{r}e^{i\frac{\theta}{n}}$, where $-\pi < \theta \leq \pi$.

Example 15.6: Let's compute all the eighth roots of 1 (also called the **8th roots of unity**). If $1 = w^n$, then $w = \sqrt[8]{1}e^{i\left(\frac{0}{8}+\frac{2k\pi}{8}\right)} = e^{\frac{k\pi}{4}i}$ for $k = 0, 1, 2, 3, 4, 5, 6, 7$. Substituting each of these values for k into the expression $e^{\frac{k\pi}{4}i}$ gives us the following 8 eighth roots of unity.

$$1, \frac{1}{\sqrt{2}} + \frac{1}{\sqrt{2}}i, i, -\frac{1}{\sqrt{2}} + \frac{1}{\sqrt{2}}i, -1, -\frac{1}{\sqrt{2}} - \frac{1}{\sqrt{2}}i, -i, \frac{1}{\sqrt{2}} - \frac{1}{\sqrt{2}}i$$

Note: Notice how the eight 8th roots of unity are uniformly distributed on the unit circle.

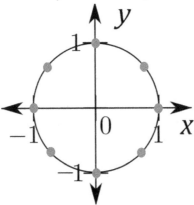

Functions of a Complex Variable

We will be considering functions $f: A \to \mathbb{C}$, where $A \subseteq \mathbb{C}$. If $z \in A$, then $f(z) = w$ for some $w \in \mathbb{C}$.

If we write both z and w in standard form, then we have $z = x + yi$ and $w = u + vi$ for some real numbers $x, y, u,$ and v. Note that the values of u and v depend upon the values of x and y. It follows that the complex function f is equivalent to a pair of real functions $u, v: \mathbb{R}^2 \to \mathbb{R}$. That is, we have $f(z) = f(x + yi) = u(x, y) + iv(x, y)$.

If we write z in the exponential form $z = re^{i\theta}$, we have $f(z) = f(re^{i\theta}) = u(r,\theta) + iv(r,\theta)$.

Notes: (1) If $f: A \to \mathbb{C}$, $z = x + yi$ and $f(z) = u + vi$, then the function f takes the point (x,y) in the Complex Plane to the point (u,v) in the Complex Plane.

Compare this to a real-valued function, where a point x on the real line is taken to a point y on the real line. The usual treatment here is to draw two real lines perpendicular to each other, label one of them the x-axis and the other the y-axis. This forms a plane and we can plot points $(x, f(x))$ in the usual way.

With complex-valued functions, we **cannot** visualize the situation in an analogous manner. The problem is that a visualization using this method would require us to plot points of the form (x, y, u, v). So, we would need a four-dimensional version of the two-dimensional plane, but humans are capable of perceiving only three dimensions. Therefore, we will need to come up with other methods for visualizing complex-valued functions.

(2) One way to visualize a complex-valued function is to simply stay in the same plane and to analyze how a typical point moves or how a certain set is transformed. For example, let $f: \mathbb{C} \to \mathbb{C}$ be defined by $f(z) = z - 1$. Then the function f takes the point (x, y) to the point $(x - 1, y)$. That is, each point is shifted one unit to the left. Similarly, if $S \subseteq \mathbb{C}$, then each point of the set S is shifted one unit to the left by the function f. Both these situations are demonstrated in the figure to the right.

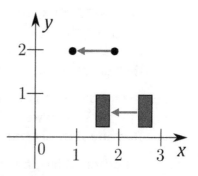

This method may work well for very simple functions, but for more complicated functions, the method in Note 3 below will usually be preferable.

(3) A second way to visualize a complex-valued function is to draw two separate planes: an xy-plane and a uv-plane. We can then draw a point or a set in the xy-plane and its image under f in the uv-plane. Let's see how this works for the function f defined by $f(z) = z - 1$ (the same function we used in Note 2).

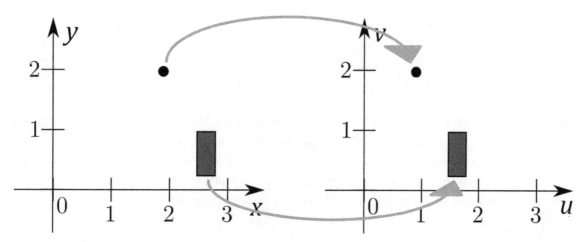

Example 15.7:

1. Let $f(z) = z + i$.

   If we write $z = x + yi$, then we have $f(x + yi) = x + yi + i = x + (y + 1)i$.

   So, $u(x, y) = x$ and $v(x, y) = y + 1$.

   Geometrically, f is a **translation**. It takes any point (x, y) in the Complex Plane and translates it up one unit. For example, the point $(1, 2)$ is translated to $(1, 3)$ under the function f because $f(1 + 2i) = (1 + 2i) + i = 1 + 3i$. We can see this in the figure to the right.

   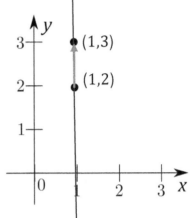

   Observe that any vertical line is mapped to itself under the function f. We can see this geometrically because given a vertical line in the Complex Plane, each point is just moved up one unit along that same vertical line. The vertical line in the figure on the right has equation $x = 1$. If we let L be the set of points on the line $x = 1$, then we see that $f[L] = L$. In fact, the function f maps L bijectively onto L. It might be more precise to say that f maps the vertical line $x = 1$ in the xy-plane to the vertical line $u = 1$ in the uv-plane.

   If a subset X of $\mathbb{C}$ satisfies $f[X] \subseteq X$, we will say that X is **invariant** under the function f. If $f[X] = X$, then we will say that X is **surjectively invariant** under f. So, in this example, we see that any vertical line L is surjectively invariant under f.

   A horizontal line, however, is **not** invariant under the function f. For example, the horizontal line $y = 1$ in the xy-plane is mapped bijectively to the horizontal line $v = 2$ in the uv-plane. We can visualize this mapping as follows:

   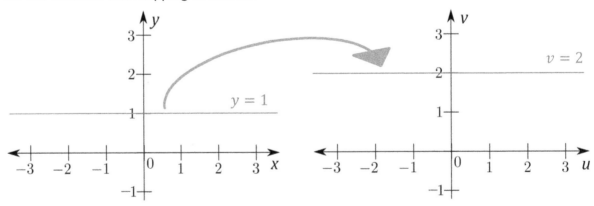

   In fact, for any "shape" in the xy-plane, after applying the function f, we wind up with the same shape shifted up 1 unit in the uv-plane. We can even think of this function as shifting the whole plane up 1 unit. More specifically, the image of the xy-plane under f is the entire uv-plane, where each point in the xy-plane is mapped to the point in the uv-plane that is shifted up 1 unit from the original point. So, $\mathbb{C}$ is surjectively invariant under f.

2. Let $g(z) = \bar{z}$.

   If we write $z = x + yi$, then we have $g(x + yi) = x - yi$.

So, $u(x, y) = x$ and $v(x, y) = -y$.

Geometrically, g is a **reflection** in the x-axis (or real axis). It takes any point (x, y) in the Complex Plane and reflects it through the x-axis to the point $(x, -y)$. For example, the point $(1, 2)$ is reflected through the x-axis to the point $(1, -2)$ under the function g because $g(1 + 2i) = 1 - 2i$. We can see this in the figure to the right.

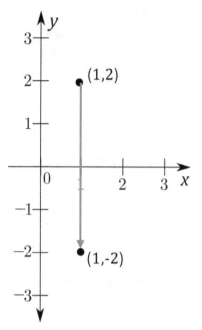

Observe that the x-axis is invariant under g. To see this, note that any point on the x-axis has the form $(a, 0)$ for some $a \in \mathbb{C}$ and $g(a + 0i) = a - 0i = a = a + 0i$. Notice that g actually maps each point on the x-axis to itself. Therefore, we call each point on the x-axis a **fixed point** of g.

It's not hard to see that the subsets of $\mathbb{C}$ that are invariant under g are precisely the subsets that are symmetric with respect to the x-axis. However, points above and below the x-axis are **not** fixed points of g, as they are reflected across the x-axis. The figure below should help to visualize this. Note that in this example, invariant is equivalent to surjectively invariant.

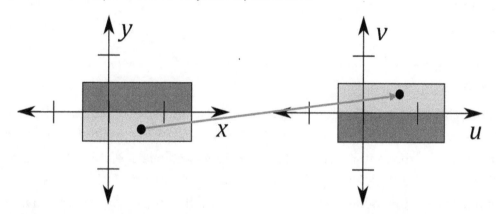

In the figure, the rectangle displayed is invariant under g. The fixed points of g in the rectangle are the points on the x-axis. We see that points below the x-axis in the xy-plane are mapped to points above the u-axis in the uv-plane. A typical point below the x-axis and its image under g above the u-axis are shown. Similarly, points above the x-axis in the xy-plane are mapped to points below the u-axis in the uv-plane.

3. Let $h(z) = iz$.

If we write $z = x + yi$, then we have $h(x + yi) = i(x + yi) = xi + yi^2 = xi - y = -y + xi$.

So, the function h takes any point (x, y) to the point $(-y, x)$. To understand what this means geometrically, it is useful to analyze what the image looks like in exponential form.

If we write $z = re^{i\theta}$, then we have $h(re^{i\theta}) = i(re^{i\theta}) = e^{i\frac{\pi}{2}}(re^{i\theta}) = re^{i\frac{\pi}{2}}e^{i\theta} = re^{i(\theta + \frac{\pi}{2})}$.

Notice that r remains unchanged under this transformation. So, $h(z)$ is the same distance from the origin as z. However, the angle changes from θ to $\theta + \frac{\pi}{2}$. Geometrically, g is a **rotation** about the origin by $\frac{\pi}{2}$ radians, or equivalently, 90°. As an example, the point $(1, 1)$ is rotated 90° about the origin to the point $(-1, 1)$ (see the figure to the right). We can see this in one of two ways. If we use the standard form of $1 + i$, then we have $h(1 + i) = -1 + i$. If we use exponential form, then by Example 15.4, $1 + i = \sqrt{2}e^{\frac{\pi}{4}i}$. So, $h\left(\sqrt{2}e^{\frac{\pi}{4}i}\right) = \sqrt{2}e^{\left(\frac{\pi}{4} + \frac{\pi}{2}\right)i} = \sqrt{2}e^{\frac{3\pi}{4}i}$. Therefore, we have $u = \sqrt{2}\cos\frac{3\pi}{4} = \sqrt{2}\left(-\frac{1}{\sqrt{2}}\right) = -1$ and $v = \sqrt{2}\sin\frac{3\pi}{4} = \sqrt{2}\left(\frac{1}{\sqrt{2}}\right) = 1$. So, once again, $g(1 + i) = -1 + 1i = -1 + i$.

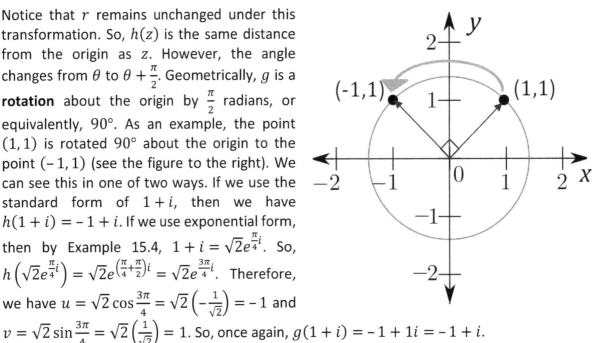

Observe that any circle centered at the origin is surjectively invariant under h and the only fixed point of h is the origin.

4. Let $p(z) = z^2$.

If we write $z = re^{i\theta}$, then we have $p\left(re^{i\theta}\right) = \left(re^{i\theta}\right)^2 = r^2\left(e^{i\theta}\right)^2 = r^2 e^{i(2\theta)}$ by De Moivre's Theorem.

Under this function, the modulus of the complex number z is squared and the argument is doubled. As an example, let's see what happens to the point $(1, 1)$ under this function. Changing to exponential form, by Example 15.4, we have $1 + i = \sqrt{2}e^{\frac{\pi}{4}i}$. So, $p(1 + i) = 2e^{\frac{\pi}{2}i}$. We see that the modulus of $p(1 + i)$ is 2 and the argument of $p(1 + i)$ is $\frac{\pi}{2}$. So, in the Complex Plane, this is the point that is 2 units from the origin on the positive y-axis (because $W\left(\frac{\pi}{2}\right) = (0, 1)$ and $(0, 1)$ lies on the positive y-axis). In standard form, we have $p(1 + i) = 2i$.

The only fixed points of p are $z = 0$ and $z = 1$. To see this, note that if $r^2 e^{i(2\theta)} = re^{i\theta}$, then $r^2 = r$ and $2\theta = \theta + 2k\pi$ for some $k \in \mathbb{Z}$. The equation $r^2 = r$ is equivalent to $r^2 - r = 0$ or $r(r - 1) = 0$. So, $r = 0$ or $r = 1$. If $r = 0$, then $z = 0$. So, assume $r = 1$. We see that $2\theta = \theta + 2k\pi$ is equivalent to $\theta = 2k\pi$. So, $z = 1 \cdot e^{i(2k\pi)} = e^0 = 1$.

Observe that the unit circle is surjectively invariant under p. To see this, first note that if $z = re^{i\theta}$ lies on the unit circle, then $r = 1$ and $p\left(e^{i\theta}\right) = e^{i(2\theta)}$, which also has modulus 1.

Furthermore, every point z on the unit circle has the form $z = e^{i\theta}$ and $p\left(e^{i\frac{\theta}{2}}\right) = \left(e^{i\frac{\theta}{2}}\right)^2 = e^{i\theta}$ by De Moivre's Theorem.

What other subsets of $\mathbb{C}$ are surjectively invariant under p? Here are a few:

- The positive real axis: $\{z \in \mathbb{C} \mid \operatorname{Re} z > 0 \wedge \operatorname{Im} z = 0\}$

222

- The open unit disk: $\{z \in \mathbb{C} \mid |z| < 1\}$

- The complement of the open unit disk: $\{z \in \mathbb{C} \mid |z| \geq 1\}$

The dedicated reader should prove that these sets are surjectively invariant under p. Are there any other sets that are surjectively invariant under p? What about sets that are invariant, but not surjectively invariant?

Limits and Continuity

Let $A \subseteq \mathbb{C}$, let $f: A \to \mathbb{C}$, let $L \in \mathbb{C}$, and let $a \in \mathbb{C}$ be a point such that A contains some deleted neighborhood of a. We say that the **limit of f as z approaches a is L**, written $\lim_{z \to a} f(z) = L$, if for every positive number ϵ, there is a positive number δ such that $0 < |z - a| < \delta \to |f(z) - L| < \epsilon$.

Notes: (1) The statement of this definition of limit is essentially the same as the statement of the $\epsilon - \delta$ definition of a limit of a real-valued function (see Lesson 13). However, the geometry looks very different.

For a real-valued function, a deleted neighborhood of a has the form $N_\epsilon^\odot(a) = (a - \epsilon, a) \cup (a, a + \epsilon)$ and we can visualize this neighborhood as follows:

$$a - \epsilon \qquad\qquad a \qquad\qquad a + \epsilon$$

For a complex-valued function, a deleted neighborhood of a, say $N_\epsilon^\odot(a) = \{z \in \mathbb{C} \mid 0 < |z - a| < \epsilon\}$, is a punctured disk with center a. We can see a visualization of such a neighborhood to the right.

(2) In $\mathbb{R}$, there is a simple one to one correspondence between neighborhoods (open intervals) and (vertical or horizontal) strips.

In $\mathbb{C}$ there is no such correspondence. Therefore, for complex-valued functions, we start right away with the $\epsilon - \delta$ definition.

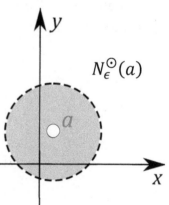

(3) Recall that in $\mathbb{R}$, the expression $|x - a| < \delta$ is equivalent to $a - \delta < x < a + \delta$, or $x \in (a - \delta, a + \delta)$.

Also, the expression $0 < |x - a|$ is equivalent to $x - a \neq 0$, or $x \neq a$.

Therefore, $0 < |x - a| < \delta$ is equivalent to $x \in (a - \delta, a) \cup (a, a + \delta)$.

In $\mathbb{C}$, if we let $z = x + yi$ and $a = b + ci$, then

$$|z - a| = |(x + yi) - (b + ci)| = |(x - b) + (y - c)i| = \sqrt{(x - b)^2 + (y - c)^2}.$$

So, $|z - a| < \delta$ is equivalent to $(x - b)^2 + (y - c)^2 < \delta^2$. In other words, (x, y) is inside the disk with center (b, c) and radius δ.

Also, we have

$$0 < |z - a| \Leftrightarrow (x - b)^2 + (y - c)^2 \neq 0 \Leftrightarrow x - b \neq 0 \text{ or } y - c \neq 0 \Leftrightarrow x \neq b \text{ or } x \neq c \Leftrightarrow z \neq a.$$

Therefore, $0 < |z - a| < \delta$ is equivalent to "z is in the punctured disk with center a and radius δ."

(4) Similarly, in $\mathbb{R}$, we have that $|f(x) - L| < \epsilon$ is equivalent to $f(x) \in (L - \epsilon, L + \epsilon)$, while in $\mathbb{C}$, we have $|f(z) - L| < \epsilon$ is equivalent to "$f(z)$ is in the disk with center L and radius ϵ."

(5) Just like for real-valued functions, we can think of determining if $\lim_{z \to a} f(z) = L$ as the result of an $\epsilon - \delta$ game. Player 1 "attacks" by choosing a positive number ϵ. This is equivalent to Player 1 choosing the disk $N_\epsilon(L) = \{w \in \mathbb{C} \mid |w - L| < \epsilon\}$.

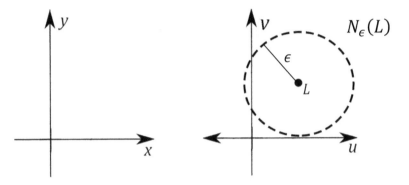

Player 2 then tries to "defend" by finding a positive number δ. This is equivalent to Player 2 choosing the punctured disk $N_\delta^{\odot}(a) = \{z \in \mathbb{C} \mid 0 < |z - a| < \delta\}$.

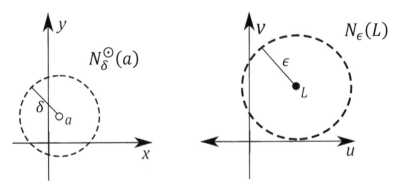

The defense is successful if $z \in N_\delta^{\odot}(a)$ implies $f(z) \in N_\epsilon(L)$, or equivalently, $f\left[N_\delta^{\odot}(a)\right] \subseteq N_\epsilon(L)$.

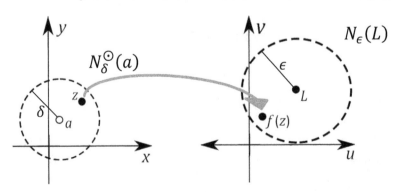

224

If Player 2 defends successfully, then Player 1 chooses a new positive number ϵ', or equivalently, a new neighborhood $N_{\epsilon'}(L) = \{w \in \mathbb{C} \mid |w - L| < \epsilon'\}$. If Player 1 is smart, then he/she will choose ϵ' to be less than ϵ (otherwise, Player 2 can use the same δ). The smaller the value of ϵ', the smaller the neighborhood $N_{\epsilon'}(L)$, and the harder it will be for Player 2 to defend. Player 2 once again tries to choose a positive number δ' so that $f\left[N_{\delta'}^{\odot}(a)\right] \subseteq N_{\epsilon}'(L)$. This process continues indefinitely. Player 1 wins the $\epsilon - \delta$ game if at some stage, Player 2 cannot defend successfully. Player 2 wins the $\epsilon - \delta$ game if he or she defends successfully at every stage.

(6) If for a given $\epsilon > 0$, we have found a $\delta > 0$ such that $f\left[N_{\delta}^{\odot}(a)\right] \subseteq N_{\epsilon}(L)$, then any positive number smaller than δ works as well. Indeed, if $0 < \delta' < \delta$, then $N_{\delta'}^{\odot}(a) \subseteq N_{\delta}^{\odot}(a)$. It then follows that $f\left[N_{\delta'}^{\odot}(a)\right] \subseteq f\left[N_{\delta}^{\odot}(a)\right] \subseteq N_{\epsilon}(L)$.

Example 15.8: Let's use the $\epsilon - \delta$ definition of limit to prove that $\lim\limits_{z \to 3+6i} \left(\frac{iz}{3} + 2\right) = i$.

Analysis: Given $\epsilon > 0$, we will find $\delta > 0$ so that $0 < |z - (3 + 6i)| < \delta$ implies $\left|\left(\frac{iz}{3} + 2\right) - i\right| < \epsilon$. First note that

$$\left|\left(\frac{iz}{3} + 2\right) - i\right| = \left|\frac{1}{3}(iz + 6) - \frac{1}{3}(3i)\right| = \left|\frac{1}{3}i(z - 6i - 3)\right| = \left|\frac{1}{3}i\right| |z - 3 - 6i| = \frac{1}{3}|z - (3 + 6i)|.$$

So, $\left|\left(\frac{iz}{3} + 2\right) - i\right| < \epsilon$ is equivalent to $|z - (3 + 6i)| < 3\epsilon$. Therefore, $\delta = 3\epsilon$ should work.

Proof: Let $\epsilon > 0$ and let $\delta = 3\epsilon$. Suppose that $0 < |z - (3 + 6i)| < \delta$. Then we have

$$\left|\left(\frac{iz}{3} + 2\right) - i\right| = \frac{1}{3}|z - (3 + 6i)| < \frac{1}{3}\delta = \frac{1}{3}(3\epsilon) = \epsilon.$$

Since $\epsilon > 0$ was arbitrary, we have $\forall \epsilon > 0 \, \exists \delta > 0 \left(0 < |z - (3 + 6i)| < \delta \to \left|\left(\frac{iz}{3} + 2\right) - i\right| < \epsilon\right)$.

Therefore, $\lim\limits_{z \to 3+6i} \left(\frac{iz}{3} + 2\right) = i$. $\square$

Example 15.9: Let's use the $\epsilon - \delta$ definition of limit to prove that $\lim\limits_{z \to i} z^2 = -1$.

Analysis: Given $\epsilon > 0$, we need to find $\delta > 0$ so that $0 < |z - i| < \delta$ implies $|z^2 - (-1)| < \epsilon$. First note that $|z^2 - (-1)| = |z^2 + 1| = |(z - i)(z + i)| = |z - i||z + i|$. Therefore, $|z^2 - (-1)| < \epsilon$ is equivalent to $|z - i||z + i| < \epsilon$.

As in Example 13.9 from Lesson 13, $|z - i|$ is not an issue because we're going to be choosing δ so that this expression is small enough. But to make the argument work we need to make $|z + i|$ small too. Remember from Note 6 above that if we find a value for δ that works, then any smaller positive number will work too. This allows us to start by assuming that δ is smaller than any positive number we choose. So, let's just assume that $\delta \leq 1$ and see what effect that has on $|z + i|$.

Well, if $\delta \leq 1$ and $0 < |z - i| < \delta$, then $|z + i| = |(z - i) + 2i| \leq |z - i| + |2i| < 1 + 2 = 3$. Here we used the Standard Advanced Calculus Trick (SACT) from Note 7 after Example 4.5 in Lesson 4, followed by the Triangle Inequality (Theorem 7.3), and then the computation $|2i| = |2||i| = 2 \cdot 1 = 2$.

So, if we assume that $\delta \leq 1$, then $|z^2 - (-1)| = |z - i||z + i| < \delta \cdot 3 = 3\delta$. Therefore, if we want to make sure that $|z^2 - (-1)| < \epsilon$, then is suffices to choose δ so that $3\delta \leq \epsilon$, as long as we also have $\delta \leq 1$. So, we will let $\delta = \min\left\{1, \frac{\epsilon}{3}\right\}$.

Proof: Let $\epsilon > 0$ and let $\delta = \min\left\{1, \frac{\epsilon}{3}\right\}$. Suppose that $0 < |z - i| < \delta$. Then since $\delta \leq 1$, we have $|z + i| = |(z - i) + 2i| \leq |z - i| + |2i| = |z - i| + |2||i| = |z - i| + 2 < 1 + 2 = 3$, and therefore, $|z^2 - (-1)| = |z^2 + 1| = |(z - i)(z + i)| = |z - i||z + i| < \delta \cdot 3 \leq \frac{\epsilon}{3} \cdot 3 = \epsilon$.

Since $\epsilon > 0$ was arbitrary, we have $\forall \epsilon > 0 \; \exists \delta > 0 \; (0 < |z - i| < \delta \rightarrow |z^2 - (-1)| < \epsilon)$. Therefore, $\lim_{z \to i} z^2 = -1$. $\qquad\square$

Theorem 15.3: If $\lim_{z \to a} f(z)$ exists, then it is unique.

Proof: Suppose that $\lim_{z \to a} f(z) = L$ and $\lim_{z \to a} f(z) = K$. Let $\epsilon > 0$. Since $\lim_{z \to a} f(z) = L$, we can find $\delta_1 > 0$ such that $0 < |z - a| < \delta_1 \rightarrow |f(z) - L| < \frac{\epsilon}{2}$. Since $\lim_{z \to a} f(z) = K$, we can find $\delta_2 > 0$ such that $0 < |z - a| < \delta_2 \rightarrow |f(z) - K| < \frac{\epsilon}{2}$. Let $\delta = \min\{\delta_1, \delta_2\}$. Suppose that $0 < |z - a| < \delta$. Then $|L - K| = |(f(z) - K) - (f(z) - L)|$ **(SACT)** $\leq |f(z) - K| + |f(z) - L|$ **(TI)** $< \frac{\epsilon}{2} + \frac{\epsilon}{2} = \epsilon$. Since ϵ was an arbitrary positive real number, by Problem 8 from Lesson 5, we have $|L - K| = 0$. So, $L - K = 0$, and therefore, $L = K$. $\qquad\square$

Note: SACT stands for the Standard Advanced Calculus Trick and **TI** stands for the Triangle Inequality.

Example 15.10: Let's show that $\lim_{z \to 0} \left(\frac{z}{\bar{z}}\right)^2$ does not exist.

Proof: If we consider complex numbers of the form $x + 0i$, $\left(\frac{z}{\bar{z}}\right)^2 = \left(\frac{x+0i}{x-0i}\right)^2 = \left(\frac{x}{x}\right)^2 = 1^2 = 1$. Since every deleted neighborhood of 0 contains points of the form $x + 0i$, we see that if $\lim_{z \to 0} \left(\frac{z}{\bar{z}}\right)^2$ exists, it must be equal to 1.

Next, let's consider complex numbers of the form $x + xi$. In this case, $\left(\frac{z}{\bar{z}}\right)^2 = \left(\frac{x+xi}{x-xi}\right)^2 = \frac{2x^2 i}{-2x^2 i} = -1$. Since every deleted neighborhood of 0 contains points of the form $x + xi$, we see that if $\lim_{z \to 0} \left(\frac{z}{\bar{z}}\right)^2$ exists, it must be equal to -1.

By Theorem 15.3, the limit does not exist. $\qquad\square$

Define $d: \mathbb{C} \times \mathbb{C} \to \mathbb{R}$ by $d(z, w) = |z - w|$. By Example 14.10 (part 1), $(\mathbb{C}, d)$ is a metric space. So, by Theorem 14.4, we have the following definition of continuity for complex-valued functions:

Let $A \subseteq \mathbb{C}$, let $f: A \to \mathbb{C}$, and let $a \in A$ be a point such that A contains some neighborhood of a. f is continuous at a if and only if for every positive number ϵ, there is a positive number δ such that

$$|z - a| < \delta \rightarrow |f(z) - f(a)| < \epsilon.$$

Example 15.11: Let $f: \mathbb{C} \to \mathbb{C}$ be defined by $f(z) = \frac{iz}{3} + 2$. In Example 15.8, we showed that $\lim\limits_{z \to 3+6i} f(z) = i$. Since $f(3 + 6i) = \frac{i(3+6i)}{3} + 2 = \frac{3i-6}{3} + 2 = \frac{3(i-2)}{3} + 2 = i - 2 + 2 = i$, we see from the proof in Example 15.8 that if $|z - (3 + 6i)| < \delta$, then $|f(z) - f(3 + 6i)| = \left|\left(\frac{iz}{3} + 2\right) - i\right| < \epsilon$. It follows that f is continuous at $3 + 6i$.

More generally, let's show that for all $a \in \mathbb{C}$, f is continuous at a.

Proof: Let $a \in \mathbb{C}$, let $\epsilon > 0$ and let $\delta = 3\epsilon$. Suppose that $|z - a| < \delta$. Then we have

$$|f(z) - f(a)| = \left|\left(\frac{iz}{3} + 2\right) - \left(\frac{ia}{3} + 2\right)\right| = \left|\frac{i}{3}(z - a)\right| = \left|\frac{i}{3}\right| |z - a| < \frac{1}{3}\delta = \frac{1}{3}(3\epsilon) = \epsilon.$$

Since $\epsilon > 0$ was arbitrary, we have $\forall \epsilon > 0 \, \exists \delta > 0 \, (|z - a| < \delta \to |f(z) - f(a)| < \epsilon)$.

Therefore, f is continuous at a. $\qquad\qquad\qquad\qquad\qquad\qquad\qquad\qquad\qquad\qquad\qquad\qquad$ $\square$

Notes: (1) We proved $\forall a \in \mathbb{C} \, \forall \epsilon > 0 \, \exists \delta > 0 \, \forall z \in \mathbb{C}(|z - a| < \delta \to |f(z) - f(a)| < \epsilon)$. In words, we proved that for every complex number a, given a positive real number ϵ, we can find a positive real number δ such that whenever the distance between z and a is less than δ, the distance between $f(z)$ and $f(a)$ is less than ϵ. And of course, a simpler way to say this is "for every complex number a, f is continuous at a," or $\forall a \in \mathbb{C} \, (f$ is continuous at $a)$."

(2) If we move the expression $\forall a \in \mathbb{C}$ next to $\forall z \in \mathbb{C}$, we get a concept that is stronger than continuity. We say that a function $f: A \to \mathbb{C}$ is uniformly continuous on A if

$$\forall \epsilon > 0 \, \exists \delta > 0 \, \forall a, z \in A \, (|z - a| < \delta \to |f(z) - f(a)| < \epsilon).$$

(3) As a quick example of uniform continuity, let's prove that the function $f: \mathbb{C} \to \mathbb{C}$ defined by $f(z) = \frac{iz}{3} + 2$ is uniformly continuous on $\mathbb{C}$.

New proof: Let $\epsilon > 0$ and let $\delta = 3\epsilon$. Let $a, z \in \mathbb{C}$ and suppose that $|z - a| < \delta$. Then we have

$$|f(z) - f(a)| = \left|\left(\frac{iz}{3} + 2\right) - \left(\frac{ia}{3} + 2\right)\right| = \left|\frac{i}{3}(z - a)\right| = \left|\frac{i}{3}\right| |z - a| < \frac{1}{3}\delta = \frac{1}{3} \cdot 3\epsilon = \epsilon.$$

Since $\epsilon > 0$ was arbitrary, we have $\forall \epsilon > 0 \, \exists \delta > 0 \, \forall a, z \in \mathbb{C} \, (|z - a| < \delta \to |f(z) - f(a)| < \epsilon)$. Therefore, f is uniformly continuous.

(4) The difference between continuity and uniform continuity on a set A can be described as follows: In both cases, an ϵ is given and then a δ is chosen. For continuity, for each value of a, we can choose a different δ. For uniform continuity, once we choose a δ for some value of a, we need to be able to use the **same** δ for every other value of a in A.

In terms of disks, once a disk of radius ϵ is given, we need to be more careful how we choose our disk of radius δ. As we check different z-values, we can translate our chosen disk as much as we like around the xy-plane. However, we are not allowed to decrease the radius of the disk.

The Riemann Sphere

We have used the symbols $-\infty$ and ∞ (or $+\infty$) to describe unbounded intervals of real numbers, as well as certain limits of real-valued functions. These symbols are used to express a notion of "infinity." If we pretend for a moment that we are standing on the real line at 0, and we begin walking to the right, continuing indefinitely, then we might say we are walking toward ∞. Similarly, if we begin walking to the left instead, continuing indefinitely, then we might say we are walking toward $-\infty$.

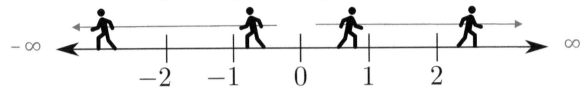

We would like to come up with a coherent notion of infinity with respect to the Complex Plane. There is certainly more than one way to do this. A method that is most analogous to the picture described above would be to define a set of infinities $\{\infty_\theta \mid 0 \le \theta < 2\pi\}$, the idea being that for each angle θ in standard position, we have an infinity, ∞_θ, describing where we would be headed if we were to start at the origin and then begin walking along the terminal ray of θ, continuing indefinitely.

The method in the previous paragraph, although acceptable, has the disadvantage of having to deal with uncountably many "infinities." Instead, we will explore a different notion that involves just a single **point at infinity**. The idea is relatively simple. Pretend you have a large sheet of paper balancing on the palm of your hand. The sheet of paper represents the Complex plane with the origin right at the center of your palm. The palm of your hand itself represents the unit circle together with its interior.

Now, imagine using the pointer finger on your other hand to press down on the origin of that sheet of paper (the Complex Plane), forcing your hand to form a unit sphere (reshaping the Complex Plane into a unit sphere as well). Notice that the origin becomes the "south pole" of the sphere, while all the "infinities" described in the last paragraph are forced together at the "north pole" of the sphere. Also, notice that the unit circle stays fixed, the points interior to the unit circle form the lower half of the sphere, and the points exterior to the unit circle form the upper half of the sphere with the exception of the "north pole."

When we visualize the unit sphere in this way, we refer to it as the **Reimann Sphere**.

Let's let $\mathbb{S}^2$ be the Reimann Sphere and let's officially define the **north pole** and **south pole** of $\mathbb{S}^2$ to be the points $N = (0,0,1)$ and $S = (0,0,-1)$, respectively.

Also, since $\mathbb{S}^2$ is a subset of three-dimensional space (formally known as $\mathbb{R}^3$), while $\mathbb{C}$ is only two dimensional, let's identify $\mathbb{C}$ with $\mathbb{C} \times \{0\}$ so that we write points in the Complex Plane as $(a, b, 0)$ instead of (a, b). We can then visualize the Complex Plane as intersecting the Reimann sphere in the unit circle. To the right we have a picture of the Reimann Sphere together with the Complex Plane.

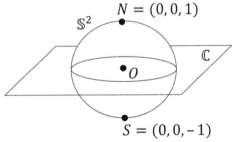

For each point z in the Complex Plane, consider the line passing through the points N and z. This line intersects $\mathbb{S}^2$ in exactly one point P_z. This observation allows us to define a bijection $f: \mathbb{C} \to \mathbb{S}^2 \setminus N$ (called defined by $f(z) = P_z$. An explicit definition of f can be given by

$$f(z) = \left(\frac{z + \overline{z}}{1 + |z|^2}, \frac{z - \overline{z}}{i(1 + |z|^2)}, \frac{|z|^2 - 1}{|z|^2 + 1} \right)$$

Below is a picture of a point z in the Complex Plane and its image $f(z) = P_z$ on the Riemann Sphere.

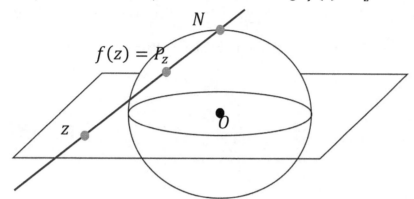

In Challenge Problem 21 below, you will be asked to verify that f is a homeomorphism. If we let $\overline{\mathbb{C}} = \mathbb{C} \cup \{\infty\}$, then we can extend f to a function $\overline{f}: \overline{\mathbb{C}} \to \mathbb{S}^2$ by defining $\overline{f}(\infty) = N$. $\overline{\mathbb{C}}$ is called the **Extended Complex Plane**. If we let $\overline{\mathcal{T}} = \mathcal{T} \cup \{U \cup \{\infty\} | U \in \mathcal{T}\}$, where $\mathcal{T}$ is the standard topology on $\mathbb{C}$, then $\overline{\mathcal{T}}$ defines a topology on $\overline{\mathbb{C}}$, and $\overline{f}$ is a homeomorphism from $(\overline{\mathbb{C}}, \overline{\mathcal{T}})$ to $(\mathbb{S}^2, \mathcal{U}_{\mathbb{S}^2})$, where $\mathcal{U}$ is the product topology on $\mathbb{R}^3$ with respect to the standard topology on $\mathbb{R}$.

Note: Subspace and **product topologies** were defined in Problems 8 and 11 in Lesson 14.

If ϵ is a small positive number, then $\frac{1}{\epsilon}$ is a large positive number. We see that the set $N_{\frac{1}{\epsilon}} = \left\{ z \mid |z| > \frac{1}{\epsilon} \right\}$ is a neighborhood of ∞ in the following sense. Notice that $N_{\frac{1}{\epsilon}}$ consists of all points outside of the circle of radius $\frac{1}{\epsilon}$ centered at the origin. The image of this set under the function f is a deleted neighborhood of N.

We can now extend our definition of limit to include various infinite cases. We will do one example here and you will look at others in Problem 18 below.

$$\lim_{z \to a} f(z) = \infty \text{ if and only if } \forall \epsilon > 0 \, \exists \delta > 0 \left(0 < |z - a| < \delta \to |f(z)| > \frac{1}{\epsilon} \right).$$

Theorem 15.4: $\lim_{z \to a} f(z) = \infty$ if and only $\lim_{z \to a} \frac{1}{f(z)} = 0$.

Proof: Suppose that $\lim_{z \to a} f(z) = \infty$ and let $\epsilon > 0$. There is $\delta > 0$ so that $0 < |z - a| < \delta \to |f(z)| > \frac{1}{\epsilon}$. But, $|f(z)| > \frac{1}{\epsilon}$ is equivalent to $\left| \frac{1}{f(z)} - 0 \right| < \epsilon$. So, $\lim_{z \to a} \frac{1}{f(z)} = 0$.

Now, suppose $\lim_{z \to a} \frac{1}{f(z)} = 0$ and let $\epsilon > 0$. There is $\delta > 0$ so that $0 < |z - a| < \delta \to \left| \frac{1}{f(z)} - 0 \right| < \epsilon$. But, $\left| \frac{1}{f(z)} - 0 \right| < \epsilon$ is equivalent to $|f(z)| > \frac{1}{\epsilon}$. So, $\lim_{z \to a} f(z) = \infty$. $\qquad \square$

Problem Set 15

Full solutions to these problems are available for free download here:

www.SATPrepGet800.com/PMFBXSG

LEVEL 1

1. In Problems 11 and 12 below, you will be asked to show that $W\left(\frac{\pi}{3}\right) = \left(\frac{1}{2}, \frac{\sqrt{3}}{2}\right)$ and $W\left(\frac{\pi}{6}\right) = \left(\frac{\sqrt{3}}{2}, \frac{1}{2}\right)$. Use this information to compute the sine, cosine, and tangent of each of the following angles:

   (i) $\frac{\pi}{6}$

   (ii) $\frac{\pi}{3}$

   (iii) $\frac{2\pi}{3}$

   (iv) $\frac{5\pi}{6}$

   (v) $\frac{7\pi}{6}$

   (vi) $\frac{4\pi}{3}$

   (vii) $\frac{5\pi}{3}$

   (viii) $\frac{11\pi}{6}$

2. Use the sum identities (Theorem 15.1) to compute the cosine, sine, and tangent of each of the following angles:

   (i) $\frac{5\pi}{12}$

   (ii) $\frac{\pi}{12}$

   (iii) $\frac{11\pi}{12}$

   (iv) $\frac{19\pi}{12}$

3. Each of the following complex numbers is written in exponential form. Rewrite each complex number in standard form:

    (i) $e^{\pi i}$

    (ii) $e^{-\frac{5\pi}{2}i}$

    (iii) $3e^{\frac{\pi}{4}i}$

    (iv) $2e^{\frac{\pi}{3}i}$

    (v) $\sqrt{2}e^{\frac{7\pi}{6}i}$

    (vi) $\pi e^{-\frac{5\pi}{4}i}$

    (vii) $e^{\frac{19\pi}{12}}$

4. Each of the following complex numbers is written in standard form. Rewrite each complex number in exponential form:

    (i) $-1-i$

    (ii) $\sqrt{3}+i$

    (iii) $1-\sqrt{3}i$

    (iv) $\left(\frac{\sqrt{6}+\sqrt{2}}{4}\right)+\left(\frac{\sqrt{6}-\sqrt{2}}{4}\right)i$

5. Write the following complex numbers in standard form:

    (i) $\left(\frac{\sqrt{2}}{2}+\frac{\sqrt{2}}{2}i\right)^4$

    (ii) $\left(1+\sqrt{3}i\right)^5$

6. Use De Moivre's Theorem to prove the following identities:

    (i) $\cos 2\theta = \cos^2\theta - \sin^2\theta$

    (ii) $\sin 2\theta = 2\sin\theta\cos\theta$

    (iii) $\cos 3\theta = \cos^3\theta - 3\cos\theta\sin^2\theta$

7. Suppose that $z = re^{i\theta}$ and $w = se^{i\phi}$ are complex numbers written in exponential form. Express each of the following in exponential form. Provide a proof in each case:

    (i) zw

    (ii) $\frac{z}{w}$

8. Write each function in the form $f(z) = u(x, y) + iv(x, y)$ and $f(z) = u(r, \theta) + iv(r, \theta)$:

  (i) $f(z) = 2z^2 - 5$

  (ii) $f(z) = \frac{1}{z}$

  (iii) $f(z) = z^3 + z^2 + z + 1$

9. Let $f(z) = x^2 - y^2 - 2x + 2y(x + 1)i$. Rewrite $f(z)$ in terms of z.

10. Find all complex numbers that satisfy the given equation:

  (i) $z^6 - 1 = 0$

  (ii) $z^4 + 4 = 0$

LEVEL 4

11. Consider triangle AOP, where $O = (0, 0)$, $A = (1, 0)$, and P is the point on the unit circle so that angle POA has radian measure $\frac{\pi}{3}$. Prove that triangle AOP is equilateral, and then use this to prove that $W\left(\frac{\pi}{3}\right) = \left(\frac{1}{2}, \frac{\sqrt{3}}{2}\right)$. You may use the following facts about triangles: (i) The interior angle measures of a triangle sum to π radians; (ii) Two sides of a triangle have the same length if and only if the interior angles of the triangle opposite these sides have the same measure; (iii) If two sides of a triangle have the same length, then the line segment beginning at the point of intersection of those two sides and terminating on the opposite base midway between the endpoints of that base is perpendicular to that base.

12. Prove that $W\left(\frac{\pi}{6}\right) = \left(\frac{\sqrt{3}}{2}, \frac{1}{2}\right)$. You can use facts (i), (ii), and (iii) described in Problem 11.

13. Let θ and ϕ be the radian measure of angles A and B, respectively. Prove the following identity:

$$\cos(\theta - \phi) = \cos\theta \cos\phi + \sin\theta \sin\phi$$

14. Let θ and ϕ be the radian measure of angles A and B, respectively. Prove the following identities:

  (i) $\cos(\theta + \phi) = \cos\theta \cos\phi - \sin\theta \sin\phi$

  (ii) $\cos(\pi - \theta) = -\cos\theta$

  (iii) $\cos\left(\frac{\pi}{2} - \theta\right) = \sin\theta$

  (iv) $\sin\left(\frac{\pi}{2} - \theta\right) = \cos\theta$

  (v) $\sin(\theta + \phi) = \sin\theta \cos\phi + \cos\theta \sin\phi$

  (vi) $\sin(\pi - \theta) = -\sin\theta$

15. Let $z, w \in \mathbb{C}$. Prove that $\arg zw = \arg z + \arg w$ in the sense that if two of the three terms in the equation are specified, then there is a value for the third term so that the equation holds. Similarly, prove that $\arg\frac{z}{w} = \arg z - \arg w$. Finally, provide examples to show that the corresponding equations are false if we replace "arg" by "Arg."

16. Define the function $f: \mathbb{C} \to \mathbb{C}$ by $f(z) = z^2$. Determine the images under f of each of the following sets:

    (i) $A = \{x + yi \mid x^2 - y^2 = 1\}$

    (ii) $B = \{x + yi \mid x > 0 \wedge y > 0 \wedge xy < 1\}$

    (iii) $C = \{x + yi \mid x \geq 0 \wedge y \geq 0\}$

    (iv) $D = \{x + yi \mid y \geq 0\}$

17. Let $A \subseteq \mathbb{C}$, let $f: A \to \mathbb{C}$, let $L = j + ki \in \mathbb{C}$, and let $a = b + ci \in \mathbb{C}$ be a point such that A contains some deleted neighborhood of a. Suppose that $f(x + yi) = u(x, y) + iv(x, y)$. Prove that $\lim_{z \to a} f(z) = L$ if and only if $\lim_{(x,y) \to (b,c)} u(x, y) = j$ and $\lim_{(x,y) \to (b,c)} v(x, y) = k$.

18. Give a reasonable definition for each of the following limits (like what was done right before Theorem 15.4). L is a finite real number.

    (i) $\lim_{z \to \infty} f(z) = L$

    (ii) $\lim_{z \to \infty} f(z) = \infty$

19. Prove each of the following:

    (i) $\lim_{z \to \infty} f(z) = L$ if and only $\lim_{z \to 0} f\left(\frac{1}{z}\right) = L$

    (ii) $\lim_{z \to \infty} f(z) = \infty$ if and only $\lim_{z \to 0} \dfrac{1}{f\left(\frac{1}{z}\right)} = 0$.

20. Let $f, g: \mathbb{R} \to \mathbb{R}$ be defined by $f(x) = \cos x$ and $g(x) = \sin x$. Prove that f and g are uniformly continuous on $\mathbb{R}$. Hint: Use the fact that the least distance between two points is a straight line.

CHALLENGE PROBLEM

21. Consider $\mathbb{C}$ with the standard topology and $\mathbb{S}^2$ with its subspace topology, where $\mathbb{S}^2$ is being considered as a subspace of $\mathbb{R}^3$. Let $f: \mathbb{C} \to \mathbb{S}^2 \setminus N$ be defined as follows:

$$f(z) = \left(\frac{z + \overline{z}}{1 + |z|^2}, \frac{z - \overline{z}}{i(1 + |z|^2)}, \frac{|z|^2 - 1}{|z|^2 + 1} \right)$$

Prove that f is a homeomorphism.

LESSON 16 – LINEAR ALGEBRA
LINEAR TRANSFORMATIONS

Linear Transformations

Recall from Lesson 8 that a **vector space** over a field $\mathbb{F}$ is a set V together with a binary operation $+$ on V (called **addition**) and an operation called **scalar multiplication** satisfying the following properties:

(1) **(Closure under addition)** For all $v. w \in V, v + w \in V$.

(2) **(Associativity of addition)** For all $v, w, u \in V, (v + w) + u = v + (w + u)$.

(3) **(Commutativity of addition)** For all $v, w \in V, v + w = w + v$.

(4) **(Additive identity)** There exists an element $0 \in V$ such that for all $v \in V, 0 + v = v + 0 = v$.

(5) **(Additive inverse)** For each $v \in V$, there is $-v \in V$ such that $v + (-v) = (-v) + v = 0$.

(6) **(Closure under scalar multiplication)** For all $k \in \mathbb{F}$ and $v \in V, kv \in V$.

(7) **(Scalar multiplication identity)** If 1 is the multiplicative identity of $\mathbb{F}$ and $v \in V$, then $1v = v$.

(8) **(Associativity of scalar multiplication)** For all $j, k \in \mathbb{F}$ and $v \in V, (jk)v = j(kv)$.

(9) **(Distributivity of 1 scalar over 2 vectors)** For all $k \in \mathbb{F}$ and $v, w \in V, k(v + w) = kv + kw$.

(10) **(Distributivity of 2 scalars over 1 vector)** For all $j, k \in \mathbb{F}$ and $v \in V, (j + k)v = jv + kv$.

The simplest examples of vector spaces are $\mathbb{Q}^n$, $\mathbb{R}^n$, and $\mathbb{C}^n$, the vector spaces consisting of n-tuples of rational numbers, real numbers, and complex numbers, respectively. As a specific example, we have $\mathbb{R}^3 = \{(x, y, z) \mid x, y, z \in \mathbb{R}\}$ with addition defined by $(x, y, z) + (s, t, u) = (x + s, y + t, z + u)$ and scalar multiplication defined by $k(x, y, z) = (kx, ky, kz)$. Note that unless specified otherwise, we would usually consider $\mathbb{R}^3$ as a vector space over $\mathbb{R}$, so that the scalars k are all real numbers.

Let V and W be vector spaces over a field $\mathbb{F}$, and let $T: V \to W$ be a function from V to W.

We say that T is **additive** if for all $u, v \in V, T(u + v) = T(u) + T(v)$.

We say that T is **homogenous** if for all $k \in \mathbb{F}$ and all $v \in V, T(kv) = kT(v)$.

T is a **linear transformation** if it is additive and homogeneous.

Example 16.1:

1. Let $V = W = \mathbb{C}$ be vector spaces over $\mathbb{R}$ and define $T: \mathbb{C} \to \mathbb{C}$ by $T(z) = 5z$. We see that $T(z + w) = 5(z + w) = 5z + 5w = T(z) + T(w)$. So, T is additive. Furthermore, we have $T(kz) = 5(kz) = k(5z) = kT(z)$. So, T is homogenous. Therefore, T is a linear transformation.

   More generally, for any vector space V over $\mathbb{R}$ and any $m \in \mathbb{R}$, the function $S: V \to V$ defined by $S(v) = mv$ is a linear transformation. The verification is nearly identical to what we did in the last paragraph. This type of linear transformation is called a **dilation**.

234

Note that if $m, b \in \mathbb{R}$ with $b \neq 0$, then the function $R: V \to V$ defined by $R(v) = mv + b$ is **not** a linear transformation. To see this, observe that $R(2v) = m(2v) + b = 2mv + b$ and $2R(v) = 2(mv + b) = 2mv + 2b$. If $R(2v) = 2R(v)$, then $2mv + b = 2mv + 2b$, or equivalently, $b = 2b$. Subtracting b from each side of this equation yields $b = 0$, contrary to our assumption that $b \neq 0$. So, the linear functions that we learned about in high school are usually not linear transformations. The only linear functions that **are** linear transformations are the ones that pass through the origin (in other words, b must be 0).

2. Let $V = \mathbb{R}^4$ and $W = \mathbb{R}^3$ be vector spaces over $\mathbb{R}$ and define $T: \mathbb{R}^4 \to \mathbb{R}^3$ by

$$T\big((x, y, z, w)\big) = (x + z, 2x - 3y, 5y - 2w).$$

We have

$$
\begin{aligned}
T\big((x, y, z, w) + (s, t, u, v)\big) &= T\big((x + s, y + t, z + u, w + v)\big) \\
&= \big((x + s) + (z + u), 2(x + s) - 3(y + t), 5(y + t) - 2(w + v)\big) \\
&= \big((x + z) + (s + u), (2x - 3y) + (2s - 3t), (5y - 2w) + (5t - 2v)\big) \\
&= (x + z, 2x - 3y, 5y - 2w) + (s + u, 2s - 3t, 5t - 2v) \\
&= T\big((x, y, z, w)\big) + T\big((s, t, u, v)\big).
\end{aligned}
$$

So, T is additive. Also, we have

$$
\begin{aligned}
T\big(k(x, y, z, w)\big) &= T\big((kx, ky, kz, kw)\big) \\
&= \big(kx + kz, 2(kx) - 3(ky), 5(ky) - 2(kw)\big) \\
&= \big(k(x + z), k(2x - 3y), k(5y - 2w)\big) \\
&= k(x + z, 2x - 3y, 5y - 2w) = kT\big((x, y, z, w)\big).
\end{aligned}
$$

So, T is homogenous. Therefore, T is a linear transformation.

3. Let $V = \mathbb{R}^2$ and $W = \mathbb{R}$ be vector spaces over $\mathbb{R}$ and define $T: \mathbb{R}^2 \to \mathbb{R}$ by $T\big((x, y)\big) = xy$. Then T is **not** a linear transformation. Indeed, consider $(1, 0), (0, 1) \in \mathbb{R}^2$. We have

$$T\big((1, 0) + (0, 1)\big) = T\big((1, 1)\big) = 1 \cdot 1 = 1.$$

$$T\big((1, 0)\big) + T\big((0, 1)\big) = 1 \cdot 0 + 0 \cdot 1 = 0 + 0 = 0.$$

So, $T\big((1, 0) + (0, 1)\big) \neq T\big((1, 0)\big) + T\big((0, 1)\big)$. This shows that T is **not** additive, and therefore, T is not a linear transformation.

Observe that T is also **not** homogeneous. To see this, consider $(1, 1) \in \mathbb{R}^2$ and $2 \in \mathbb{R}$. We have $T\big(2(1, 1)\big) = T\big((2, 2)\big) = 2 \cdot 2 = 4$, but $2T(1, 1) = 2(1 \cdot 1) = 2 \cdot 1 = 2$.

In Problem 3 below, you will be asked to show that neither additivity nor homogeneity alone is enough to guarantee that a function is a linear transformation.

Recall from Lesson 8 that if $v, w \in V$ and $j, k \in \mathbb{F}$, then $jv + kw$ is called a **linear combination** of the vectors v and w with weights j and k. The next theorem says that a function is a linear transformation if and only if it "behaves well" with respect to linear combinations.

Theorem 16.1: Let V and W be vector spaces over a field $\mathbb{F}$. A function $T: V \to W$ is a linear transformation if and only if for all $v, w \in V$ and all $a, b \in \mathbb{F}$, $T(av + bw) = aT(v) + bT(w)$.

Proof: Suppose that $T: V \to W$ is a linear transformation, let $v, w \in V$, and let $a, b \in \mathbb{F}$. Since T is additive, $T(av + bw) = T(av) + T(bw)$. Since T is homogenous, $T(av) = aT(v)$ and $T(bw) = bT(w)$. Therefore, $T(av + bw) = T(av) + T(bw) = aT(v) + bT(w)$, as desired.

Conversely, suppose that for all $a, b \in \mathbb{F}$, $T(av + bw) = aT(v) + bT(w)$. Let $v, w \in V$ and let $a = b = 1$. Then $T(v + w) = T(1v + 1w) = 1T(v) + 1T(w) = T(v) + T(w)$. Therefore, T is additive. Now, let $v \in V$ and $k \in \mathbb{F}$. Then $T(kv) = T(kv + 0v) = kT(v) + 0T(v) = kT(v)$. Therefore, T is homogenous. It follows that T is a linear transformation. $\qquad\square$

We can use induction to extend Theorem 16.1 to arbitrary linear combinations. If $v \in V$ can be written as a linear combination of vectors $v_1, v_2, \dots, v_n \in V$, then $T(v)$ is determined by $T(v_1), T(v_2), \dots, T(v_n)$. Specifically, if $v = c_1 v_1 + c_2 v_2 + \cdots + c_n v_n$, then we have

$$T(v) = T(c_1 v_1 + c_2 v_2 + \cdots + c_n v_n) = c_1 T(v_1) + c_2 T(v_2) + \cdots + c_n T(v_n).$$

In particular, if $B = \{v_1, v_2, \dots, v_n\}$ is a basis of V, then T is completely determined by the values of $T(v_1), T(v_2), \dots, T(v_n)$.

Notes: (1) Recall from Lesson 8 that the vectors $v_1, v_2, \dots, v_n \in V$ are **linearly independent** if whenever $k_1 v_1 + k_2 v_2 + \cdots + k_n v_n = 0$, it follows that all the weights $k_1, k_2, \dots, k_n$ are 0.

(2) Also, recall that the set of all linear combinations of $v_1, v_2, \dots, v_n \in V$ is called the **span** of $v_1, v_2, \dots, v_n$, written span$\{ v_1, v_2, \dots, v_n \}$.

(3) The set of vectors $\{v_1, v_2, \dots, v_n\}$ is a **basis** of V if $v_1, v_2, \dots, v_n$ are linearly independent and span$\{ v_1, v_2, \dots, v_n \} = V$.

In particular, if $\{v_1, v_2, \dots, v_n\}$ is a basis of V, then every vector in V can be written as a linear combination of $v_1, v_2, \dots, v_n$.

So, if we know the values of $T(v_1), T(v_2), \dots, T(v_n)$, then we know the value of $T(v)$ for any $v \in V$, as shown above.

In other words, given a basis B of V, any function $f: B \to W$ extends uniquely to a linear transformation $T: V \to W$.

Let V and W be vector spaces over a field $\mathbb{F}$. We define $\mathcal{L}(V, W)$ to be the set of all linear transformations from V to W. Symbolically, $\mathcal{L}(V, W) = \{T: V \to W \mid T \text{ is a linear transformation}\}$.

Theorem 16.2: Let V and W be vector spaces over a field $\mathbb{F}$. Then $\mathcal{L}(V, W)$ is a vector space over $\mathbb{F}$, where addition and scalar multiplication are defined as follows:

$S + T \in \mathcal{L}(V, W)$ is defined by $(S + T)(v) = S(v) + T(v)$ for $S, T \in \mathcal{L}(V, W)$.

$kT \in \mathcal{L}(V, W)$ is defined by $(kT)(v) = kT(v)$ for $T \in \mathcal{L}(V, W)$ and $k \in \mathbb{F}$.

The reader will be asked to prove Theorem 16.2 in Problem 8 below.

If V, W, and U are vector spaces over $\mathbb{F}$, and $T: V \to W, S: W \to U$ are linear transformations, then the composition $S \circ T: V \to U$ is a linear transformation, where $S \circ T$ is defined by $(S \circ T)(v) = S(T(v))$ for all $v \in V$. To see this, let $v, w \in V$ and $a, b \in \mathbb{F}$. Then we have

$$(S \circ T)(av + bw) = S(T(av + bw)) = S(aT(v) + bT(w))$$
$$= a\left(S(T(v))\right) + b\left(S(T(w))\right) = a(S \circ T)(v) + b(S \circ T)(w).$$

Example 16.2: Let $T: \mathbb{R}^2 \to \mathbb{R}^3$ be the linear transformation defined by $T((x, y)) = (x, x + y, y)$ and let $S: \mathbb{R}^3 \to \mathbb{R}^2$ be the linear transformation defined by $S((x, y, z)) = (z - y, x - z)$. Then $S \circ T: \mathbb{R}^2 \to \mathbb{R}^2$ is a linear transformation and we have

$$(S \circ T)((x, y)) = S\left(T((x, y))\right) = S((x, x + y, y)) = (-x, x - y).$$

Notes: (1) In Example 16.2, the composition $T \circ S: \mathbb{R}^3 \to \mathbb{R}^3$ is also a linear transformation and we have

$$(T \circ S)((x, y, z)) = T\left(S((x, y, z))\right) = T((z - y, x - z)) = (z - y, x - y, x - z).$$

(2) In general, if $T: V \to W, S: X \to U$ are linear transformations, then $S \circ T$ is defined if and only if $W = X$. So, just because $S \circ T$ is defined, it does not mean that $T \circ S$ is also defined. For example, if $T: \mathbb{R} \to \mathbb{R}^2$ and $S: \mathbb{R}^2 \to \mathbb{R}^3$, then $S \circ T$ is defined and $S \circ T: \mathbb{R} \to \mathbb{R}^3$. However, $T \circ S$ is not defined. The "outputs" of the linear transformation S are ordered triples of real numbers, while the "inputs" of the linear transformation T are real numbers. They just don't "match up."

(3) If S and T are both linear transformations from a vector space V to itself (that is $S, T: V \to V$), then the compositions $S \circ T$ and $T \circ S$ will both also be linear transformations from V to itself.

By Note 3 above, in the vector space $\mathcal{L}(V, V)$, we can define a multiplication by $ST = S \circ T$. This definition of multiplication gives $\mathcal{L}(V, V)$ a ring structure. In fact, with addition, scalar multiplication, and composition as previously defined, $\mathcal{L}(V, V)$ is a structure called a **linear algebra**.

A **linear algebra** over a field $\mathbb{F}$ is a triple $(A, +, \cdot)$, where $(A, +)$ is a vector space over $\mathbb{F}$, $(A, +, \cdot)$ is a ring, and for all $u, v \in A$ and $k \in \mathbb{F}$, $k(uv) = (ku)v = u(kv)$.

We will call the last property "**compatibility of scalar and vector multiplication.**"

Notes: (1) There are two multiplications defined in a linear algebra. As for a vector space, we have **scalar multiplication**. We will refer to the ring multiplication as **vector multiplication**.

(2) Recall from Lesson 4 that a ring $(A, +, \cdot)$ satisfies the first 5 properties of a vector space listed above (with A in place of V) together with the following three additional properties of vector multiplication:

- **(Closure)** For all $u, v \in A, u \cdot v \in A$.

- **(Associativity)** For all $u, v, w \in A, (u \cdot v) \cdot w = u \cdot (v \cdot w)$.

- **(Identity)** There exists an element $1 \in A$ such that for all $v \in A, 1 \cdot v = v \cdot 1 = v$.

Example 16.3:

1. $(\mathbb{R}, +, \cdot)$ is a linear algebra over $\mathbb{R}$, where addition and multiplication are defined in the usual way. In this example, scalar and vector multiplication are the same.

2. Similarly, $(\mathbb{C}, +, \cdot)$ is a linear algebra over $\mathbb{C}$, where addition and multiplication are defined in the usual way (see Lesson 7). Again, in this example, scalar and vector multiplication are the same.

3. If V is a vector space over a field $\mathbb{F}$, then $\mathcal{L}(V, V)$ is a linear algebra over $\mathbb{F}$, where addition and scalar multiplication are defined as in Theorem 16.2, and vector multiplication is given by composition of linear transformations. You will be asked to verify this in Problem 9 below.

Recall from Lesson 10 that a function $f: A \to B$ is **injective** if $a, b \in A$ and $a \neq b$ implies $f(a) \neq f(b)$. Also, f is **surjective** if for all $b \in B$, there is $a \in A$ with $f(a) = b$. A **bijective** function is one that is both injective and surjective.

Also recall that a bijective function f is **invertible**. The **inverse** of f is then the function $f^{-1}: B \to A$ defined by $f^{-1}(b) = $ "the unique $a \in A$ such that $f(a) = b$."

By Theorem 10.6 from Lesson 10, $f^{-1} \circ f = i_A$ and $f \circ f^{-1} = i_B$, where i_A and i_B are the identity functions on A and B, respectively. Furthermore, f^{-1} is the **only** function that satisfies these two equations. Indeed, if $h: B \to A$ also satisfies $h \circ f = i_A$ and $f \circ h = i_B$, then

$$h = h \circ i_B = h \circ (f \circ f^{-1}) = (h \circ f) \circ f^{-1} = i_A \circ f^{-1} = f^{-1}.$$

A bijection $T: V \to W$ that is also a linear transformation is called an **isomorphism**. If an isomorphism $T: V \to W$ exists, we say that V and W are isomorphic. As is always the case with algebraic structures, isomorphic vector spaces are essentially identical. The only difference between them are the "names" of the elements. Isomorphisms were covered in more generality in Lesson 11.

If a bijective function happens to be a linear transformation between two vector spaces, it's nice to know that the inverse function is also a linear transformation. We prove this now.

Theorem 16.3: Let $T: V \to W$ be an invertible linear transformation. Then $T^{-1}: W \to V$ is also a linear transformation.

Proof: Let $T: V \to W$ be an invertible linear transformation, let $u, v \in W$, and let $a, b \in \mathbb{F}$. Then by the linearity of T, we have

$$T\left(aT^{-1}(u) + bT^{-1}(v)\right) = aT\left(T^{-1}(u)\right) + bT\left(T^{-1}(v)\right) = au + bv.$$

Since T is injective, $aT^{-1}(u) + bT^{-1}(v)$ is the unique element of V whose image under T is $au + bv$. By the definition of T^{-1}, $T^{-1}(au + bv) = aT^{-1}(u) + bT^{-1}(v)$. $\qquad\square$

Example 16.4:

1. Let $V = W = \mathbb{C}$ be vector spaces over $\mathbb{R}$ and define $T: \mathbb{C} \to \mathbb{C}$ by $T(z) = 5z$, as we did in part 1 of Example 16.1. if $z \neq w$, then $5z \neq 5w$, and so T is injective. Also, if $w \in \mathbb{C}$, then we have $T\left(\frac{1}{5}w\right) = 5\left(\frac{1}{5}w\right) = w$. So, T is surjective. It follows that T is invertible and that the inverse of T is defined by $T^{-1}(z) = \frac{1}{5}z$. By Theorem 16.3, $T^{-1}: \mathbb{C} \to \mathbb{C}$ is also a linear transformation. In the terminology of Lesson 11, T is an **automorphism**. In other words, T is an isomorphism from $\mathbb{C}$ to itself.

2. Let V be a vector space over a field $\mathbb{F}$ with basis $\{v_1, v_2, v_3\}$. Then let $T: V \to \mathbb{F}^3$ be the unique linear transformation such that $T(v_1) = (1, 0, 0)$, $T(v_2) = (0, 1, 0)$, and $T(v_3) = (0, 0, 1)$. In other words, if $v \in V$, since $\{v_1, v_2, v_3\}$ is a basis of V, we can write $v = c_1 v_1 + c_2 v_2 + c_3 v_3$, and T is defined by $T(v) = c_1 T(v_1) + c_2 T(v_2) + c_3 T(v_3) = (c_1, c_2, c_3)$.

   To see that T is injective, suppose that $T(c_1 v_1 + c_2 v_2 + c_3 v_3) = T(d_1 v_1 + d_2 v_2 + d_3 v_3)$. Then $(c_1, c_2, c_3) = (d_1, d_2, d_3)$. It follows that $c_1 = d_1$, $c_2 = d_2$, and $c_3 = d_3$. Therefore, $c_1 v_1 + c_2 v_2 + c_3 v_3 = d_1 v_1 + d_2 v_2 + d_3 v_3$ and so, T is injective.

   Now, if $(a, b, c) \in \mathbb{F}^3$, then $T(av_1 + bv_2 + cv_3) = (a, b, c)$ and so, T is surjective. From this computation, we also see that $T^{-1}: \mathbb{F}^3 \to V$ is defined by $T^{-1}((a, b, c)) = av_1 + bv_2 + cv_3$.

   It follows that $T: V \to \mathbb{F}^3$ is an isomorphism, so that V is isomorphic to $\mathbb{F}^3$.

   Essentially the same argument as above can be used to show that if V is a vector space over a field $\mathbb{F}$ with a basis consisting of n vectors, then V is isomorphic to $\mathbb{F}^n$.

Matrices

Recall from Lesson 8 that for $m, n \in \mathbb{Z}^+$, an $m \times n$ **matrix** over a field $\mathbb{F}$ is a rectangular array with m rows and n columns, and entries in $\mathbb{F}$. For example, the matrix $H = \begin{bmatrix} i & 2 - 5i & \frac{1}{5} \\ -1 & \sqrt{3} & 7 + i \end{bmatrix}$ is a 2×3 matrix over $\mathbb{C}$. We will generally use a capital letter to represent a matrix, and the corresponding lowercase letter with double subscripts to represent the entries of the matrix. We use the first subscript for the row and the second subscript for the column. Using the matrix H above as an example, we see that $h_{11} = i$, $h_{12} = 2 - 5i$, $h_{13} = \frac{1}{5}$, $h_{21} = -1$, $h_{22} = \sqrt{3}$, and $h_{23} = 7 + i$.

If A is an $m \times n$ matrix, then we can visualize A as follows:

$$A = \begin{bmatrix} a_{11} & \cdots & a_{1n} \\ \vdots & & \vdots \\ a_{m1} & \cdots & a_{mn} \end{bmatrix}$$

We let $M_{mn}^{\mathbb{F}}$ be the set of all $m \times n$ matrices over the field $\mathbb{F}$. Recall that we add two matrices $A, B \in M_{mn}^{\mathbb{F}}$ to get $A + B \in M_{mn}^{\mathbb{F}}$ using the rule $(a + b)_{ij} = a_{ij} + b_{ij}$. We multiply a matrix $A \in M_{mn}^{\mathbb{F}}$ by a scalar $k \in \mathbb{F}$ using the rule $(ka)_{ij} = ka_{ij}$. We can visualize these computations as follows:

$$\begin{bmatrix} a_{11} & \cdots & a_{1n} \\ \vdots & & \vdots \\ a_{m1} & \cdots & a_{mn} \end{bmatrix} + \begin{bmatrix} b_{11} & \cdots & b_{1n} \\ \vdots & & \vdots \\ b_{m1} & \cdots & b_{mn} \end{bmatrix} = \begin{bmatrix} a_{11} + b_{11} & \cdots & a_{1n} + b_{1n} \\ \vdots & & \vdots \\ a_{m1} + b_{m1} & \cdots & a_{mn} + b_{mn} \end{bmatrix}$$

$$k \begin{bmatrix} a_{11} & \cdots & a_{1n} \\ \vdots & & \vdots \\ a_{m1} & \cdots & a_{mn} \end{bmatrix} = \begin{bmatrix} ka_{11} & \cdots & ka_{1n} \\ \vdots & & \vdots \\ ka_{m1} & \cdots & ka_{mn} \end{bmatrix}$$

With these operations of addition and scalar multiplication, $M_{mn}^{\mathbb{F}}$ is a vector space over $\mathbb{F}$.

We would now like to turn $M_{nn}^{\mathbb{F}}$ into a linear algebra over $\mathbb{F}$ by defining a vector multiplication in $M_{nn}^{\mathbb{F}}$. Notice that we will not be turning all vector spaces $M_{mn}^{\mathbb{F}}$ into linear algebras. We will be able to do this only when $m = n$. That is, the linear algebra will consist only of **square matrices** of a specific size.

We first define the product of an $m \times n$ matrix with an $n \times p$ matrix, where m, n, p are positive integers. Notice that to take the product AB we first insist that the number of columns of A be equal to the number of rows of B (these are the "inner" two numbers in the expressions "$m \times n$" and "$n \times p$").

So, how do we actually multiply two matrices? This is a bit complicated and requires just a little practice. Let's begin by walking through an example while informally describing the procedure, so that we can get a feel for how matrix multiplication works before getting caught up in the "messy looking" definition.

Let $A = \begin{bmatrix} 0 & 1 \\ 3 & 2 \end{bmatrix}$ and $B = \begin{bmatrix} 1 & 2 & 0 \\ 0 & 3 & 6 \end{bmatrix}$. Notice that A is a 2×2 matrix and B is a 2×3 matrix. Since A has 2 columns and B has 2 rows, we will be able to multiply the two matrices.

For each row of the first matrix and each column of the second matrix, we add up the products entry by entry. Let's compute the product AB as an example.

$$AB = \begin{bmatrix} 0 & 1 \\ 3 & 2 \end{bmatrix} \cdot \begin{bmatrix} 1 & 2 & 0 \\ 0 & 3 & 6 \end{bmatrix} = \begin{bmatrix} x & y & z \\ u & v & w \end{bmatrix}$$

Since x is in the first row and first column, we use the first row of A and the first column of B to get $x = \begin{bmatrix} 0 & 1 \end{bmatrix} \begin{bmatrix} 1 \\ 0 \end{bmatrix} = 0 \cdot 1 + 1 \cdot 0 = 0 + 0 = 0$.

Since u is in the second row and first column, we use the second row of A and the first column of B to get $u = \begin{bmatrix} 3 & 2 \end{bmatrix} \begin{bmatrix} 1 \\ 0 \end{bmatrix} = 3 \cdot 1 + 2 \cdot 0 = 3$.

The reader should attempt to follow this procedure to compute the values of the remaining entries. The final product is

$$AB = \begin{bmatrix} 0 & 3 & 6 \\ 3 & 12 & 12 \end{bmatrix}$$

Notes: (1) The product of a **2 × 2** matrix and a **2 × 3** matrix is a **2 × 3** matrix.

(2) More generally, the product of an $m \times n$ matrix and an $n \times p$ matrix is an $m \times p$ matrix. Observe that the inner most numbers (both n) must agree, and the resulting product has dimensions given by the outermost numbers (m and p).

We formally define matrix multiplication as follows. Let A be the $m \times n$ matrix $A = \begin{bmatrix} a_{11} & \cdots & a_{1n} \\ \vdots & & \vdots \\ a_{m1} & \cdots & a_{mn} \end{bmatrix}$

and let B be the $n \times p$ matrix $B = \begin{bmatrix} b_{11} & \cdots & b_{1p} \\ \vdots & & \vdots \\ b_{n1} & \cdots & b_{np} \end{bmatrix}$. We define the product AB to be the $m \times p$ matrix

$C = \begin{bmatrix} c_{11} & \cdots & c_{1p} \\ \vdots & & \vdots \\ c_{m1} & \cdots & c_{mp} \end{bmatrix}$ such that

$$c_{ij} = a_{i1}b_{1j} + a_{i2}b_{2j} + \cdots + a_{in}b_{nj} = \sum_{k=1}^{n} a_{ik}b_{kj}.$$

Notes: (1) The symbol Σ is the Greek letter Sigma. In mathematics, this symbol is often used to denote a sum. Σ is generally used to abbreviate a very large sum or a sum of unknown length by specifying what a typical term of the sum looks like. Let's look at a simpler example first before we analyze the more complicated one above:

$$\sum_{k=1}^{5} k^2 = 1^2 + 2^2 + 3^2 + 4^2 + 5^2 = 1 + 4 + 9 + 16 + 25 = 55.$$

The expression "$k = 1$" written underneath the symbol indicates that we get the first term of the sum by replacing k by 1 in the given expression. When we replace k by 1 in the expression k^2, we get 1^2.

For the second term, we simply increase k by 1 to get $k = 2$. So, we replace k by 2 to get $k^2 = 2^2$.

We continue in this fashion, increasing k by 1 each time until we reach the number written above the symbol. In this case, that is $k = 5$.

(2) Let's now get back to the expression that we're interested in.

$$c_{ij} = \sum_{k=1}^{n} a_{ik}b_{kj} = a_{i1}b_{1j} + a_{i2}b_{2j} + \cdots + a_{in}b_{nj}$$

Once again, the expression "$k = 1$" written underneath the symbol indicates that we get the first term of the sum by replacing k by 1 in the given expression. When we replace k by 1 in the expression $a_{ik}b_{kj}$, we get $a_{i1}b_{1j}$. Notice that this is the first term of c_{ij}.

For the second term, we simply increase k by 1 to get $k = 2$. So, we replace k by 2 to get $a_{i2}b_{2j}$.

We continue in this fashion, increasing k by 1 each time until we reach the number written above the symbol. In this case, that is $k = n$. So, the last term is $a_{in}b_{nj}$.

(3) In general, we get the entry c_{ij} in the ith row and jth column of $C = AB$ by "multiplying" the ith row of A with the jth column of B. We can think of the computation like this:

$$[a_{i1} \quad a_{i2} \cdots a_{in}] \begin{bmatrix} b_{1j} \\ b_{2j} \\ \vdots \\ b_{nj} \end{bmatrix} = a_{i1}b_{1j} + a_{i2}b_{2j} + \cdots + a_{in}b_{nj}$$

Notice how we multiply the leftmost entry a_{i1} by the topmost entry b_{1j}. Then we move one step to the right to a_{i2} and one step down to b_{2j} to form the next product, ... and so on.

It is fairly straightforward to verify that with our definitions of addition, scalar multiplication, and matrix multiplication, for each $n \in \mathbb{Z}^+$, $M_{nn}^{\mathbb{F}}$ is a linear algebra over $\mathbb{F}$. I leave this as an exercise for the reader. Note that it is important that the number of rows and columns of our matrices are the same. Otherwise, the matrix products will not be defined.

Example 16.5:

1. $[1 \quad 2 \quad 3 \quad 4] \cdot \begin{bmatrix} 5 \\ 1 \\ -2 \\ 3 \end{bmatrix} = [1 \cdot 5 + 2 \cdot 1 + 3(-2) + 4 \cdot 3] = [5 + 2 - 6 + 12] = [13]$.

    We generally identify a 1×1 matrix with its only entry. So, $[1 \quad 2 \quad 3 \quad 4] \cdot \begin{bmatrix} 5 \\ 1 \\ -2 \\ 3 \end{bmatrix} = \mathbf{13}$.

2. $\begin{bmatrix} 5 \\ 1 \\ -2 \\ 3 \end{bmatrix} \cdot [1 \quad 2 \quad 3 \quad 4] = \begin{bmatrix} 5 & 10 & 15 & 20 \\ 1 & 2 & 3 & 4 \\ -2 & -4 & -6 & -8 \\ 3 & 6 & 9 & 12 \end{bmatrix}$.

    Notice that $[1 \quad 2 \quad 3 \quad 4] \cdot \begin{bmatrix} 5 \\ 1 \\ -2 \\ 3 \end{bmatrix} \neq \begin{bmatrix} 5 \\ 1 \\ -2 \\ 3 \end{bmatrix} \cdot [1 \quad 2 \quad 3 \quad 4]$, and in fact, the two products do not even have the same size. This shows that if AB and BA are both defined, then they **do not** need to be equal.

3. $\begin{bmatrix} 1 & 2 \\ 0 & 1 \end{bmatrix} \cdot \begin{bmatrix} 0 & 2 \\ 3 & 2 \end{bmatrix} = \begin{bmatrix} 0+6 & 2+4 \\ 0+3 & 0+2 \end{bmatrix} = \begin{bmatrix} 6 & 6 \\ 3 & 2 \end{bmatrix}$.

    $\begin{bmatrix} 0 & 2 \\ 3 & 2 \end{bmatrix} \cdot \begin{bmatrix} 1 & 2 \\ 0 & 1 \end{bmatrix} = \begin{bmatrix} 0+0 & 0+2 \\ 3+0 & 6+2 \end{bmatrix} = \begin{bmatrix} 0 & 2 \\ 3 & 8 \end{bmatrix}$.

    Notice that $\begin{bmatrix} 1 & 2 \\ 0 & 1 \end{bmatrix} \cdot \begin{bmatrix} 0 & 2 \\ 3 & 2 \end{bmatrix} \neq \begin{bmatrix} 0 & 2 \\ 3 & 2 \end{bmatrix} \cdot \begin{bmatrix} 1 & 2 \\ 0 & 1 \end{bmatrix}$.

    This shows that even if A and B are square matrices of the same size, in general $AB \neq BA$. So, matrix multiplication is **not** commutative. $M_{nn}^{\mathbb{F}}$ is a **noncommutative linear algebra**.

The Matrix of a Linear Transformation

Let $T \in \mathcal{L}(V, W)$ and let $B = \{v_1, v_2, \dots, v_n\}$ and $C = \{w_1, w_2, \dots, w_m\}$ be bases of V and W, respectively. Recall that T is completely determined by the values of $T(v_1), T(v_2), \dots, T(v_n)$. Furthermore, since $T(v_1), T(v_2), \dots, T(v_n) \in W$ and C is a basis for W, each of $T(v_1), T(v_2), \dots, T(v_n)$ can be written as a linear combination of the vectors in C. So, we have

$$T(v_1) = a_{11}w_1 + a_{21}w_2 + \cdots + a_{m1}w_m$$
$$T(v_2) = a_{12}w_1 + a_{22}w_2 + \cdots + a_{m2}w_m$$
$$\vdots$$
$$T(v_j) = a_{1j}w_1 + a_{2j}w_2 + \cdots + a_{mj}w_m$$
$$\vdots$$
$$T(v_n) = a_{1n}w_1 + a_{2n}w_2 + \cdots + a_{mn}w_m$$

Here, we have $a_{ij} \in \mathbb{F}$ for each $i = 1, 2, \ldots, m$ and $j = 1, 2, \ldots, n$. We form the following matrix:

$$\mathcal{M}_T(B, C) = \begin{bmatrix} a_{11} & \cdots & a_{1n} \\ \vdots & & \vdots \\ a_{m1} & \cdots & a_{mn} \end{bmatrix}$$

$\mathcal{M}_T(B, C)$ is called the **matrix of the linear transformation T with respect to the bases B and C.**

Note: The coefficients in the expression $T(v_j) = a_{1j}w_1 + a_{2j}w_2 + \cdots + a_{mj}w_m$ become the jth **column** of $\mathcal{M}_T(B, C)$. Your first instinct might be to form the row $[a_{1j} \ a_{2j} \cdots a_{mj}]$, but this is incorrect. Pay careful attention to how we form $\mathcal{M}_T(B, C)$ in part 2 of Example 16.6 below to make sure that you avoid this error.

Example 16.6:

1. Consider the linear transformation $T: \mathbb{C} \to \mathbb{C}$ from part 1 of Example 16.1. We are considering $\mathbb{C}$ as a vector space over $\mathbb{R}$ and T is defined by $T(z) = 5z$. Let's use the standard basis for $\mathbb{C}$, so that $B = C = \{1 + 0i, 0 + 1i\} = \{1, i\}$. We have

$$T(1) = 5 = 5 \cdot 1 + 0 \cdot i$$
$$T(i) = 5i = 0 \cdot 1 + 5 \cdot i$$

The matrix of T with respect to the standard basis is $\mathcal{M}_T(\{1, i\}, \{1, i\}) = \begin{bmatrix} 5 & 0 \\ 0 & 5 \end{bmatrix}$.

In this case, since T is being mapped from a vector space to itself and we are using the same basis for both "copies" of $\mathbb{C}$, we can abbreviate $\mathcal{M}_T(\{1, i\}, \{1, i\})$ as $\mathcal{M}_T(\{1, i\})$. Furthermore, since we are using the standard basis, we can abbreviate $\mathcal{M}_T(\{1, i\}, \{1, i\})$ even further as $\mathcal{M}_T$. So, we can simply write $\mathcal{M}_T = \begin{bmatrix} 5 & 0 \\ 0 & 5 \end{bmatrix}$.

Now, let $z = a + bi \in \mathbb{C}$ and write z as the column vector $z = \begin{bmatrix} a \\ b \end{bmatrix}$. We have

$$\mathcal{M}_T \cdot z = \begin{bmatrix} 5 & 0 \\ 0 & 5 \end{bmatrix} \begin{bmatrix} a \\ b \end{bmatrix} = \begin{bmatrix} 5a \\ 5b \end{bmatrix} = 5 \begin{bmatrix} a \\ b \end{bmatrix} = 5z = T(z).$$

So, multiplication on the left by $\mathcal{M}_T$ gives the same result as applying the transformation T.

2. Consider the linear transformation $T: \mathbb{R}^4 \to \mathbb{R}^3$ from part 2 of Problem 16.1. We are considering $\mathbb{R}^4$ and $\mathbb{R}^3$ as vector spaces over $\mathbb{R}$ and T is defined by

$$T\big((x, y, z, w)\big) = (x + z, 2x - 3y, 5y - 2w).$$

Let's use the standard bases for $\mathbb{R}^4$ and $\mathbb{R}^3$, so that

$$B = \{(1, 0, 0, 0), (0, 1, 0, 0), (0, 0, 1, 0), (0, 0, 0, 1)\} \quad \text{and} \quad C = \{(1, 0, 0), (0, 1, 0), (0, 0, 1)\}.$$

We have

$$T\big((1,0,0,0)\big) = (1,2,0)$$
$$T\big((0,1,0,0)\big) = (0,-3,5)$$
$$T\big((0,0,1,0)\big) = (1,0,0)$$
$$T\big((0,0,0,1)\big) = (0,0,-2)$$

The matrix of T with respect to the standard bases is $\mathcal{M}_T = \begin{bmatrix} 1 & 0 & 1 & 0 \\ 2 & -3 & 0 & 0 \\ 0 & 5 & 0 & -2 \end{bmatrix}$

Once again, we abbreviate $\mathcal{M}_T(B,C)$ as $\mathcal{M}_T$ because we are using the standard bases.

Now, let $v = (x,y,z,w) \in \mathbb{R}^4$ and write v as the column vector $v = \begin{bmatrix} x \\ y \\ z \\ w \end{bmatrix}$. We have

$$\mathcal{M}_T \cdot v = \begin{bmatrix} 1 & 0 & 1 & 0 \\ 2 & -3 & 0 & 0 \\ 0 & 5 & 0 & -2 \end{bmatrix} \begin{bmatrix} x \\ y \\ z \\ w \end{bmatrix} = \begin{bmatrix} x + z \\ 2x - 3y \\ 5y - 2w \end{bmatrix} = T(v).$$

So, once again, multiplication on the left by $\mathcal{M}_T$ gives the same result as applying the transformation T.

Let V be a vector space over $\mathbb{F}$ with a finite basis. Then we say that V is **finite-dimensional**. If $B = \{v_1, v_2, \dots, v_n\}$, then by Problem 12 from Lesson 8, all bases of V have n elements. In this case, we say that V is **n-dimensional**, and we write $\dim V = n$.

Theorem 16.4: Let V be an n-dimensional vector space over a field $\mathbb{F}$. Then there is a linear algebra isomorphism $F: \mathcal{L}(V,V) \to M_{nn}^{\mathbb{F}}$

You will be asked to prove Theorem 16.4 in Problem 15 below.

Images and Kernels

Let $T: V \to W$ be a linear transformation. The **image** (or **range**) of T is the set $T[V] = \{T(v) \mid v \in V\}$ and the **kernel** (or **null space**) of T is the set $\ker(T) = \{v \in V \mid T(v) = 0\}$.

Example 16.7: Let $T: \mathbb{R}^4 \to \mathbb{R}^3$ be defined by $T\big((x,y,z,w)\big) = (x+y, x-z, x+2w)$. Let's compute $T[\mathbb{R}^4]$ and $\ker(T)$. First, $T[\mathbb{R}^4]$ consists of all vectors of the form

$$(x+y, x-z, x+2w) = (x+y)(1,0,0) + (x-z)(0,1,0) + (x+2w)(0,0,1)$$

So, if $(v_1, v_2, v_3) \in \mathbb{R}^3$, let $x = 0, y = v_1, z = -v_2,$ and $w = \frac{1}{2}v_3$. Then we see that

$$(x+y)(1,0,0) + (x-z)(0,1,0) + (x+2w)(0,0,1)$$
$$= v_1(1,0,0) + v_2(0,1,0) + v_3(0,0,1) = (v_1, v_2, v_3)$$

Therefore, $\mathbb{R}^3 \subseteq T[\mathbb{R}^4]$. Since it is clear that $T[\mathbb{R}^4] \subseteq \mathbb{R}^3$, we have $T[\mathbb{R}^4] = \mathbb{R}^3$.

Now, $(x, y, z, w) \in \ker(T)$ if and only if $(x + y, x - z, x + 2w) = (0, 0, 0)$ if and only if $x + y = 0$, $x - z = 0$, and $x + 2w = 0$ if and only if $y = -x$, $z = x$, and $w = -\frac{x}{2}$ if and only if $(x, y, z, w) = \left(x, -x, x, -\frac{x}{2}\right) = x\left(1, -1, 1, -\frac{1}{2}\right)$.

So, every element of $\ker(T)$ is a scalar multiple of $\left(1, -1, 1, -\frac{1}{2}\right)$. Thus, $\ker(T) \subseteq \text{span}\left\{\left(1, -1, 1, -\frac{1}{2}\right)\right\}$.

Conversely, an element of $\text{span}\left\{\left(1, -1, 1, -\frac{1}{2}\right)\right\}$ has the form $\left(v, -v, v, -\frac{1}{2}v\right)$, and we have $T\left(\left(v, -v, v, -\frac{1}{2}v\right)\right) = \left(v - v, v - v, v + 2\left(-\frac{1}{2}v\right)\right) = (0, 0, 0)$. So, $\text{span}\left\{\left(1, -1, 1, -\frac{1}{2}\right)\right\} \subseteq \ker(T)$

Therefore, $\ker(T) = \text{span}\left\{\left(1, -1, 1, -\frac{1}{2}\right)\right\}$.

Notice that $T[\mathbb{R}^4]$ is a subspace of $\mathbb{R}^3$ (in fact, $T[\mathbb{R}^4] = \mathbb{R}^3$) and $\ker(T)$ is a subspace of $\mathbb{R}^4$. Also, the sum of the dimensions of $T[\mathbb{R}^4]$ and $\ker(T)$ is $3 + 1 = 4$, which is the dimension of $\mathbb{R}^4$. None of this is a coincidence, as we will see in the next few theorems.

Theorem 16.5: Let V and W be vector spaces over a field $\mathbb{F}$ and let $T: V \to W$ be a linear transformation. Then $T[V] \leq W$.

Proof: We have $T(0) = T(0 + 0) = T(0) + T(0)$. Therefore, $T(0) = 0$. It follows that $0 \in T[V]$.

Let $w, t \in T[V]$. Then there are $u, v \in V$ with $T(u) = w$ and $T(v) = t$. It then follows that $T(u + v) = T(u) + T(v) = w + t$. So, $w + t \in T[V]$.

Let $w \in T[V]$ and $k \in \mathbb{F}$. Then there is $u \in V$ with $T(u) = w$. We have $T(ku) = kT(u) = kw$. Therefore, $kw \in T[V]$.

By Theorem 8.1 from Lesson 8, $T[V] \leq W$. $\square$

Theorem 16.6: Let V and W be vector spaces over a field $\mathbb{F}$ and let $T: V \to W$ be a linear transformation. Then $\ker(T) \leq V$.

Proof: As in the proof of Theorem 16.5, we have $T(0) = 0$. So, $0 \in \ker(T)$.

Let $u, v \in \ker(T)$. Then $T(u + v) = T(u) + T(v) = 0 + 0 = 0$. So, $u + v \in \ker(T)$.

Let $u \in \ker(T)$ and $k \in \mathbb{F}$. Then $T(ku) = kT(u) = k \cdot 0 = 0$. Therefore, $ku \in \ker(T)$.

By Theorem 8.1 from Lesson 8, $\ker(T) \leq V$. $\square$

Theorem 16.7: Let V and W be vector spaces over a field $\mathbb{F}$ and let $T: V \to W$ be a linear transformation. Then $\ker(T) = \{0\}$ if and only if T is injective.

Proof: Suppose that $\ker(T) = \{0\}$, let $u, v \in V$, and let $T(u) = T(v)$. Then $T(u) - T(v) = 0$. It follows that $T(u - v) = T(u) - T(v) = 0$. So, $u - v \in \ker(T)$. Since $\ker(T) = \{0\}$, $u - v = 0$. Therefore, $u = v$. Since $u, v \in V$ were arbitrary, T is injective.

Conversely, suppose that T is injective, and let $u \in \ker(T)$. Then $T(u) = 0$. But also, by the proof of Theorem 16.5, $T(0) = 0$. So, $T(u) = T(0)$. Since T is injective, $u = 0$. Since $u \in V$ was arbitrary, $\ker(T) \subseteq \{0\}$. By the proof of Theorem 16.5, $T(0) = 0$, so that $0 \in \ker(T)$, and so, $\{0\} \subseteq \ker(T)$. It follows that $\ker(T) = \{0\}$. $\quad\square$

If V and W are vector spaces over a field $\mathbb{F}$, and $T: V \to W$ is a linear transformation, then the **rank** of T is the dimension of $T[V]$ and the **nullity** of T is the dimension of $\ker(T)$.

Theorem 16.8: Let V and W be vector spaces over a field $\mathbb{F}$ with $\dim V = n$ and let $T: V \to W$ be a linear transformation. Then $\text{rank } T + \text{nullity } T = n$.

Note: Before proving the theorem, let's observe that in a finite-dimensional vector space V, any vectors that are linearly independent can be extended to a basis of V.

To see this, let $v_1, v_2, \ldots v_k$ be linearly independent and let $u_1, u_2, \ldots, u_m$ be any vectors such that $\text{span}\{u_1, u_2, \ldots, u_m\} = V$. We will decide one by one if we should throw in or exclude each u_j. Specifically, we start by first letting $B_0 = \{v_1, v_2, \ldots v_k\}$ and then $B_1 = \begin{cases} B_0 & \text{if } u_1 \in \text{span } B_0. \\ B_0 \cup \{u_1\} & \text{if } u_1 \notin \text{span } B_0. \end{cases}$ In general, for each $j = 1, 2, \ldots m$, we let $B_j = \begin{cases} B_{j-1} & \text{if } u_j \in \text{span } B_{j-1}. \\ B_{j-1} \cup \{u_j\} & \text{if } u_j \notin \text{span } B_{j-1}. \end{cases}$ By Problem 6 from Lesson 8, for each j, B_j is linearly independent. Since for each j, $u_j \in \text{span } B_j$ and $B_j \subseteq B_m$, $V = \text{span}\{u_1, u_2, \ldots, u_m\} = \text{span } B_m$. Therefore, B_m is a basis of V.

Proof of Theorem 16.8: Suppose nullity $T = k$, where $0 \leq k \leq n$. Then there is a basis $\{v_1, v_2, \ldots, v_k\}$ of $\ker(T)$ (note that if $k = 0$, this basis is the empty set). In particular, the vectors $v_1, v_2, \ldots, v_k$ are linearly independent. By the note above, we can extend these vectors to a basis B of V, let's say $B = \{v_1, v_2, \ldots, v_k, u_1, u_2, \ldots, u_m\}$. So, we have $n = k + m$. Let's show that $\{T(u_1), T(u_2), \ldots, T(u_m)\}$ is a basis of $T[V]$.

For linear independence of $T(u_1), T(u_2), \ldots, T(u_m)$, note that since T is a linear transformation, $c_1 T(u_1) + c_2 T(u_2) + \cdots + c_m T(u_m) = 0$ is equivalent to $T(c_1 u_1 + c_2 u_2 + \cdots + c_m u_m) = 0$, which is equivalent to $c_1 u_1 + c_2 u_2 + \cdots + c_m u_m \in \ker(T)$. Since $\{v_1, v_2, \ldots, v_k\}$ is a basis of $\ker(T)$, we can find weights $d_1, d_2, \ldots, d_k$ such that $c_1 u_1 + c_2 u_2 + \cdots + c_m u_m = d_1 v_1 + d_2 v_2 + \cdots + d_k v_k$. Since B is a basis of V, all weights (the c_i's and d_j's) are 0. So, $T(u_1), T(u_2), \ldots, T(u_m)$ are linearly independent.

To see that $T[V] = \text{span}\{T(u_1), T(u_2), \ldots, T(u_m)\}$, let $v \in V$. Since B is a basis of V, we can write v as a linear combination $v = c_1 v_1 + c_2 v_2 + \cdots c_k v_k + d_1 u_1 + d_2 u_2 + \cdots + d_m u_m$. Applying the linear transformation T gives us

$$T(v) = T(c_1 v_1 + c_2 v_2 + \cdots + c_k v_k + d_1 u_1 + d_2 u_2 + \cdots + d_m u_m)$$
$$= c_1 T(v_1) + c_2 T(v_2) + \cdots + c_k T(v_k) + d_1 T(u_1) + d_2 T(u_2) + \cdots + d_m T(u_m)$$
$$= d_1 T(u_1) + d_2 T(u_2) + \cdots + d_m T(u_m).$$

Note that $T(v_1), T(v_2), \ldots, T(v_k)$ are all 0 because $v_1, v_2, \ldots, v_k \in \ker(T)$.

Since each vector of the form $T(v)$ can be written as a linear combination of $T(u_1), T(u_2), \ldots, T(u_m)$, we have shown that $T[V] = \text{span}\{T(u_1), T(u_2), \ldots, T(u_m)\}$.

Since $T(u_1), T(u_2), \ldots, T(u_m)$ are linearly independent and $T[V] = \text{span}\{T(u_1), T(u_2), \ldots, T(u_m)\}$, it follows that $\{T(u_1), T(u_2), \ldots, T(u_m)\}$ is a basis of $T[V]$. Therefore, rank $T = m$. $\qquad\square$

Eigenvalues and Eigenvectors

We now restrict our attention to linear transformations from a vector space to itself. For a vector space V, we will abbreviate the linear algebra $\mathcal{L}(V, V)$ by $\mathcal{L}(V)$.

If $U \leq V$, we say that U is **invariant** under $T \in \mathcal{L}(V)$ if $T[U] \subseteq U$.

Example 16.8: Let V be a vector space and let $T \in \mathcal{L}(V)$.

1. $\{0\}$ is invariant under T. Indeed, $T(0) = 0$ by the proof of Theorem 16.5.

2. V is invariant under T. Indeed, if $v \in V$, then $T(v) \in V$.

3. $\ker(T)$ is invariant under T. To see this, let $v \in \ker(T)$. Then $T(v) = 0 \in \ker(T)$.

4. $T[V]$ is invariant under T. To see this, let $w \in T[V]$. Then $T(w)$ is clearly also in $T[V]$.

Let V be a vector space over a field $\mathbb{F}$. We call a subspace $U \leq V$ a **simple** subspace if it consists of all scalar multiples of a single vector. In other words, U is simple if there is a $u \in V$ such that $U = \{ku \mid k \in \mathbb{F}\}$.

Theorem 16.9: Let V be a vector space over a field $\mathbb{F}$, let $U = \{ku \mid k \in \mathbb{F}\}$ be a simple subspace of V, and let $T \in \mathcal{L}(V)$. Then U is invariant under T if and only if there is $\lambda \in \mathbb{F}$ such that $T(u) = \lambda u$.

Proof: Suppose that $U = \{ku \mid k \in \mathbb{F}\}$ is invariant under T. Then $T(u) \in U$. It follows that $T(u) = \lambda u$ for some $\lambda \in \mathbb{F}$.

Conversely, suppose there is $\lambda \in \mathbb{F}$ such that $T(u) = \lambda u$. Let $v \in U$. Then there is $k \in \mathbb{F}$ such that $v = ku$. Then $T(v) = T(ku) = kT(u) = k(\lambda u) = (k\lambda)u \in U$. Since $v \in U$ was arbitrary, $T[U] \subseteq U$. Therefore, U is invariant under T. $\qquad\square$

Let V be a vector space over a field $\mathbb{F}$ and let $T \in \mathcal{L}(V)$. A scalar $\lambda \in \mathbb{F}$ is called an **eigenvalue** of T if there is a **nonzero** vector $v \in V$ such that $T(v) = \lambda v$. The vector v is called an **eigenvector** of T.

Notes: (1) If v is the zero vector, Then $T(v) = T(0) = 0 = \lambda \cdot 0$ for every scalar λ. This is why we exclude the zero vector from being an eigenvector. An eigenvector **must be nonzero**.

(2) If we let $I: V \to V$ be the identity linear transformation defined by $I(v) = v$ for all $v \in V$, then we can write λv as $\lambda I(v)$. So, the equation $T(v) = \lambda v$ is equivalent to the equation $(T - \lambda I)(v) = 0$.

(3) It follows from Note 2 that λ is an eigenvalue of T if and only if $\ker(T - \lambda I) \neq \{0\}$. By Theorem 16.7, λ is an eigenvalue of T if and only if $T - \lambda I$ is **not** injective.

(4) By Note 2, v is an eigenvector of T corresponding to eigenvalue λ if and only if v is a nonzero vector such that $(T - \lambda I)(v) = 0$. So, the set of eigenvectors of T corresponding to λ is $\ker(T - \lambda I)$. By Theorem 16.6, $\ker(T - \lambda I)$ is a subspace of V. We call this subspace the **eigenspace** of V corresponding to the eigenvalue λ.

Example 16.9:

1. Let V be any vector space over a field $\mathbb{F}$ and let $I: V \to V$ be the identity linear transformation. Then for any $v \in V$, $I(v) = v = 1v$. So, we see that 1 is the only eigenvalue of I and every nonzero vector $v \in V$ is an eigenvector of I for the eigenvalue 1.

2. More generally, if $k \in \mathbb{F}$, then the linear transformation kI satisfies $(kI)(v) = kI(v) = kv$ for all $v \in V$. So, we see that k is the only eigenvalue of kI and every nonzero vector $v \in V$ is an eigenvector of kI for the eigenvalue k.

3. Consider $\mathbb{C}^2$ as a vector space over $\mathbb{C}$ and define $T: \mathbb{C}^2 \to \mathbb{C}^2$ by $T\big((z, w)\big) = (-w, z)$. Observe that $\lambda = i$ is an eigenvalue of T with corresponding eigenvector $(1, -i)$. Indeed, we have $T\big((1, -i)\big) = (i, 1)$ and $i(1, -i) = (i, -i^2) = (i, 1)$. So, $T\big((1, -i)\big) = i(1, -i)$.

   Let's find all the eigenvalues of this linear transformation. We need to solve the equation $T\big((z, w)\big) = \lambda(z, w)$, or equivalently, $(-w, z) = (\lambda z, \lambda w)$. Equating the first components and second components gives us the two equations $-w = \lambda z$ and $z = \lambda w$. Solving the first equation for w yields $w = -\lambda z$. Substituting into the second equation gives us $z = \lambda(-\lambda z) = -\lambda^2 z$. So, $z + \lambda^2 z = 0$. Using distributivity on the left-hand side of this equation gives $z(1 + \lambda^2) = 0$. So, $z = 0$ or $1 + \lambda^2 = 0$. If $z = 0$, then $w = -\lambda \cdot 0 = 0$. So, $(z, w) = (0, 0)$. Since an eigenvector must be nonzero, we reject $z = 0$. The equation $1 + \lambda^2 = 0$ has the two solutions $\lambda = i$ and $\lambda = -i$. These are the two eigenvalues of T.

   Next, let's find the eigenvectors corresponding to the eigenvalue $\lambda = i$. In this case, we have $T\big((z, w)\big) = i(z, w)$, or equivalently, $(-w, z) = (iz, iw)$. So, $-w = iz$ and $z = iw$. These two equations are actually equivalent. Indeed, if we multiply each side of the second equation by i, we get $iz = i^2 w$, or equivalently, $iz = -w$ or $-w = iz$.

   So, we use only one of the equations, say $-w = iz$, or equivalently, $w = -iz$. So, the eigenvectors of T corresponding to the eigenvalue $\lambda = i$ are all nonzero vectors of the form $(z, -zi)$. For example, letting $z = 1$, we see that $(1, -i)$ is an eigenvector corresponding to the eigenvalue $\lambda = i$.

   Let's also find the eigenvectors corresponding to the eigenvalue $\lambda = -i$. In this case, we have $T\big((z, w)\big) = -i(z, w)$, or equivalently, $(-w, z) = (-iz, -iw)$. So, $-w = -iz$ and $z = -iw$. Once again, these two equations are equivalent. Indeed, if we multiply each side of the second equation by $-i$, we get $-iz = i^2 w$, or equivalently, $-iz = -w$ or $-w = -iz$.

   So, we use only one of the equations, say $-w = -iz$, or equivalently, $w = iz$. So, the eigenvectors of T corresponding to the eigenvalue $\lambda = -i$ are all nonzero vectors of the form (z, zi). For example, letting $z = 1$, we see that $(1, i)$ is an eigenvector corresponding to the eigenvalue $\lambda = -i$.

Note that if we consider the vector space $\mathbb{R}^2$ over the field $\mathbb{R}$ instead of $\mathbb{C}^2$ over $\mathbb{C}$, then the linear transformation $T: \mathbb{R}^2 \to \mathbb{R}^2$ defined by $T((z, w)) = (-w, z)$ has no eigenvalues (and therefore, no eigenvectors). Algebraically, this follows from the fact that $1 + \lambda^2 = 0$ has no real solutions.

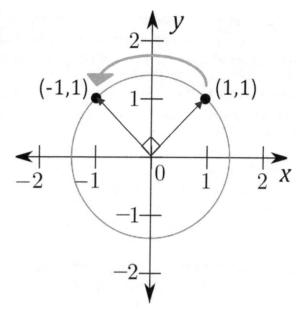

It is also easy to see geometrically that this transformation has no eigenvalues. The given transformation rotates any nonzero point $(z, w) \in \mathbb{R}^2$ counterclockwise by $90°$. Since no multiple of (z, w) results in such a rotation, we see that there is no eigenvalue. The figure to the right shows how T rotates the point $(1, 1)$ counterclockwise $90°$ to the point $(-1, 1)$.

Let V be a vector space over a field $\mathbb{F}$, let $v_1, v_2, \ldots, v_n \in V$, and $k_1, k_2, \ldots, k_n \in \mathbb{F}$. Recall from Lesson 8 that the expression $k_1 v_1 + k_2 v_2 + \cdots + k_n v_n$ is called a **linear combination** of the vectors $v_1, v_2, \ldots, v_n$ with **weights** $k_1, k_2, \ldots, k_n$.

Also recall once more that $v_1, v_2, \ldots, v_n$ are **linearly dependent** if there exist weights $k_1, k_2, \ldots, k_n \in \mathbb{F}$, with at least one weight nonzero, such that $k_1 v_1 + k_2 v_2 + \cdots + k_n v_n = 0$. Otherwise, we say that $v_1, v_2, \ldots, v_n$ are **linearly independent**.

In Problem 6 from Lesson 8, you were asked to prove that if a finite set of at least two vectors is linearly dependent, then one of the vectors in the set can be written as a linear combination of the other vectors in the set. To prove the next theorem (Theorem 16.11), we will need the following slightly stronger result.

Lemma 16.10: Let V be a vector space over a field $\mathbb{F}$ and let $v_1, v_2, \ldots, v_k \in V$ be linearly dependent with $k \geq 2$. Also assume that $v_1 \neq 0$. Then there is $t \leq k$ such that v_t can be written as a linear combination of $v_1, v_2, \ldots, v_{t-1}$.

Proof: Suppose that $v_1, v_2, \ldots, v_k$ are linearly dependent and $v_1 \neq 0$. Let $c_1 v_1 + c_2 v_2 + \cdots + c_k v_k = 0$ be a nontrivial dependence relation (in other words, not all the c_i are 0). Since $v_1 \neq 0$, we must have $c_i \neq 0$ for some $i \neq 1$ (otherwise $c_1 v_1 + c_2 v_2 + \cdots + c_k v_k = 0$ implies $c_1 v_1 = 0$, which implies that $c_1 = 0$, contradicting that the dependence relation is nontrivial). Let t be the largest value such that $c_t \neq 0$. Then we have $c_1 v_1 + c_2 v_2 + \cdots + c_k v_k = c_1 v_1 + c_2 v_2 + \cdots + c_t v_t + 0 v_{t+1} \cdots + 0 v_k$, and so, $c_1 v_1 + c_2 v_2 + \cdots + c_t v_t = 0$. Since $c_t \neq 0$, we can solve for v_t to get

$$v_t = -\frac{c_1}{c_t} v_1 - \cdots - \frac{c_{t-1}}{c_t} v_{t-1}.$$

So, v_t can be written as a linear combination of $v_1, v_2, \ldots, v_{t-1}$. $\square$

Note: A **lemma** is a theorem whose primary purpose it to prove a more important theorem. Although Lemma 16.10 is an important result in Linear Algebra, the main reason we are mentioning it now is to help us prove the next theorem (Theorem 16.11).

Theorem 16.11: Let V be a vector space over a field $\mathbb{F}$, let $T \in \mathcal{L}(V)$, and let $\lambda_1, \lambda_2, \ldots, \lambda_k$ be distinct eigenvalues of T with corresponding eigenvectors $v_1, v_2, \ldots, v_k$. Then $v_1, v_2, \ldots, v_k$ are linearly independent.

Proof: Suppose toward contradiction that $v_1, v_2, \ldots, v_k$ are linearly dependent. Let t be the least integer such that v_t can be written as a linear combination of $v_1, v_2, \ldots, v_{t-1}$ (we can find such a t by Lemma 16.10). Then there are weights $c_1, c_2, \ldots, c_{t-1}$ such that $v_t = c_1 v_1 + c_2 v_2 + \cdots + c_{t-1} v_{t-1}$. Apply the linear transformation T to each side of this last equation to get the equation $T(v_t) = T(c_1 v_1 + c_2 v_2 + \cdots + c_{t-1} v_{t-1}) = c_1 T(v_1) + c_2 T(v_2) + \cdots + c_{t-1} T(v_{t-1})$. Since each v_i is an eigenvector corresponding to eigenvalue λ_i, we have $\lambda_t v_t = c_1 \lambda_1 v_1 + c_2 \lambda_2 v_2 + \cdots + c_{t-1} \lambda_{t-1} v_{t-1}$. We can also multiply each side of the equation $v_t = c_1 v_1 + c_2 v_2 + \cdots + c_{t-1} v_{t-1}$ by λ_t to get the equation $\lambda_t v_t = c_1 \lambda_t v_1 + c_2 \lambda_t v_2 + \cdots + c_{t-1} \lambda_t v_{t-1}$. We now subtract:

$$\lambda_t v_t = c_1 \lambda_t v_1 + c_2 \lambda_t v_2 + \cdots + c_{t-1} \lambda_t v_{t-1}$$
$$\lambda_t v_t = c_1 \lambda_1 v_1 + c_2 \lambda_2 v_2 + \cdots + c_{t-1} \lambda_{t-1} v_{t-1}$$
$$\overline{ 0 = c_1(\lambda_t - \lambda_1)v_1 + c_2(\lambda_t - \lambda_2)v_2 + \cdots + c_{t-1}(\lambda_t - \lambda_{t-1})v_{t-1}}$$

Since we chose t to be the least integer such that v_t can be written as a linear combination of $v_1, v_2, \ldots, v_{t-1}$, it follows that $v_1, v_2, \ldots, v_{t-1}$ are linearly independent. Therefore, the constants $c_1(\lambda_t - \lambda_1), c_2(\lambda_t - \lambda_2), \ldots, c_{t-1}(\lambda_t - \lambda_{t-1})$ are all 0. Since the eigenvalues are all distinct, we must have $c_1 = c_2 = \cdots = c_{t-1} = 0$. Then $v_t = c_1 v_1 + c_2 v_2 + \cdots + c_{t-1} v_{t-1} = 0$, contradicting our assumption that v_t is an eigenvector. Therefore, $v_1, v_2, \ldots, v_k$ cannot be linearly dependent. So, $v_1, v_2, \ldots, v_k$ are linearly independent. $\square$

Let A be a square matrix, say $A = \begin{bmatrix} a_{11} & \cdots & a_{1n} \\ \vdots & & \vdots \\ a_{n1} & \cdots & a_{nn} \end{bmatrix}$. The **diagonal entries** of A are the entries $a_{11}, a_{22}, \ldots, a_{nn}$. All other entries of A are **nondiagonal entries**.

Example 16.10: The diagonal entries of the matrix $B = \begin{bmatrix} 1 & 5 & 2 \\ 3 & 6 & 0 \\ 2 & 9 & 8 \end{bmatrix}$ are $b_{11} = 1$, $b_{22} = 6$, and $b_{33} = 8$. The nondiagonal entries of B are $b_{12} = 5$, $b_{13} = 2$, $b_{21} = 3$, $b_{23} = 0$, $b_{31} = 2$, and $b_{32} = 9$.

A **diagonal matrix** is a square matrix that has every nondiagonal entry equal to 0.

Example 16.11: The matrix B from Example 16.10 is **not** a diagonal matrix, while the matrices $C = \begin{bmatrix} 1 & 0 & 0 \\ 0 & 6 & 0 \\ 0 & 0 & 8 \end{bmatrix}$ and $D = \begin{bmatrix} 5 & 0 & 0 \\ 0 & -2 & 0 \\ 0 & 0 & 0 \end{bmatrix}$ are diagonal matrices.

Let V be a vector space. A linear transformation $T \in \mathcal{L}(V)$ is said to be **diagonalizable** if there is a basis $\mathcal{B}$ of V for which $\mathcal{M}_T(\mathcal{B})$ is a diagonal matrix.

Example 16.12:

1. Consider $\mathbb{C}$ as a vector space over $\mathbb{R}$ and define $T : \mathbb{C} \to \mathbb{C}$ by $T(z) = 5z$, as we did in part 1 of Example 16.1. The equation $T(z) = 5z$ tells us that every nonzero vector z is an eigenvector corresponding to the eigenvalue $\lambda = 5$. $T(z) = \lambda z$ is equivalent to $5z = \lambda z$ or $(\lambda - 5)z = 0$. So, $\lambda = 5$ is the only eigenvalue. In particular, the standard basis vectors 1 and i are eigenvectors corresponding to the eigenvalue $\lambda = 5$. We have

    $$T(1) = 5 = 5 \cdot 1 + 0 \cdot i.$$
    $$T(i) = 5i = 0 \cdot 1 + 5 \cdot i.$$

    So, as we saw in part 1 of Example 16.6, the matrix of T with respect to the standard basis is $\mathcal{M}_T = \begin{bmatrix} 5 & 0 \\ 0 & 5 \end{bmatrix}$, a diagonal matrix. Therefore, T is diagonalizable.

2. Consider $\mathbb{R}^3$ as a vector space over $\mathbb{R}$ and define $T : \mathbb{R}^3 \to \mathbb{R}^3$ by

    $$T\big((x, y, z)\big) = (3x + y, y - 2z, 7z).$$

    Let's find the eigenvalues and eigenvectors of T.

    We start by solving the equation $T\big((x, y, z)\big) = \lambda(x, y, z)$. This equation is equivalent to the three equations $3x + y = \lambda x$, $y - 2z = \lambda y$, and $7z = \lambda z$. We work backwards. If $z \neq 0$, we get $\lambda = 7$. If $z = 0$ and $y \neq 0$, we get $\lambda = 1$. Finally, if $z = 0$, $y = 0$, and $x \neq 0$, we get $\lambda = 3$.

    So, the eigenvalues of T are 7, 1, and 3.

    If we let $\lambda = 7$, we get $3x + y = 7x$, $y - 2z = 7y$, and $7z = 7z$. The equation $y - 2z = 7y$ is equivalent to the equation $6y = -2z$, or $y = -\frac{1}{3}z$. The equation $3x + y = 7x$ is equivalent to $4x = y = -\frac{1}{3}z$, or $x = -\frac{1}{12}z$. So, if we let $z = -12$, we get the eigenvector $v_1 = (1, 4, -12)$.

    If we let $\lambda = 1$, we get $3x + y = x$, $y - 2z = y$, and $7z = z$. The equation $7z = z$ is equivalent to the equation $z = 0$. The equation $y - 2z = y$ is then equivalent to $y = y$. The equation $3x + y = x$ is equivalent to $2x = -y$ or $x = -\frac{1}{2}y$. So, if we let $y = -2$, we get the eigenvector $v_2 = (1, -2, 0)$.

    If we let $\lambda = 3$, we get $3x + y = 3x$, $y - 2z = 3y$, and $7z = 3z$. The equation $7z = 3z$ is equivalent to the equation $z = 0$. The equation $y - 2z = 3y$ is then equivalent to $y = 0$. The equation $3x + y = 3x$ is then equivalent to $x = x$. So, if we let $x = 1$, we get the eigenvector $v_3 = (1, 0, 0)$.

    It follows that $B = \{(1, 4, -12), (1, -2, 0), (1, 0, 0)\}$ is a basis of eigenvectors of V and we have

    $$T\big((1, 4, -12)\big) = 7(1, 4, -12)$$
    $$T\big((1, -2, 0)\big) = 1(1, -2, 0)$$
    $$T\big((1, 0, 0)\big) = 3(1, 0, 0)$$

    Therefore, the matrix of T with respect to B is $\mathcal{M}_T(B) = \begin{bmatrix} 7 & 0 & 0 \\ 0 & 1 & 0 \\ 0 & 0 & 3 \end{bmatrix}$.

    Since $\mathcal{M}_T(B)$ is a diagonal matrix, T is diagonalizable.

3. Recall from part 3 of Example 16.9, the linear transformation $T: \mathbb{R}^2 \to \mathbb{R}^2$ defined by $T\big((x, y)\big) = (-y, x)$ (where $\mathbb{R}^2$ is being viewed as a vector space over the field $\mathbb{R}$). We saw in that example that this linear transformation has no eigenvalues. It follows that there is no basis for $\mathbb{R}^2$ such that the matrix of T with respect to that basis is a diagonal matrix. In other words, T is **not** diagonalizable.

However, in the same example, we saw that the linear transformation $T: \mathbb{C}^2 \to \mathbb{C}^2$ defined by $T: \mathbb{C}^2 \to \mathbb{C}^2$ by $T\big((z, w)\big) = (-w, z)$ (where $\mathbb{C}^2$ is being viewed as a vector space over the field $\mathbb{C}$) has eigenvalues i and $-i$ with eigenvectors corresponding to these eigenvalues of $(1, -i)$ and $(1, i)$, respectively. So, we have

$$T\big((1, -i)\big) = i(1, -i)$$
$$T\big((1, i)\big) = -i(1, i)$$

So, the matrix of T with respect to the basis $B = \{(1, -i), (1, i)\}$ is $\mathcal{M}_T(B) = \begin{bmatrix} i & 0 \\ 0 & -i \end{bmatrix}$, a diagonal matrix. Therefore, T is diagonalizable.

We finish with a Theorem that gives a sufficient condition for a linear transformation to be diagonalizable.

Theorem 16.12: Let V be an n-dimensional vector space and let $T \in \mathcal{L}(V)$ have n distinct eigenvalues. Then T is diagonalizable.

Proof: Suppose that $\dim V = n$ and $T \in \mathcal{L}(V)$ has the n distinct eigenvalues $\lambda_1, \lambda_2, \ldots, \lambda_n$, with corresponding eigenvectors $v_1, v_2, \ldots, v_n$. By Theorem 16.11, $v_1, v_2, \ldots, v_n$ are linearly independent. By the note following Theorem 16.8, $v_1, v_2, \ldots, v_n$ can be extended to a basis of V. However, a basis of V has n elements and therefore, $\{v_1, v_2, \ldots, v_n\}$ is already a basis of V. Since $T(v_1) = \lambda_1 v_1$,

$T(v_2) = \lambda_2 v_2, \ldots, T(v_n) = \lambda_n v_n$, it follows that $\mathcal{M}_T(B) = \begin{bmatrix} \lambda_1 & 0 & \cdots & 0 \\ 0 & \lambda_2 & \cdots & 0 \\ \vdots & \vdots & \ddots & \vdots \\ 0 & 0 & \cdots & \lambda_n \end{bmatrix}$. Since $\mathcal{M}_T(B)$ is a diagonal

matrix, T is diagonalizable. $\qquad\qquad \square$

Full solutions to these problems are available for free download here:

www.SATPrepGet800.com/PMFBXSG

LEVEL 1

1. Let V and W be vector spaces over $\mathbb{R}$. Determine if each of the following functions is a linear transformation:

    (i) $f: \mathbb{R} \to \mathbb{R}$ defined by $f(x) = 2x + 1$

    (ii) $g: \mathbb{R} \to \mathbb{R}^2$ defined by $g(x) = (2x, 3x)$

    (iii) $h: \mathbb{R}^3 \to \mathbb{R}^3$ defined by $h\big((x, y, z)\big) = (x + y, x + z, z - y)$

2. Compute each of the following:

    (i) $\begin{bmatrix} 2 & 0 & -3 \\ 0 & 1 & 4 \end{bmatrix} \cdot \begin{bmatrix} 1 & 1 & 3 & 0 \\ 1 & -4 & 2 & 0 \\ 2 & 0 & 1 & -4 \end{bmatrix}$

    (ii) $\begin{bmatrix} 3 & -1 & 5 \end{bmatrix} \cdot \begin{bmatrix} -4 \\ -7 \\ 2 \end{bmatrix}$

    (iii) $\begin{bmatrix} -4 \\ -7 \\ 2 \end{bmatrix} \cdot \begin{bmatrix} 3 & -1 & 5 \end{bmatrix}$

    (iv) $\begin{bmatrix} a & b & c \\ d & e & f \\ g & h & i \end{bmatrix} \cdot \begin{bmatrix} 1 & 0 & 1 \\ 0 & 2 & 0 \\ 3 & 1 & 4 \end{bmatrix}$.

LEVEL 2

3. Consider $\mathbb{C}$ as a vector space over itself. Give an example of a function $f: \mathbb{C} \to \mathbb{C}$ such that f is additive, but **not** a linear transformation. Then give an example of vector spaces V and W and a homogenous function $g: V \to W$ that is **not** a linear transformation.

LEVEL 3

4. Let $P = \{ax^2 + bx + c \mid a, b, c \in \mathbb{R}\}$ be the vector space of polynomials of degree 2 with real coefficients (see part 3 of Example 8.3 from Lesson 8). Define the linear transformation $D: P \to P$ by $D(ax^2 + bx + c) = 2ax + b$. Find the matrix of T with respect to each of the following bases:

    (i)   The standard basis $B = \{1, x, x^2\}$

    (ii) $C = \{x + 1, x^2 + 1, x^2 + x\}$

5. Let V and W be vector spaces with V finite-dimensional, let $U \leq V$, and let $T \in \mathcal{L}(U, W)$. Prove that there is an $S \in \mathcal{L}(V, W)$ such that $S(v) = T(v)$ for all $v \in U$.

LEVEL 4

6. Let $T: V \to W$ be a linear transformation and let $v_1, v_2, \ldots, v_n \in V$. Prove the following:

   (i) If T is injective and $v_1, v_2, \ldots, v_n$ are linearly independent in V, then $T(v_1), T(v_2), \ldots, T(v_n)$ are linearly independent in W.

   (ii) If T is surjective and $\operatorname{span}\{v_1, v_2, \ldots, v_n\} = V$, then $\operatorname{span}\{T(v_1), T(v_2), \ldots, T(v_n)\} = W$.

7. Determine if each linear transformation is diagonalizable:

   (i) $T: \mathbb{R}^2 \to \mathbb{R}^2$ defined by $T\big((x, y)\big) = (y, 2x)$

   (ii) $U: \mathbb{C}^2 \to \mathbb{C}^2$ defined by $U\big((z, w)\big) = (z + iw, iz - w)$.

8. Let V and W be vector spaces over a field $\mathbb{F}$. Prove that $\mathcal{L}(V, W)$ is a vector space over $\mathbb{F}$, where addition and scalar multiplication are defined as in Theorem 16.2.

9. Let V be a vector space over a field $\mathbb{F}$. Prove that $\mathcal{L}(V)$ is a linear algebra over $\mathbb{F}$, where addition and scalar multiplication are defined as in Theorem 16.2 and vector multiplication is given by composition of linear transformations.

10. Let $T: V \to W$ and $S: W \to V$ be linear transformations such that $ST = i_V$ and $TS = i_W$. Prove that S and T are bijections and that $S = T^{-1}$.

11. Let V and W be finite-dimensional vector spaces and let $T \in \mathcal{L}(V, W)$. Prove the following:

    (i) If $\dim V < \dim W$, then T is **not** surjective

    (ii) If $\dim V > \dim W$, then T is **not** injective.

12. Prove that two finite-dimensional vector spaces over a field $\mathbb{F}$ are isomorphic if and only if they have the same dimension.

13. Let $T \in \mathcal{L}(V)$ be invertible and let $\lambda \in \mathbb{F} \setminus \{0\}$. Prove that λ is an eigenvalue of T if and only if $\frac{1}{\lambda}$ is an eigenvalue of T^{-1}.

LEVEL 5

14. Let V be a vector space with $\dim V > 1$. Show that $\{T \in \mathcal{L}(V) \mid T \text{ is not invertible}\} \nleq \mathcal{L}(V)$.

15. Let V be an n-dimensional vector space over a field $\mathbb{F}$. Prove that there is a linear algebra isomorphism $F: \mathcal{L}(V) \to M_{nn}^{\mathbb{F}}$.

INDEX

About the Author

Dr. Steve Warner, a New York native, earned his Ph.D. at Rutgers University in Pure Mathematics in May 2001. While a graduate student, Dr. Warner won the TA Teaching Excellence Award.

After Rutgers, Dr. Warner joined the Penn State Mathematics Department as an Assistant Professor and in September 2002, he returned to New York to accept an Assistant Professor position at Hofstra University. By September 2007, Dr. Warner had received tenure and was promoted to Associate Professor. He has taught undergraduate and graduate courses in Precalculus, Calculus, Linear Algebra, Differential Equations, Mathematical Logic, Set Theory, and Abstract Algebra.

From 2003 – 2008, Dr. Warner participated in a five-year NSF grant, "The MSTP Project," to study and improve mathematics and science curriculum in poorly performing junior high schools. He also published several articles in scholarly journals, specifically on Mathematical Logic.

Dr. Warner has nearly two decades of experience in general math tutoring and tutoring for standardized tests such as the SAT, ACT, GRE, GMAT, and AP Calculus exams. He has tutored students both individually and in group settings.

In February 2010 Dr. Warner released his first SAT prep book "The 32 Most Effective SAT Math Strategies," and in 2012 founded Get 800 Test Prep. Since then Dr. Warner has written books for the SAT, ACT, SAT Math Subject Tests, AP Calculus exams, and GRE.

Dr. Steve Warner can be reached at

steve@SATPrepGet800.com

BOOKS BY DR. STEVE WARNER

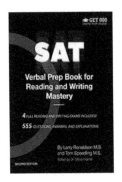 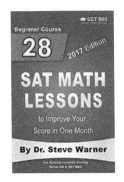 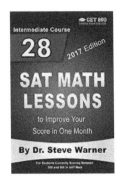 

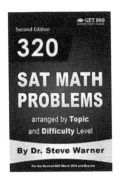   

 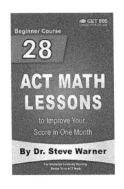  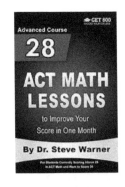

  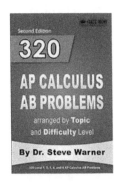 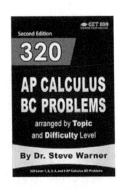

CPSIA information can be obtained
at www.ICGtesting.com
Printed in the USA
LVHW060805200119
604565LV00021B/784/P